World University Library

The World University Library is an international series of books, each of which has been specially commissioned. The authors are leading scientists and scholars from all over the world who, in an age of increasing specialisation, see the need for a broad, up-to-date presentation of their subject. The aim is to provide authoritative introductory books for university students which will be of interest also to the general reader. The series is published in Britain, France, Germany, Holland, Italy, Spain, Sweden and the United States.

Arnold Kaufmann

The Science of Decision-making

an introduction to praxeology

translated from the French by Rex Audley

World University Library

McGraw-Hill Book Company
New York Toronto

Library of Congress Catalog Card Number: 67–14681
Phototypeset by BAS Printers Limited, Wallop, Hampshire, England
Printed by Officine Grafiche Arnoldo Mondadori, Verona, Italy

Contents

Foreword

The curve showing the rate of advance of technological progress is an exponential one, and to speculate on what lies in the future for our children may well make our heads swim. One of the most haunting fears which beset us in contemplating life in the not-too-distant future is the fear of losing our intellectual liberty, of subduing our initiative to socio-economic techniques, of transferring our fundamental responsibilities to electronic machines. In the midst of all the safeguards that he seeks in the social systems presented to him, will man be able to preserve his independence? Will he remain an active performer or will he become a mere spectator, a customer satisfied with the terms offered him, renouncing individuality and enterprise?

Whether he be industrialist, politician, engineer, lawyer or artist, the intellectual looks with suspicion on the entry of the exact sciences into spheres where, traditionally, art has owed nothing to science. Already the numerous successes of mathematics in industrial economy, in planning and administration, in sociology and in many other spheres of human activity, have brought in their wake a definite change of attitude amongst management and staff. Yet with these applications of the exact sciences and this new attitude imposed by progress, meta-physical anxiety over the loss of personal liberty has increased.

Would it not be as well to take our bearings, or perhaps, less ambitiously, to try to examine how this more scientific attitude manifests itself, what its basic origins are, why it questions the traditional definition of the responsibilities of leadership, and what transformation of the world it can lead to sooner or later?

Will we have a science of action at our disposal in the near future? Will we have a more positive understanding of the machinery by which men are linked together in the social complex? Will we learn how to make a suitable choice from the countless policies or strategies which can be determined in our highly combinatorial models representing the structure of the world? Will we be able to adapt ourselves to a society becoming more and more flexible?

The literature on this subject, sparse until recently, now holds an important place. It has been developing rapidly over the past ten years throughout the world, under various titles, among which striking neologisms appear – such as econometrics, operational research, cybernetics, information theory. There is now no university or equivalent syllabus which does not contain a fairly extensive coverage of these concepts. In every country refresher courses on methods dealing with them are attended by management staff. Nearly all large administrative bodies and business concerns have reorganised themselves so that decisions can be worked out more scientifically, so that transmission of information can keep pace with rapidly changing circumstances and so that the demands of technological progress can be met.

In our present state of knowledge we are far from claiming that a science of action, or 'praxeology' (a word coined by Kotarbinski, from the Greek *praxis* = action) – can be properly defined.

Some patterns of management, some procedures for working out decisions may well seem to be in focus in certain fields, but the most important problems, especially those of macroeconomy, are being subjected to methods which are very much under discussion. We can, however, already work out a sub-optimum for administrative or industrial problems – failing an optimisation of wider problems taking in a whole firm or an entire sector of the economy.

It must be said that mathematics as used in the past did not lend itself easily to the construction of adequate models. The problems man is concerned with are essentially of a combinatorial nature and the path followed by mathematicians for the last three centuries has led to remarkable developments in the analysis of continuous functions. On the other hand the developments in combinatorial methods were given appreciably less importance until modern algebra drastically upset entrenched positions. Many researches which would once have been thought Utopian have ended in positively applicable methods and in proven processes.

One need hardly mention the part played nowadays by the large electronic centres of administration and information. Ever more powerful and efficient, endowed with rapid and wide-ranging memories, computers are linked to complicated electronic equipment for gathering and conveying information. These machines can deal in minutes with combinatorial or numerical problems so complex for man that the mere reading of their terms would take longer than the time the computer takes to reach the final solution. They are to the human brain what machine tools are to the human hand.

Yet, as ever more doors are opened and new thresholds crossed, moral questions arise which shift our deliberations on to a higher plane, and the most important problem will be to give a definition of man and the society of tomorrow.

This book develops such lines of thought. On this subject ethics cannot be separated from logic, nor the spiritual from tangible fact. Its presentation gives the book rather a didactic character, but I hope it will have the unique quality of dealing with the mathematical aspects of rather complex questions with few, if any, formulae. Moreover, a number of 'arrow diagrams' or 'graphs' have been included, to help the reader, and only elementary problems are treated. I therefore hope that the book will be comprehensible to the layman – and that scholars will not accuse me of popularising my subject by over-simplifying complicated truths.

My purpose is to encourage the reader to use, whenever he can, the exact sciences in practical situations and above all to open up wider horizons for considering the question of translating his intentions into criteria of effectiveness.

Before controlling inert structures, sets of hypotheses, economic or social models and targets of management performance, overriding all logical argument, the businessman should not neglect the function for which finding the greatest possible value is of superlative importance to the stability of the world: human relationships.

1 Decision in human actions

1 Introduction

Let me outline the reasons for writing this book. Are we to go on acting and making decisions, merely on the basis of intuition? Can anything be achieved without certain types of higher intelligence – the precious endowments of a few men of genius who, in politics, business or administration, have brought dazzling successes . . . or terrible catastrophes? Or are we now in possession of certain forms of knowledge, and more particularly of methods, enabling us to bring to intuition an additional contribution from mathematical logic, this replacing, to some extent, pure empiricism?

The arguments of all those who believe in the scientific preparation of decisions – such as are presented here – demand that we put this very valuable intuition to better use. For undoubtedly this form of intuition cannot be entirely replaced by purely logical mechanisms.

The world has become more and more complex, its physical and moral health constantly being influenced by a thousand beneficial or maleficent forms of progress. The acceleration of history, the flexibility of structures, man's essential mobility, produce a continuous reassessment of ideas. The businessman will be obliged to acquire the basic principles of a new science which has been created for him – 'Praxeology'. From the state to the family, in every group of which they will be members, our children will soon become familiar with models and diagrams which will help them to understand the mechanisms of the world. They will perhaps be better able than we to project hypotheses into the future – the *near* future. They will learn how to construct 'praxeograms' or mathematical models of action. They will learn to draw up accurate maps or representations of these models, so as to be able to communicate satisfactorily with others – maps which will possibly be called 'praxeographs' and which the PERT method (see page 32) foreshadows. Then, perhaps, this disturbing world which will one day be theirs, this dangerous and exciting world which we foresee, will be more easily controlled because it will be better understood.

2 Complexity of the world

One of the less obvious factors which make decision in human actions difficult is the complexity of the modern world. Living in the midst of this complexity we are more or less conditioned to it, but our difficulties begin when circumstances generate decisions whose consequences we consider important. We realise then that, for solving complex problems, the number of possible solutions is such that a simple statement of preference is inadequate.

The method we implicitly follow, in exercising our preference in a problem of decision, consists in breaking down the aggregate of possible solutions, be they limited or unlimited in number, into perceptibly smaller mutually exclusive sets. We then examine whether the choice of a solution set can be substituted for the choice of a factor. We carry on in this way, reducing more and more, if necessary, the number of factors or components for which in the end preference may be satisfactorily shown. This manner of simplifying the problems of reality is not only a practical method. It is also, according to Descartes, a logical method. All methods of preparation of decisions, particularly those used for the optimisation of situations from the economic standpoint on a commercial or national scale, or from a military standpoint, are reduced to this absolute principle. Fundamentally the *modus operandi* of a statistician, which consists in breaking down a vast body of objects into classes and then analysing the way in which these classes are distributed, is an example of the application of the principle in which all objects of the same class are considered homogeneous. It is also the *modus operandi* of an industrial analyst who, in dealing with a set of operations whose structures may be extremely complex in their relationship to each other, will find one limited group on which particular attention will be brought to bear and which will have a perceptibly greater influence than the others on the total time factor. Again, it is according to this general principle that we choose one group in a set of properties which is judged to be sufficiently representative to allow us to take certain decisions from a ranking of its elements.

The use of this principle of partition has become all but universal and we cannot do without it if we are to understand the increasingly intricate structures of the modern world.

While we are waiting for the complexity of these structures to be specified and quantified in a systematic manner (and this does not seem to be feasible in the near future, if it ever will be), it is as well first of all to be fully aware of this complexity and particularly of the forms under which it appears. Nature, as far as human beings are concerned, presents structures which for the most part defy analysis. The structures created by man are perhaps less complex, but since he has a power of decision in them the multiplicity of the situations to be envisaged makes the description of the possible conditions much more highly combinatorial.

When we compare the world of the mid-nineteenth century with the world of today, we realise that the main difference between men separated by four generations comes from the transformation of their environment. The walker has become a 'driver', and moves within a network of streets and roads which would bewilder his forefathers. The craftsman has become a manufacturing technician, less and less manual, with responsibilities in the assembly lines, whose electronic network contains hundreds of thousands of cables. The shopkeeper is now a 'distributor'. The clerk has given place to the 'planner' who prepares the instructions to be given to the management computers. To his grandfather the 'organigram' he uses would look like the scribbles of a lunatic. The whole of human society is involved. There is no activity which can escape the trend. Though at some point things seem to simplify themselves, they do so only to become even more complex later on, when they unite with others. They form a new unit, which takes its place in a structure which will be comprehensible only when much more highly developed language and concepts are introduced.

Building a road has always required a good technological and geographical knowledge. But today it also requires mathematical studies on the intended route, and for these combinatorial analysis and topology (in the mathematical sense) are usefully employed. A glance at a city like Los Angeles would fully bear this out.

The arrangement of a syllabus in a school or university may be so difficult that we have to have recourse to electronic means to take account of the vast number of restrictions and specifications involved. A surgical operation may require the participation of a great many assistants performing hundreds of actions. So much so that these operations are plotted by programs with a long list of contents, like the list which has to be checked before a pilot takes off, or the list of work involved in the building of a dam. The preparation of a production line requires the specification of tens of thousands of technological matters and the drawing up of descriptive graphs of similar complexity, with points representing states of existence and lines denoting restrictions on their timing.

Documentary and bibliographical research is now a vast electronic undertaking occupying the largest computers. As a compelling example I give below a list of the administrative operations necessary at present (tomorrow they will no doubt be insufficient) for the creation in France of a limited company of the simplest type. Figure 2·1 shows how such operations develop. Though the diagram might be different in the USA or in England or Germany, it would be at least as complex.

The lawyer, like the engineer, the shopkeeper or the administrator needs, as Theseus needed Ariadne's thread, efficient ways of emerging from the maze into which his activities lead him.

Networks of highways in a very advanced country, a telephone system, the entire administrative regulations of a company, a legal code, a school syllabus – all represent intricate systems, and yet they are nothing like as complex as the vast topological structure of the human brain, with its thousands of millions of neurons and even more differentiated connections. A simple house-fly, indeed, is far more complex than a factory! Though nature has endowed us with an intelligence capable of exploring phenomena through intuition and logic, she has been less generous in equipping us to tackle combinatorial investigations.

Table 1 Administrative operations necessary for forming in France a limited company without appeal to the public and without contribution in kind.

1 Drafting the articles of the company.
2 Depositing the draft in the record office.
3 Preparing the allotment letters.
4 Despatching the allotment letters.
5 Returning the allotment letters, signed and including the paid-up capital.
6 Preparing the statement of subscription and payment.
7 Depositing the statement and the capital with the notary.
8 Preparing the declaration executed and authenticated by a notary.
9 Deciding the number of directors.
10 Selecting the directors.
11 Determining of the directors' remuneration.
12 Deciding on the number of auditors.
13 Selecting the auditors.
14 Determining the auditors' remuneration.
15 Preparing the declaration of subscriptions and payments.
16 Preparing the Constitutive Assembly.
17 Preparing the first Council.
18 Meeting of the Constitutive Assembly.
19 Meeting of the Council.
20 Preparing the expedition of the original draft of the articles.
21 Writing up the minutes of the Constitutive Assembly.
22 Presenting to the Registry Office.
23 Depositing in the Record Office.
24 Articles for the cheque accounts.
25 Specimen signatures for the cheque accounts.
26 Minutes of the Constitutive Assembly for the cheque accounts.
27 Minutes of the first Council of Administration for the cheque accounts.

28 Preparing copy for publication.
29 Copy published in legal journals.
30 Sending out legal journals.
31 Despatching legal journals to the cheque account.
32 Making out *Modele B* for the purposes of the entry in the Commercial Register.
33 Birth certificates of the directors.
34 Certificate of the Housing Department (commercial premises).
35 Printing, preparing share certificates.
36 Signatures of the shares.
37 Opening the Council Register.
38 Opening the cheque accounts.
39 Registration in the Commercial Register.
40 Notifying the Health Department.
41 Notifying the Registry Office.
42 Opening the General Assembly Register.
43 Opening the Transfer Register.
44 Completing the Direct Taxation form.
45 Drafting copies of the articles.
46 Drafting copies of the minutes of the Constitutive Assembly.
47 Completing the Indirect Taxation form.
48 Notifying the Direct Taxation Office.
49 Notifying the Indirect Taxation Office.
50 Buying account books.
51 Stamping the account books.

Dummy activities The activities numbered 52 to 64 are called dummy activities' (or simply 'dummies') and show logical constraints on the succession of the real activities connected by them.

Figure 2·1

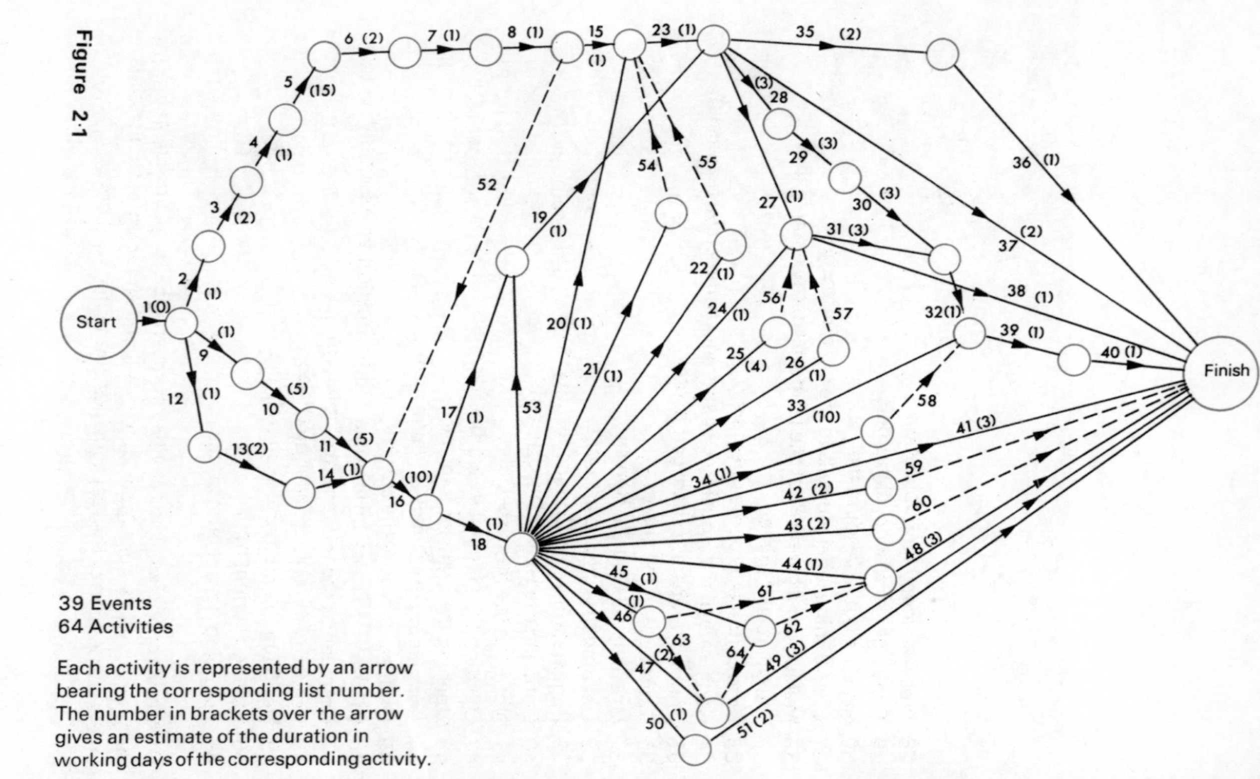
Start
Finish
39 Events
64 Activities
Each activity is represented by an arrow bearing the corresponding list number. The number in brackets over the arrow gives an estimate of the duration in working days of the corresponding activity.

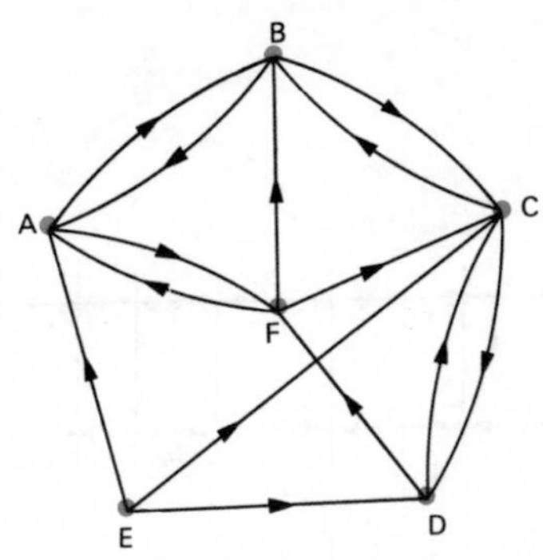

Figure 2·2

Let us consider, for example, the pattern formed by six points and fourteen arrows shown on the figure 2·2. How many sequences can we form with the letters A B C D E and F, in such a manner that they form paths starting from one point, going on to the next, and passing once and once only through all the other points? Thus, E C D F A B is such a sequence. There are seven in all; I leave my readers to enumerate the others.

Finally, it will be appreciated what a valuable help mathematics can be, when a phenomenon is combinatorial by nature, not only in giving a representation of it but also in analysing it. The phenomena on which I shall focus attention in this present work have, in general, a combinatorial structure of this sort.

3 Contraction of time

The theory of relativity in physics tells us that time is not homogeneous for all bodies in motion. It depends on the speed of the moving body, and it decreases as the speed increases. This phenomenon is called the 'contraction of time'. But we are going to consider a totally different contraction. It is also accepted, though obviously without proof, that psychological time contracts with the age of an individual (a year seeming to pass more quickly for an old man than for a young man).

The greatest density of events occurring within equal periods of passing time introduces another form of contraction. In these

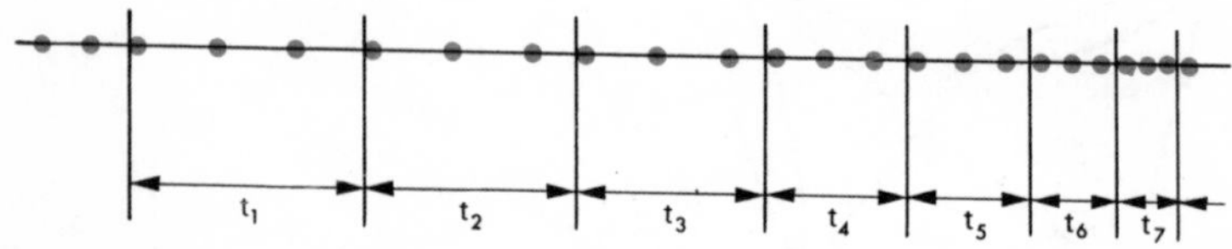

Figure 3·1

terms, this notion of contraction is very vague and we are going to explain it another way. Let us call 'fact' or 'event' a modification, whether under the influence of the environment or under the influence of a decision, of the system studied; in that case the same period of time will be richer in events for the later periods. If instead of dividing time into equal intervals, we divide it into intervals each containing the same number of facts, the duration of each of these intervals will be smaller and smaller; this phenomenon is set out in figure 3·1.

Of course this relative contraction of time is practically and theoretically impossible. It is a hypothesis which must be accepted, in the same way that a psychologist accepts the contraction of psychological time in terms of age without being able to formulate a valid mathematical law. In the case of a socio-economic system, it is advisable to remember that this hypothesis depends on the system in question, just as in psychology it depends on each individual constituting a separate case.

The causes of this relative contraction of time are chiefly: the widening of structures, the increase in the speed of communications and of transport, and the increase in the means of treating and transmitting information. Although it is very difficult in the phenomenon of organisation to detail specific events, except in the elementary structures, one can state categorically that the current of events is gathering pace.

The contraction of time we are concerned with is also called the 'acceleration of history'. I have devoted a paragraph of this book to this particular question as I think that it forms an important causal element in the development of the attitude of people at sufficiently high levels of responsibility in the systems. As we do not have the necessary time nowadays for the study of all the facts, for the preparation of decisions, it is convenient to spread such study and preparation over a group. It is also helpful to simplify problems by systematic analysis. Since this can often be achieved through mathematical models, they have an obvious interest to management. Finally, the use of sufficiently powerful media for the treatment of information and for calculation can compensate for the contraction of time by the rapidity with which the message is interpreted.

4 Speed of communications

This is another important factor which imposes on modern man a change of attitude towards his behaviour in a position of authority. With electrical transmission practically instantaneous, with the perfection over the last few decades of audio-visual methods, especially now that television has found its way into our homes and even into our factories, what is important, as far as the arguments put forward in this work are concerned, is not the instrument of communication itself but the extent of its growth.

The spread of oral and/or visual communications is leading to a considerable decrease in the waiting period for information and the reply to it. The method of working, the organisation of responsibilities, the preparation of decisions, the supervision of their implementation – all these activities are accelerating fast. Sometimes the psychological effects which result can even cause neuroses, not only among individuals but among the systems themselves, if we accept that this sort of illness can also exist in cybernetic concepts.

If the time allotted to reflection is thus curtailed, the widening, on the other hand, of the immediate range of perception makes for the better working out of decisions; but we must learn to think faster, and to accept more readily the delegation to others, at lower levels, of a part of our responsibilities.

It would be as well to take account of the means of communication, of speech, of psycho-social attitudes, of codes of behaviour, not only within a group working together in the same place but also with groups working apart. During a recent visit to North American Aviation for instance, I was impressed by the system of closed-circuit television which not only enables the various departmental heads in the same factory to communicate without moving from their offices, but equally enables the same sort of communication to be made between departments belonging to factories perhaps a hundred miles apart.

This closed-circuit television not only makes functional communications possible but also enables orders to be specified, modifications and new techniques to be taught, as well as the direct or deferred observation of certain phenomena, and so on. It also represents a kind of delocalisation – a modern way to create ubiquity. The employment of this internal TV system, which is to be found, of course, in other firms, will certainly spread when its advantages are recognised. In all probability it will bring about a completely new approach to the problems of management at all levels.

We should now perhaps proceed to a certain mental exercise, to the development of the faculty which in English is called role-changing. This word should not be taken in a pejorative sense: such mental mobility is an indispensable complement of the speed of communication.

The semantic aspect itself needs to be considered. The meaning of words and messages is sometimes modified by the system of transmission. It is no longer man talking to man, but two men talking through machines which bring about distortions. These distortions would not matter if it were only a question of language, but they also have semantic characteristics.

Stresses and strains can arise among people working in organisations equipped with internal and external communication devices which allow an extensive circulation of ideas and orders. They will probably not be reduced without careful preparation in the use of such devices. The next generation will perhaps suffer less than we do from this increase of intensity in communication, as they will have grown used to it from childhood. As for us, it is vital that we should adapt to the world of telecommunications and automatic interpretation of information.

If we take the word 'communication' in its physical sense, there is no doubt that mobility of individuals and objects, and the possibilities arising from the speed reached by various means of transport, have modified the behaviour of businessmen, and more widely speaking, the behaviour of people in authority in civil and military spheres. One consequence is that preparing and taking decisions can be accompanied by an on-the-spot study of the problems as they arise.

But, though the advance in communications has diminished the number of uncontrolled variables, thanks to improvements in the processing of information, nevertheless problems now arise at higher levels, on a higher plane of responsibility. The area of study which precedes action must in the long run be much greater.

5 Influence of technological progress

When a new scientific theory can be applied in a certain field of technology, men are involved just as much as objects. It very often means reassessing the position and the future of individuals.

At this point I would like to restate the terms of the theory developed in a chapter of a book which I wrote recently in collaboration with J. Cathelin (*Le gaspillage de la liberté*, published by Dunod, Paris, 1964).

Technological progress has always had important repercussions on men's daily lives. But previously, owing to the more limited distribution of information and the comparatively small accumulation of knowledge (see Lévi-Strauss's theory of 'Cumulative Civilisation'), its influence was slower and more diffuse. No doubt the wheel, or the printing-press, when they were invented, had an immediate effect on the ideas and living conditions of certain people. But their influence on the human condition in general was slow and limited in relation to the contraction of evolutionary time.

Thus, for example, large areas of our planet for centuries remained ignorant of both of these major inventions. (The western world had not heard of gunpowder at a time when it was being used in China; and the pre-Columbian civilisations knew nothing of the wheel.) Nowadays, on the contrary, the historical and geographical (i.e. spatio-temporal) impact (or influence) of technological progress is simultaneous on individuals or groups throughout the world. The effect of technological advances on individual or group structures is direct and immediate.

But is it possible to predict technological advances? Though it may be impossible at long range, one can make short term forecasts about the initial stages in certain spheres. These stages will be very important factors in decision-making. Judging the effect of technological progress on a short-term basis is certainly possible and this is, in fact, one of the research activities of economists and engineers with executive responsibility. But, as I shall show in another chapter, such evaluations must be made, if possible, of the accompanying risk.

In a world flexible in its structures and its methods – a flexibility which springs mainly from technological progress – a rigid attitude, firmly rooted in certain systems of valuing or measuring, is out of place. Moreover the impossibility of being specific about progress in the long term must make anyone with the responsibility of decision very wary. The soundest attitude towards such a flexible world is one of adaptability and I shall attempt to analyse its various elements.

One need hardly emphasise how grave are the consequences of overlooking, and sometimes wilfully ignoring, the influence of technological progress and the direction in which it is moving, however ignorant one may be of its nature. Wars have often been lost because of this oversight; and they have also caused economic recessions and the downfall of commercial enterprises.

Hypotheses on the evolution of techniques must be considered as parameters when one wishes to build the model of a structure. This sometimes makes the work of reflection and analysis extremely complicated but it is absolutely necessary.

One is reminded of Auguste Detoeuf's remark, 'A society is not run according to rules laid down once and for all; it is an unending creation. If the world does not run very well, the reason is that God, having created it and fixed its laws, thought he could have a rest.'

6 Electronic treatment of information

The field of applied science dealing with the electronic treatment of information includes not only the theory and the construction but also the uses of the electronic calculators which we now call 'computers'. We shall confine ourselves in this paragraph to the uses of computers, pointing out in the main how helpful and frequently how necessary they are. The list in table 2 (page 26) gives some idea of the part played by computers in human activities. For the layman I shall explain briefly the use of this equipment in several of these operations.

Let us suppose that an organisation like NASA (National Aeronautical and Space Administration) has to prepare the launching of a space capsule with one or several human passengers. Such a launching goes through five main stages:

1 Putting the missile into orbit.
2 Duplicating by ground control the pilot's handling of the capsule.
3 Manoeuvring the capsule.
4 Starting the retroactive jets, and
5 Directing the descent towards a pre-arranged landing point.

In spite of an advanced level of knowledge and reliable equipment, one cannot foresee everything needed to ensure the absolute safety of the astronaut and the successful completion of a particular mission. The equations of the trajectories linked to the planes of a

Table 2 Some uses of computers.

Organisation and forecasting in industry.
Numeric calculation.
Accountancy and statistics.
Trajectories of space vehicles and satellites.
Military detection systems.
Automatic booking for air travel.
Programming of events and operations
(PERT system and variants).
Management and supervision of production lines.
Documentation, bibliography.
Translation of foreign languages.
Legal research and analyses.
Meteorology.
Medical diagnosis.
Analysis and control of urban traffic.
Teaching.
Machine stimulation.
Business games, tactical or strategic war games.
Voting systems.
Philology.
Coding, deciphering, transcoding.
Musical composition.
Control of road traffic (electronic treatment of traffic), etc.

moving earth are extremely complex; with each deviation of the trajectory orders are given by radio to the controls, but all the decisions to be taken cannot be committed to the computers. (Several computers are needed, each of vast dimensions.) Some of the functions of decision are entrusted to men, engineers and supervisors. So the whole of the operation thus completed is made up of the following components: capsule and passengers, tracking

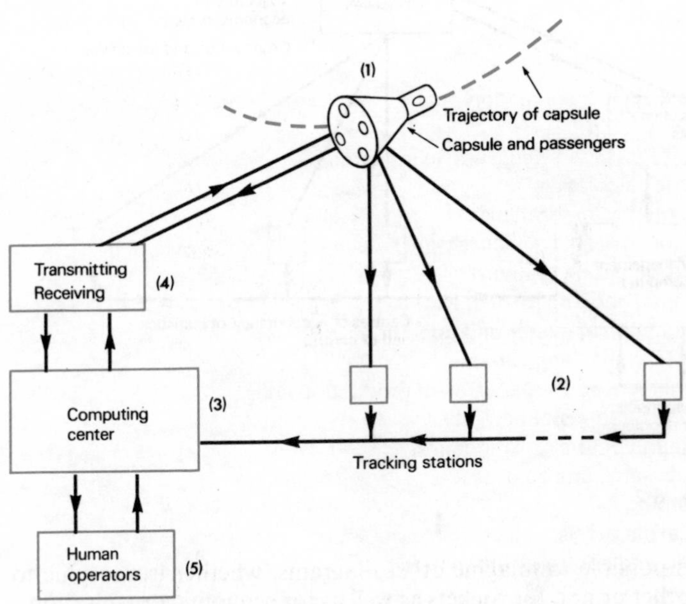

Figure 6·1

stations, calculation centre, ground supervisors. On examining the structure of such a system, a diagram such as the one on figure 6·1 can easily be made up, showing the various functions.

Now let us try to draw a diagram representing this time the structure of the organs of function and decision of a complex economic organisation such as a company. The basic diagram is shown in figure 6·2. It will be seen that it is the same as the one in figure 6·1. Of course, in both cases we have limited ourselves to the five primary functions.

1 The object and its trajectory.
2 The controls.
3 The calculation.
4 Methods of execution and reception.
5 The command.

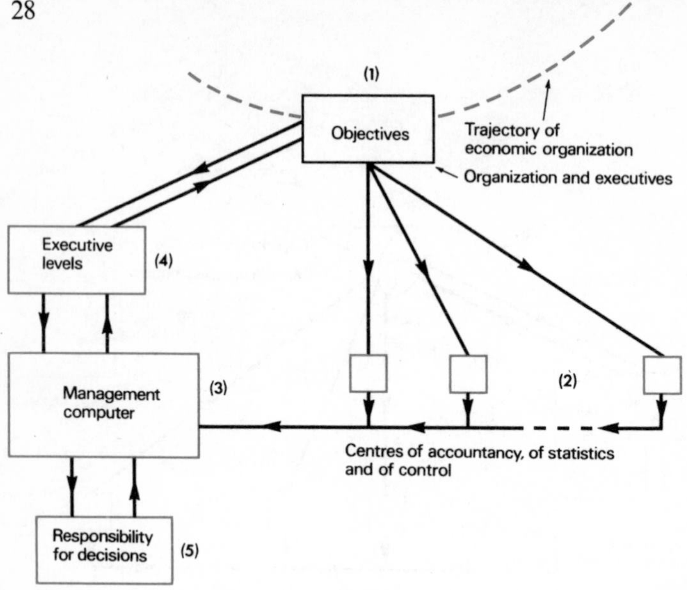

Figure 6·2

It is possible to imagine other diagrams, whether isomorphic to each other or not, for rockets as well as for economic organisations. The interest of the representation I have chosen lies in the fact that it stresses the importance of the role of the 'decision-making computer'.

The diagram used can be applied to other systems; for example the system formed by the driver and his car. In figure 6·3 the five primary functions of the system are shown.

The analogy between the system made up of the space capsule and the sum of the elements controlling its trajectory on the one hand, and an economic organisation on the other, is much closer than one might suppose – to the extent, in fact, that the mathematical instruments used are closely related. For example, the same principle, called 'the principle of optimality', which plays a fundamental role in the 'calculus of variations', and its modern version 'dynamic programming', is used by the engineers at Cape Kennedy or at Novosibirsk as well as by the economists who study the management of equipment and stocks. Economists are already

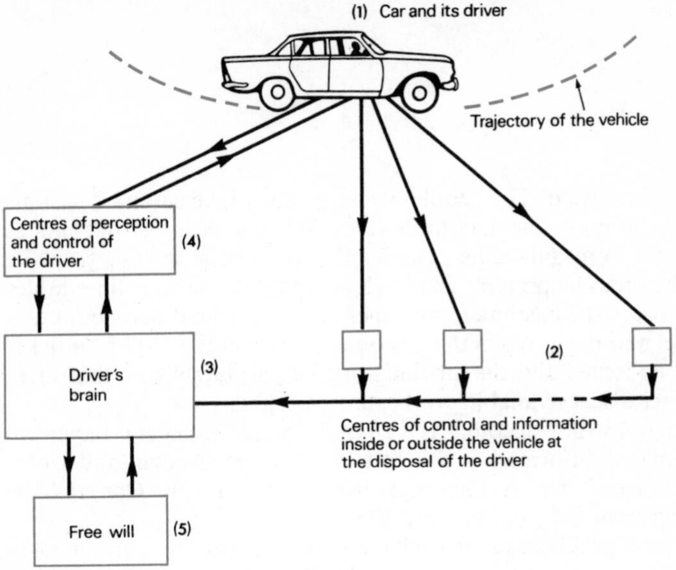

Figure 6·3

beginning to speak of the 'trajectory' of an economic system, and of 'economic geodesics'.

Let us examine some other uses of computers.

An interesting example concerns the reservation of seats with air lines. It gives a very good picture of the use of computers in 'real time'. (The expression 'real time' means that the time spent between feeding information into the computer and getting the results out corresponds to the length of time dictated by the needs of the process under control. Generally, when the computer deals with information in a very short period of time the results are stored and emerge at the appointed time. To avoid idle time in the calculation and storage units, the machine is provided with several input channels and items of information are fed in simultaneously and temporarily stored, lining up like customers in a queue.)

The problem of the reservation of seats in a large air-line is a straightforward one: how to sell the maximum number of seats. The seats represent extremely perishable goods – they cannot be stored and when a plane takes off any that remain vacant are inevitably wasted. The people in charge must take certain decisions in order to make the maximum sales. When a customer telephones or comes to an office, he explains the journey he intends to make and the times he prefers. The clerk looks up the various time-tables and advises the customer, who then makes his final decision, takes a ticket and pays. When the customer arrives at the airport, a ticket has been issued and the air-line must be absolutely sure that there is in fact a seat available on the chosen flight.

The following account is inspired by the excellent paper on 'Automated Information Systems in Planning Control and Command' (read by A. Vazsonyi before the Tenth Congress of Management Sciences in June 1963).

If passengers behaved in such a way that last-minute cancellations or bookings never had to be made, the solution to the problem would be very simple. But a large percentage of the seats have to be cancelled and re-sold, often within a few hours of the time of departure of the flight. This makes the problem considerably more complicated and has necessitated the use of computers acting in 'real time'. At the central booking office of the air-line there is a computer connected with all the main cities. This machine makes the necessary search and provides the time-tables, does the accounts, checks the seats available and any issues which may be of importance for the passengers. Let us suppose that somebody telephones or comes to the booking office to decide on a certain journey. The assistant makes use of a small control device connected to the computer. By the aid of a small plate containing appropriate perforations and notches which he inserts in the machine, and by turning certain knobs, he can communicate with the electronic centre which tells him in a very short time whether the required seat is available. If it is, the clerk books the seat for the customer, issues the ticket and the computer records a firm booking. He can also make cancellations if need be. Because of the speed of communication and of processing the information, the booking of available seats is possible until the last minute. One can see how the use of a computer can appreciably modify the administrative and commercial organisation of an air-line, even to the point of reviewing accepted practices which hitherto might have seemed unquestionably to be in the company's interest.

Another example concerns the devices used by the army for the command and control of the means to discourage air and nuclear missile attacks. When one studies the causes of the success achieved by the RAF during the Battle of Britain in the Second World War, the quality and courage of their pilots is obviously the first thing to be considered. There was also, however, the quality of the organisation of the defence system at a time when there was as yet no question of employing electronic calculating machines. Nowadays the main centres of command and control are equipped with huge computers which receive information on the possible movements of various hostile and friendly aircraft, analyse the situations, deal with and pass the information on to the people in charge, or if necessary, make an automatic decision on the appropriate orders, conveying them to the various levels of command and execution, after making all necessary verifications. A system such as SAGE (Semi-Automatic Ground Equipment System) perfected these procedures in the USA. SAGE in fact is an extremely complicated organisation possessing much bigger electronic computers than those generally in use in the great university centres or in large firms. An idea of the work of the production and preparation of such a system can be given by pointing out that the programming of all the electronic computers in use has called for more than two million hours' work on the part of the programmers. At the various levels of command and operation at large military installations for defence and attack, important problems arise concerning the men and the pattern within which they are disposed. Psycho-sociology has already made great progress, thanks to the studies of these many thousands of men placed in relation to each other like the neurons in the brain.

All the uses of electronic computers in scientific management would need hundreds of pages to be developed fully. My present comments are very much in the nature of a summary. Computers can be used as instruments for forecasting and decision, either in contracted machine time (calculation of possible solutions or optimal solutions – field of operational research), or in real machine time (management proper – field of automated management). Certain procedures thus constitute a superposition of these two uses. I shall have occasion in various chapters of the present work to refer back to the use of electronic computing in operational research and in scientific management.

Among other important applications of computers is their use in processing diagrams of supervision and control of work already mentioned (figure 2·1). In 1957 the study and the manufacture of the famous Polaris missile system had set an enormous accounting problem for the organisers of the project, who had to assume responsibility for thousands and thousands of research operations, both theoretical and practical, and of studies of manufacturing processes; hundreds of millions of dollars were at stake, but what was even more important, the effective manufacture of these arms had considerable implications for the foreign policy of the Western world. A team of mathematicians and engineers from the US Navy Department perfected a method now known the whole world over under the name of PERT (Progress Evaluation and Review Technique), or again, under another title CPM (Critical Path Method). Thanks to PERT, the Polaris programme was successfully worked out, and in fact was finished appreciably in advance of what had been forecast. To give the reader an idea of how PERT works, let us suppose that a firm is in charge of building a dam, and that the engineers have drawn up, in advance, a list of all the activities comprised in such a project, the sequence of these activities, the events which end them and their durations. One can then obtain, using an arrow diagram, a representation such as the one given in figure 6·4, in which the arrows show activities and the circles events. The PERT method will give the total time, and the critical activities and events (that is to say, those which must not be delayed). For the non-critical activities and events PERT will give the limits of permissible delay (called ‘slack time’).

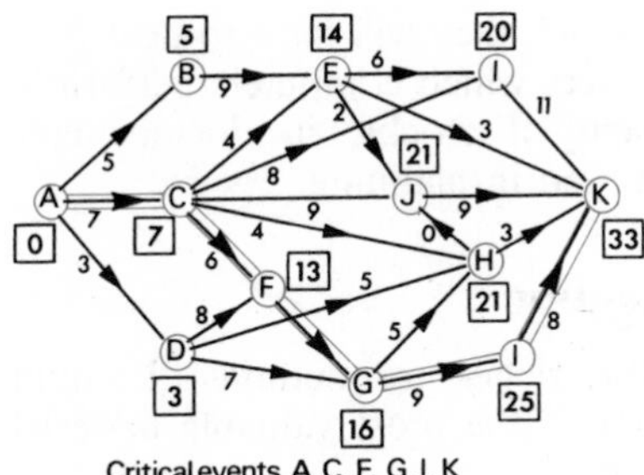

Critical events A, C, F, G, I, K

Figure 6·4

Moreover, an electronic computer can carry out exchanges or corrections of activities, to modify certain investments, to arrange the schedules so as to obtain the optimum overall duration or financial outlay. One can see the uses to which such a method can be put, in all sorts of professions; and it has become a most reliable method for studying actual situations and for the scientific preparation of decisions.[6] Opinion is practically unanimous that this method constitutes an appreciable advance on older scheduling methods.

Thus, for the Apollo project (men landing on the moon) organised by NASA, the PERT system is used at every stage. Here are a few figures which speak for themselves: 20,000 firms are working on this project; 150,000 scientists and engineers are taking part, and about 100,000 operations are being planned. The facilities for electronic calculation will, of course, be on the scale of this gigantic enterprise. There are scores of large computers being used, each one costing several millions of dollars.

The Anglo-French project Concord (Paris to New York in about two hours) should also be cited. Its production was accounted by PERT or one of its variants.

When PERT is conducted on a large scale by means of electronic calculation, the organisers of a project have at their disposal a veritable spatio-temporal map which enables them to estimate the future timing of the events with which they will have to deal.

One could cite many other services which computers perform – for example, in the management of stocks, in documentary researches, in bank management, and in planning.

7 Methods for the man of action

Nietzsche said: 'the most valuable riches are methods'. I would prefer to put more stress on virtue: 'the most valuable material riches are methods'.

The plan put forward by A. Moles[1] and by the Methodological Studies Group enables us to enumerate fifty or more separate methods used for action. There is no scarcity of methods – on the contrary, there is a surfeit, and I for one make no complaint about it. Table 3 presents on pages 36–7 a summarised list of several methods used in very different fields of science.

8 Towards a more scientific attitude

The general factors whose importance we have underlined in the preceding pages call for a more scientific attitude among people in authority. To find, to measure, to analyse, to optimise, to decide, to observe the results and to begin the cycle again; this is the way in which decision-taking should be carried out. Certainly, intuition plays a vital part in human actions and thoughts, as Descartes emphasised in his *Regulae ad directionem ingenii*. In this work he lays down rules for helping inventive reflection; it was among the first of Descartes' researches. Abundant in subject matter, his book deals with logic and methodology; he introduces heuristics, a set of rules on inventive reflection.

Our attitude in action cannot merely be logical, for it should be recognised that emotion is an influence of prime importance; without it there would be no more will in action, simply automatisms and tropisms. The correct attitude, as Descartes has said, and after him Leibnitz and Bolzano, seems to be the heuristic attitude – a mixture of inventive intuition and of logic. To maintain his independence in the midst of increasingly complex mechanisms which he must control, the man of action must remain a creator, he needs *ingenium*. The great mathematician G. Polya considers that the heuristic attitude is fundamental to the explorer, to the discoverer.

The rules of heuristics, according to Descartes, are also the ones which seem to be important in the conduct of men, as well as in the conduct of research and in creativity. Here too, talent and experience are not everything; we need an intense desire to get at the truth. The man of action finds it in scientific method. Above all else, there must be, in his mental make-up, an uncompromising spirit of truth which, in order to emerge, needs methods and means of processing of information. A business deal cannot now be conducted merely with subtlety or even cunning. One has to see the facts and the situations mapped out as exactly as possible. Models must be produced on which discussion can be based, models closer and closer to reality; incomplete perhaps, because they are models and not objects, but solidly built on logical foundations. Too many businessmen have tried to be miracle workers, risking all on a hunch, following only their lucky stars.

The happy marriage of intuition and logic can be achieved through the use, where possible, of mathematical methods.

Obviously, to bring the mathematical genie into human science, one must first understand it. It does not rush meekly to obey the commands of each and every would-be usurper who summons it. And it is when it seems easiest to master that it is most dangerous. Yet it is possible, from the clues, the measurements, and the models it provides, to make decisions manifestly better than rules of thumb.

Table 3 Methods and their application.

Method	**Brief Description**	**Example and application**
Direct application of a theory.	Starting from the fact that a mathematical or abstract rational theory, wholly enunciable, exists, this theory is applied to the actual problem considered.	This is the method of mathematical models used by physicists or economists. It is a real mechanisation which enables us to pass from the general theory to the feasible domain.
Method of revising hypotheses.	From a criticism of basic hypotheses or their developments, construction of a new system of more acceptable hypotheses.	From the faults of an organisation or of a machine set up according to certain principles, construction of a more efficient system.
Critical or dialectic method.	Setting up a new system of hypothesis from the destruction of the previous system.	Intervention into a work of research or classification of an effective dissenter who succeeds in modifying the trend of the research, or the choice of a different classification.
Renovation method.	An older theory or organisation is supposed to exist. The renovation consists in modifying the theory or organisation, taking into consideration fresh facts or new methods, but without modifying the objective of the action.	One of the most widely used practical methods in research and organisation. In physics, revising the theory of conductivity in the light of atomic science. Introducing punched cards into a firm without changing its accounting principles.
Method of transfer of concepts.	Concepts are taken from one particular field and an attempt is made to transfer them to a new one.	To take the concept of a transient state from physics and to try and use it in the study of certain problems of business management.
Method of analogical transfer.	A phenomenon is examined with the considerations, and from the viewpoint of a different phenomenon.	Analogy between certain problems of flux in physics and flow in a problem of traffic. Analogy between the mortality of living cells and the wear and tear of equipment.
Method of prolongation.	Certain limitations are imposed in order that they may be exceeded, leading to new limitations, and so on.	This is the introduction into reasoning of induction, as is often done in mathematics.

Method	Brief description	Example and application
Phenomeno-logical method.	Advocated by the philosopher Husserl, it consists in isolating a phenomenon from its background in order to study and use it, though the discarded connections may be taken into account later on.	Frame-by-frame analysis of film. Certain methods of simulation. Visual study of flow in a fluid by using dyes.
Teratological method.	Consists in formulating hypotheses beyond the normal limits of rationality, then imagining their effect in the given pattern.	To consider in a problem of business management extreme values of certain parameters, in order to find a reasonable compromise.
Dichotomy method.	Faced with a given problem we ask ourselves a series of questions which can be answered by yes or no.	This is the classical procedure in mathematics for many demonstrations. An element in the problem is defined as possessing or not possessing certain characteristics – choice between several types of investment through successive dichotomies.
Matrices of discovery method.	Universal method permitting a rationalised study of the field of possibilities. A square table or matrix is made up giving the reactions of studied features in relation to each other. Can be generalised into hypercubes, when one looks for the reactions of features when *n* is greater than 3.	Mendeleev table. Economic or sociological interactions. Problems of information in business. Factorial analysis.
Morphological method.	Determination of groups of elements which can be part of the morphology of a concept, or of a machine.	Research into technological innovation. Great success in space research. Astronony.
Brainstorming method.	There is a negative correlation between the creative and the critical mind. In team work all criticism is forbidden and as many different suggestions as possible are encouraged.	Research into new selling and publicity processes. Industrial aesthetics.

2 The choice of a criterion

9 Introduction

The trickiest problem in the rational preparation for action is, in the opinion of psychologists and economists, the conversion of objectives into criteria. This chapter will be devoted to this difficult but interesting question, which can be satisfactorily answered only in certain relatively simple cases. The arguments used in the mathematical theory of sets constitute reliable guides for the choice of an order of preference, or value function which corresponds with sufficient accuracy to objectives.

I shall purposely use very elementary and sometimes artificial examples, to avoid too long or complicated statements. By using examples where the objects studied are in a finite number, I shall be able to present the characteristics studied without using mathematical formulae, which would make difficult reading for some. The notion of a graph in the sense of the theory of sets, will give an easy introduction to the concept I shall need.

10 Some important characteristics of the theory of sets

A set is a collection of objects (concrete or abstract) which are 'well defined' and 'distinct from one another'. Such a definition, intuitive though it be, will suffice for this work.

One can talk of a set of pupils in a class, of a set of numbers, of a set of points on a map; but one cannot talk of a set of ideas.

In particular, objectives constitute a set only when well defined and distinct. This is the first difficulty to overcome in order to be able to deal with collections of objects as whole sets. However, this first attempt at definition will be of great help in the scientific investigation of intentions. Here we shall rediscover the considerations that Descartes passed on to us in his *Discours* and that later on, economists – in particular Pareto – have chosen as a starting point for their theories.

What is a graph?

Let us start by an example. Suppose we have a set $A = (a, b, c, d)$

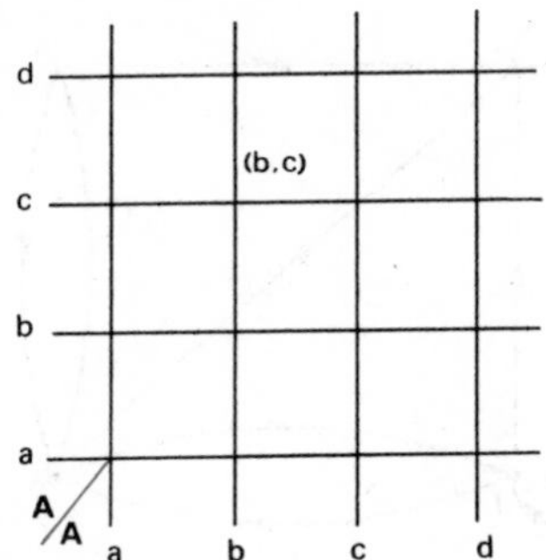

Figure 10·1

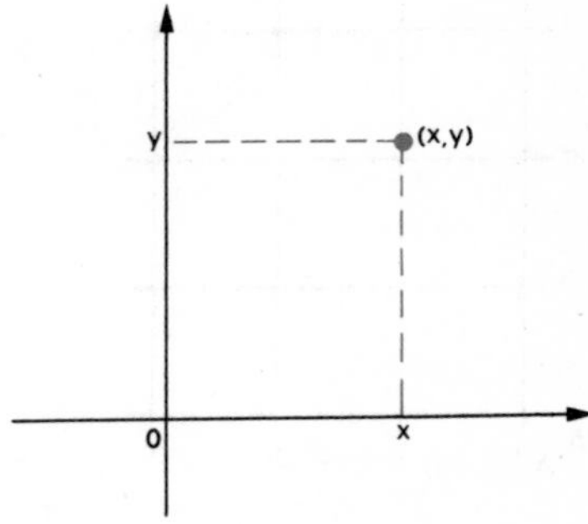

Figure 10·2

i.e. a collection of four letters, quite distinct. Let us form pairs with these four letters, say (a, a) (a, b) (a, c) (a, d) (b, a) (b, b) (b, c) (b, d) (c, a) (c, b) (c, c) (c, d) (d, a) (d, b) (d, c) (d, d). These pairs in turn form a set called the product of set A by set A. But this notion can also be extended to infinite sets. Thus the set of the points of the map *xoy* is really a set of the pair (x, y) in which x is one co-ordinate and y the other. Figures 10·1 and 10·2 represent the products of the sets which have just been described. The sixteen pairs formed from the set (a, b, c, d) appear at the intersection of the lines drawn in figure 10·1. In figure 10·2, the points with co-ordinates x, y are infinite in number, but the principle of representing them remains the same.

Now let us return to the example of figure 10·1 and let us suppose that we can break down the set of sixteen pairs into two parts, one of these parts having certain properties, and the other part not having them. The part possessing the properties will be called 'graph', and be denoted by **G**. Figure 10·3 and figure 10·4 give examples of graphs. In figure 10·3 the ●'s placed at the inter-sections of the lattice work (figure 10·3(a)) or the arrows on figure 10·3(b) which gives another representation, show the pairs belong-

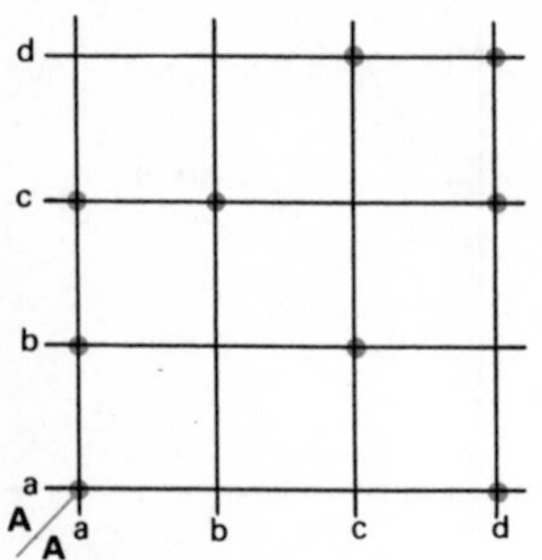

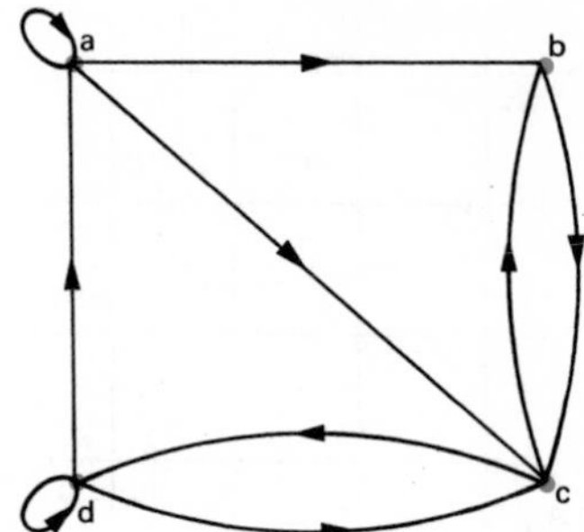

Figure 10·3 (a) and (b)

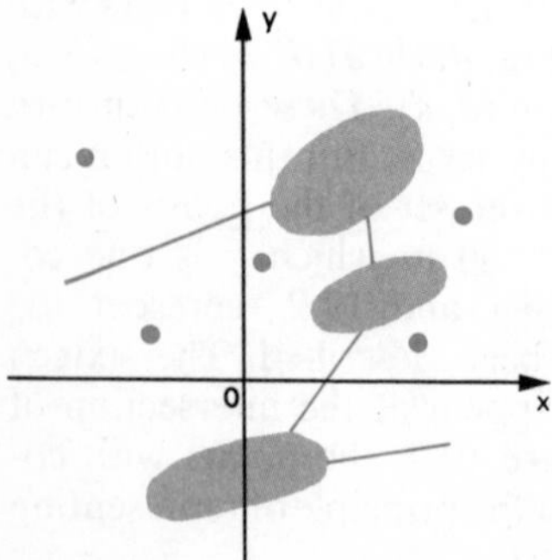

Figure 10·4

ing to the graph. Figure 10·4 represents a graph of an infinite set **A** which is the set of all real numbers from $-\infty$ to $+\infty$; for this last figure all shaded areas, lines and isolated points belong to the graph.

We are now going to study the principal properties of graphs, because these properties will be essential in the arguments relating

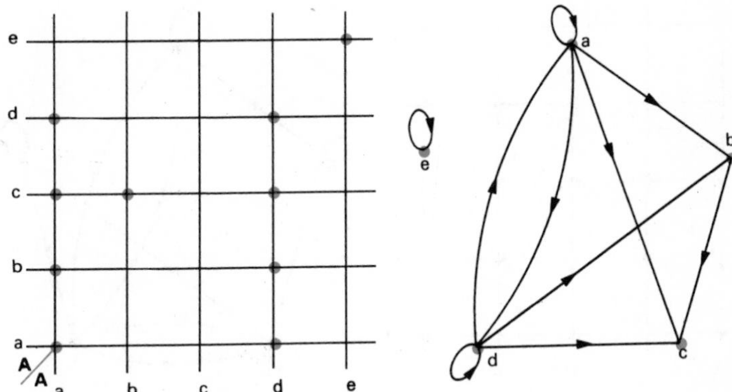

Figure 10·5 (a) and (b)

to the notion of preference. Then we shall see in which simple cases it is possible to convert a graph of precedence into a criterion.

Transitivity. A graph is 'transitive' when it possesses the following properties: if two pairs (x, y) and (y, z) belong to the graph, the pair (x, z) belongs to it also. This is a fundamental property.

Figure 10·5 shows a transitive graph. Thus (a, b) and (b, c) belong to **G** as does (a, c). In the same way (a, d) and (d, a) belong to **G** and (a, a) also.

The property of transitivity is that of the syllogism, whence its importance. The well-known properties $x < y$ (x smaller than y), straight line D_1 is parallel to straight line D_2, the numbers n_1 and n_2 are divisible by the same number p, produce transitive graphs, but on the other hand, the relationship '*A* resembles *B*' is not a transitive relation; in fact *A* may resemble *B* and *B* resemble *C* without *A* resembling *C*.

Reflexivity. A graph is reflexive when it contains all the pairs (n, n), i.e. all the pairs (x, y) where $x = y$. Figure 10·6 gives an

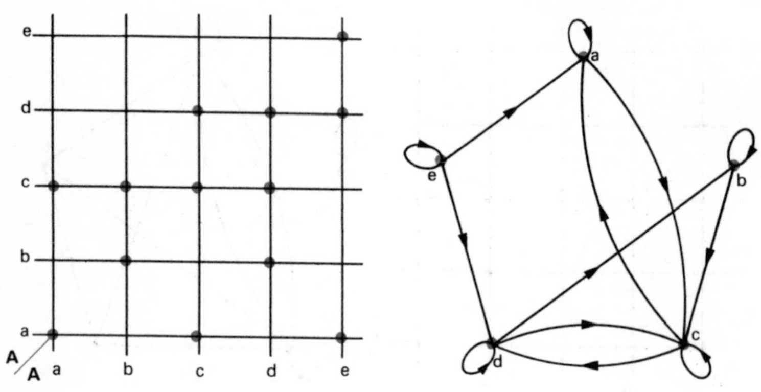

Figure 10·6 (a) and (b)

example of a reflexive graph. The pairs (a, a) (b, b) (c, c) (d, d) and (e, e) are all part of the graph.

Relation of pre-order or low order. A graph which is both transitive and reflexive represents a 'relation of pre-order'.

Figure 10·7 gives an example of a relation of pre-order. The relations $x \leqslant y$, $x = y$, D_1 is $\parallel$ to D_2 are relations which possess the property of forming pre-orders.

Symmetry. A graph **S** 'symmetrical' is such that: if a pair (x, y) belongs to **S** then the pair (y, x) belongs to it also. Figure 10·8 represents a symmetrical graph.

Relation of equivalence. A graph which is at the same time transitive – reflexive – symmetrical, represents a relation of equivalence. Figure 10·9 gives the graph of a relation of equivalence; so does figure 10·10 but on this figure (figure 10·10(a)), the elements of the set **A** have been placed in such a way that the parts of **A** equivalent

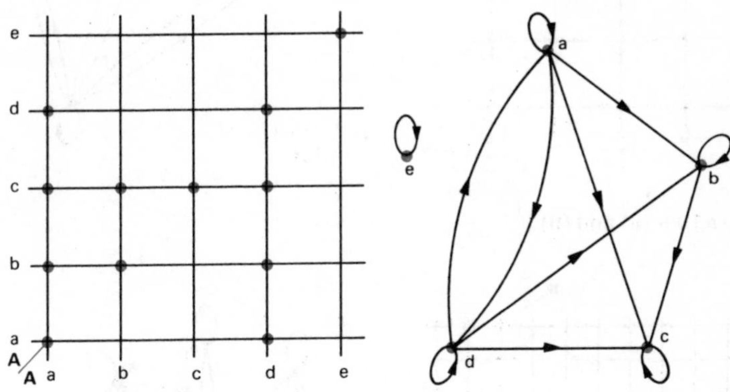

Figure 10·7 (a) and (b)

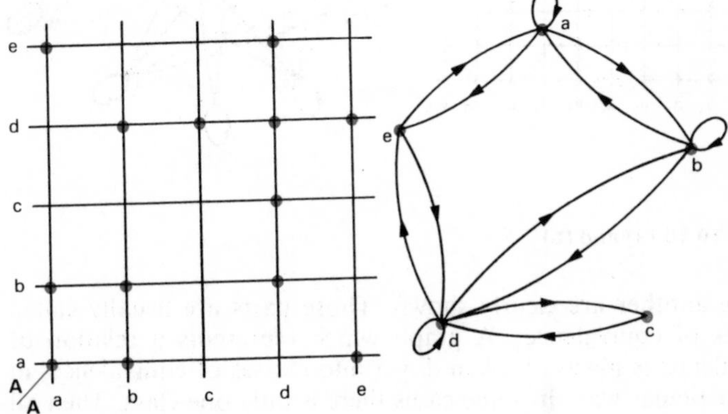

Figure 10·8 (a) and (b)

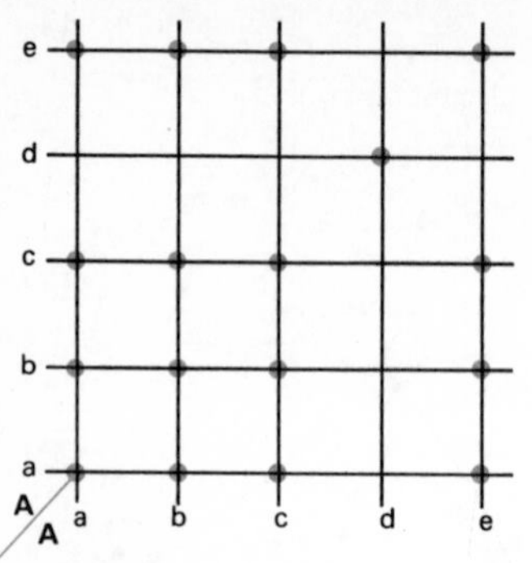

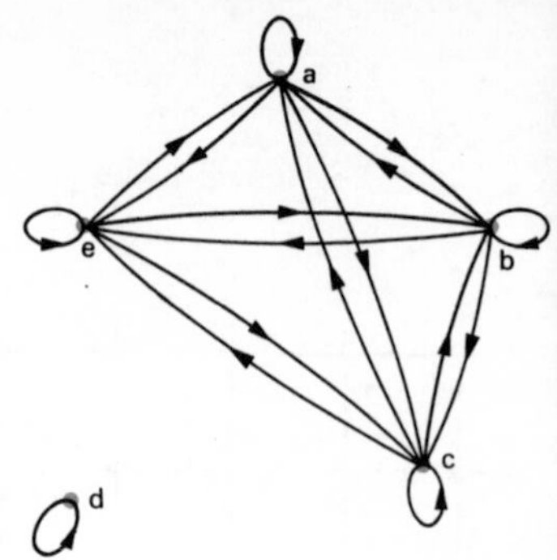

Figure 10·9 (a) and (b)

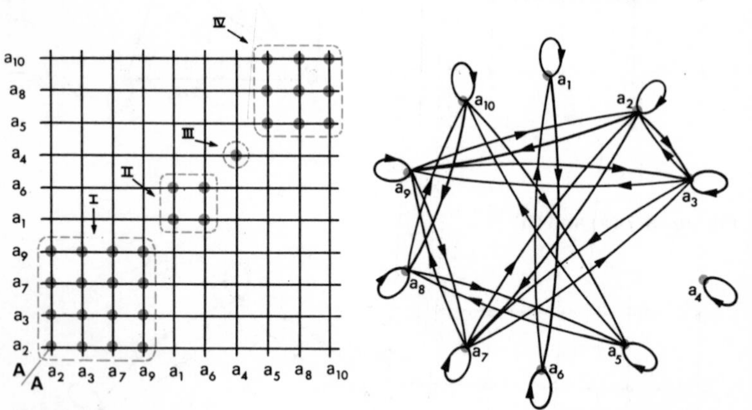

Figure 10·10 (a) and (b)

to one another are clearly shown. Those parts are usually called 'classes of equivalence'. A graph which represents a relation of equivalence is always broken down into classes of equivalence, in one particular way. In some cases there is only one class. Then all the pairs without exception belong to the graph.

Let us mention some examples of relations of equivalence: $x = y$, $D_1 \parallel D_2$, A belongs to the same family as B, $x - y$ is divisible by p, etc.

Antisymmetry. A graph **G** is 'antisymmetric' if: x being different from y, the presence in **G** of (x, y) excludes the presence of (y, x).

Figure 10·11 gives the example of an antisymmetric graph. The relations $x<y$, A is the son of B, p_1 precedes p_2, are antisymmetric relations.

Ordered relationships. A graph which is at the same time transitive, reflexive and antisymmetric, represents an 'ordered' relationship.

The symbol $\prec$ is generally used to indicate that an order exists between two elements x and y of a set. If x precedes y, we write $x \prec y$. If x precedes or is equal to y, we write $x \preccurlyeq y$. Figure 10·12 and 10·13 represent graphs of ordered relationships.

For figure 10·12 we can write

$$a \prec e \prec d$$
$$a \prec b$$
$$c \prec b$$

For figure 10·13

$$e \prec a \prec b \prec d \prec c$$

Figure 10·12 represents a partially ordered relationship. The order is not given by a single sequence of elements. Figure 10·13 represents a completely ordered relationship, the order being given by a single sequence. The relationships $x \preccurlyeq y$, A is included in B, p_1 is less heavy than or as heavy as p_2, are ordered relationships. They are also completely ordered relationships.

11 Preference graph: preference function: decision rules

Let us begin by studying a simple and amusing little problem. Let us consider a gourmet who can buy, without worrying about the price, one of the following four pies: Thrush pie (T), Skylark pie (S), Blackbird pie (E) or Hare pie (H). Let us suppose that if any pair (x, y) of pies is presented to the gourmet he can express one

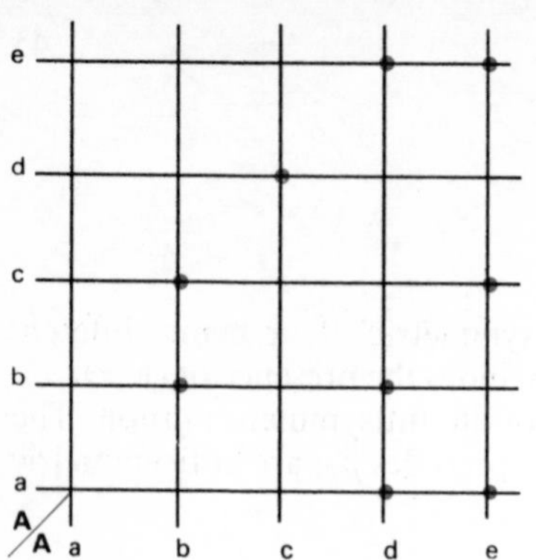

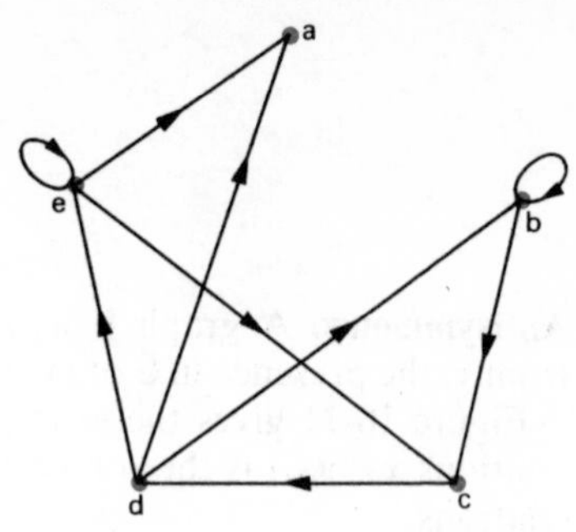

Figure 10·11 (a) and (b)

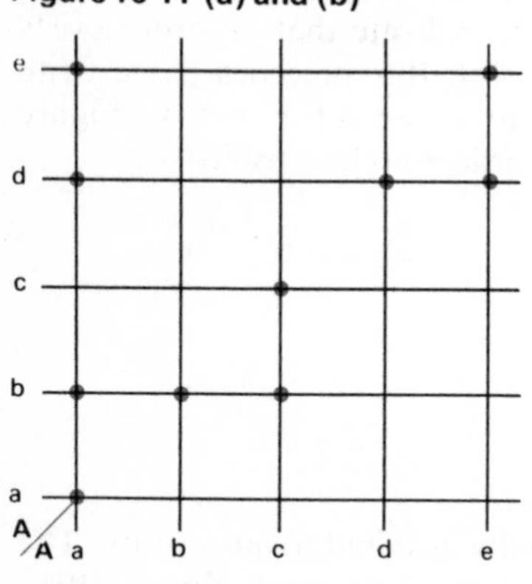

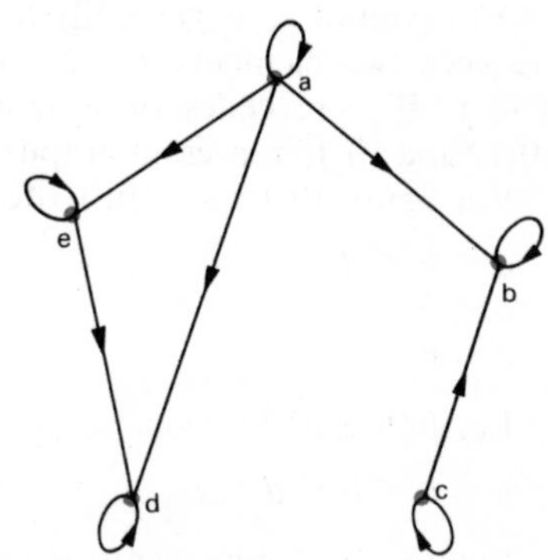

Figure 10·12 (a) and (b)

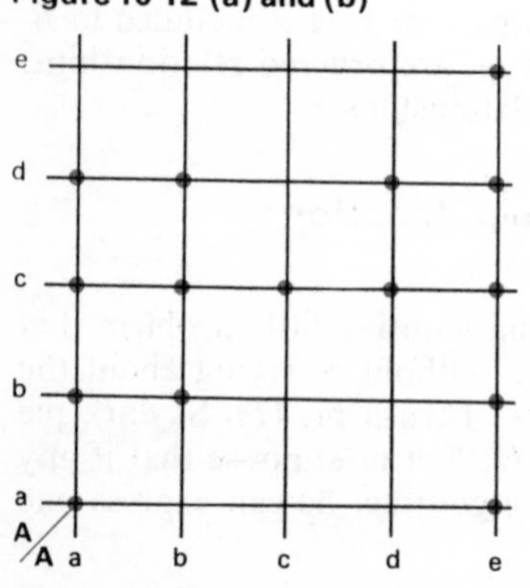

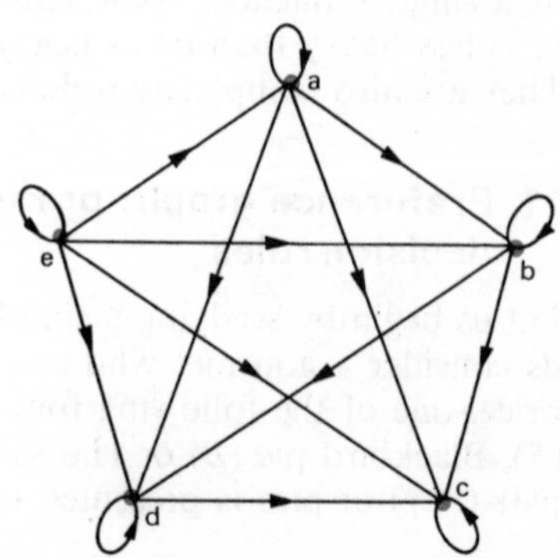

Figure 10·13 (a) and (b)

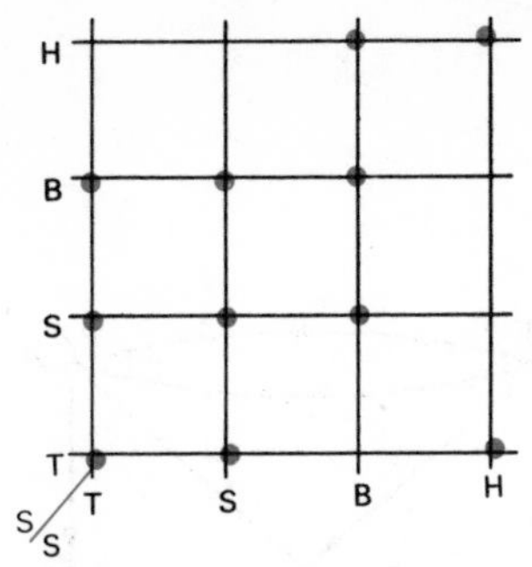

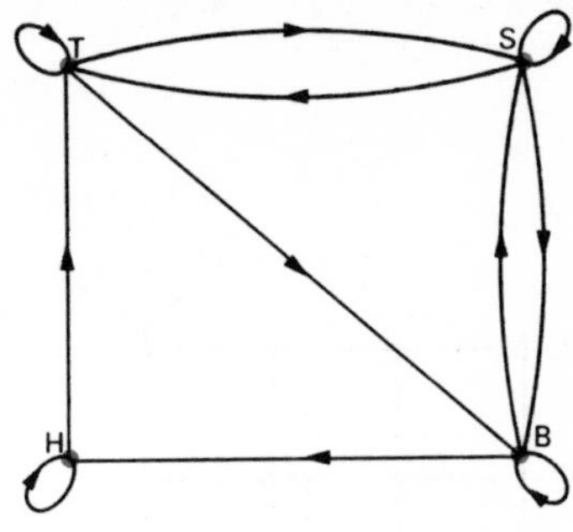

Figure 11·1 (a) and (b)

of the three following judgments: 'I prefer *y* to *x*, or *x* to *y* (this 'or' is exclusive). '*x* and *y* are a matter of indifference to me.' 'I cannot compare *x* and *y*.'

Let us suppose that the six pairs of pies have been presented to the gourmet in this way and that he has expressed for each pair one of the three judgments.

To be able to give later on a suitable mathematical formulation, we shall accept, by definition: (1) that the proposition '*x* and *y* are a matter of indifference to me' and 'I prefer *x* to *y*, and *y* to *x*' have the same meaning; (2) that a proposition 'I prefer *x* to *y*' is always true.

If *y* is preferred to *x*, we shall say that the pair (*x*, *y*) belongs to the graph which represents the set of judgments. If *x* and *y* are indifferent we shall say that the pairs (*x*, *y*) and (*y*, *x*) belong to the graph. Finally the pairs (*x*, *y*) and (*y*, *x*) which do not belong to the graph will correspond to an inability to compare.

Let us suppose that the gourmet has expressed the judgments shown on the graph of figure 11·1. If we study this graph we can see certain logical difficulties. First, *H* is preferred to *B*, *T* is preferred to *H* and *B* is preferred to *T*. These preferences are not transitive. Another factor is embarrassing: *S* and *T* are a matter of indifference, so are *B* and *S*, but *B* is preferred to *T*. The indifference is not transitive. The behaviour of a consumer and more broadly speaking the behaviour of a man of action, which corresponds to the graph of preference in which the transitivity of preferences or of indifferences is not always verified, is quite conceivable, even if it is not logical. Such a graph will be called 'graph

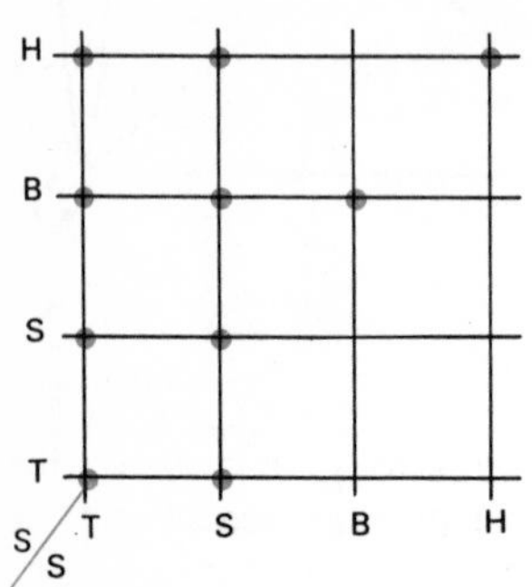

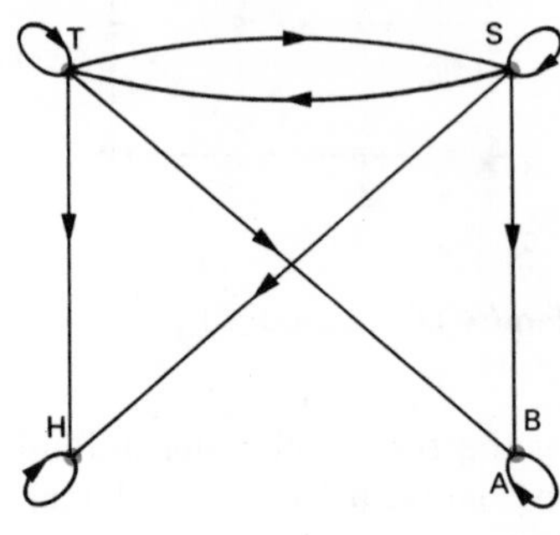

Figure 11·2 (a) and (b)

of free preference', and the corresponding relation called 'a free preference'; we shall also say that 'a free preference is not a pre-order'.

Let us suppose now that the man who likes pies is logical, that is to say, imposes transitivity on his preferences or indifferences, and that the graph of preference which he adopts is the graph of figure 11·2. (It would seem that this pie-lover is a Corsican because of his preference of B to T, and to S: it is well known in France that Corsicans are partial to blackbird pies.) The graph of figure 11·2 is transitive. We shall say in that case that it is a graph of logical preference, and the corresponding relation will be called a 'logical preference' which, this time, constitutes a pre-order.

Now, in a 'relation of logical preference', i.e. a pre-order, let us consider all the elements indifferent to one another as forming a single element; that is to say for all the elements for which we have a relation of equivalence (a transitive, reflexive, symmetric relation). Thus simplified, the graph becomes the graph corresponding to a relation of order, which can be partial or complete. If the order is partial, we shall say that it is a graph of 'logical preference, partially decidable'. If the order is complete we shall say that it is a graph of 'logical preference totally decidable'.

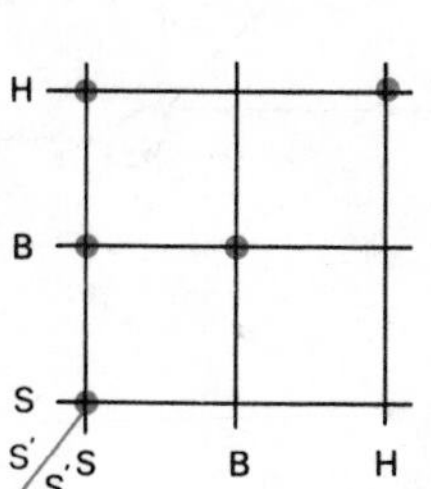

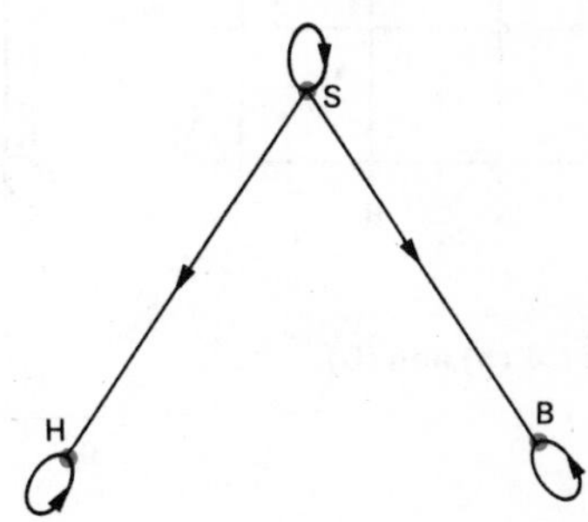

Figure 11·3 (a) and (b)

Let us go back to our Corsican gourmet. Since he is indifferent to *S* and *T*, let us take *S* as representative of this class of equivalence (*S* then represents *S* as well as *T*). We now have the graph of figure 11·3 reduced to three pies. It is easy to see that it is a relation of partial order.

$S \prec B$ and $S \prec H$

This Corsican gourmet is logical, but if he can decide between *S* and *B* on the one hand, and *S* and *H* on the other, he cannot do so between *H* and *B*. Such an attitude is perfectly acceptable from a logical point of view.

Now, let us suppose that the graph of preference of one gourmet is the one represented in figure 11·4 which is immediately reduced to the graph of figure 11·5. We then get a total order

$S \prec B \prec H$

The graph of figure 11·4 is a graph of 'totally decidable logical preference'.

Thus four stronger and stronger levels appear in the notions of preference, if we add to them the level of 'total incapacity of preference'.

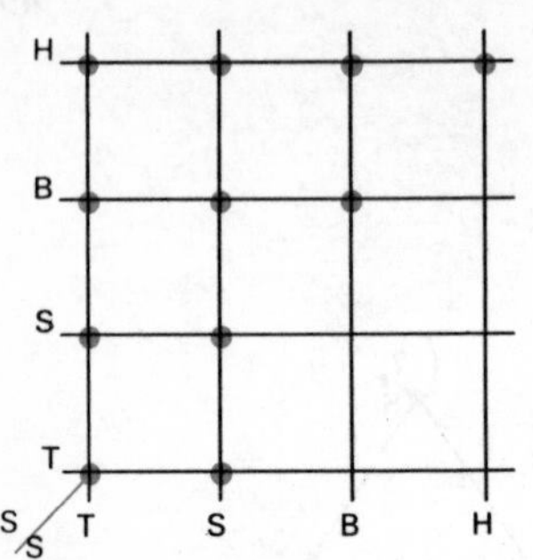

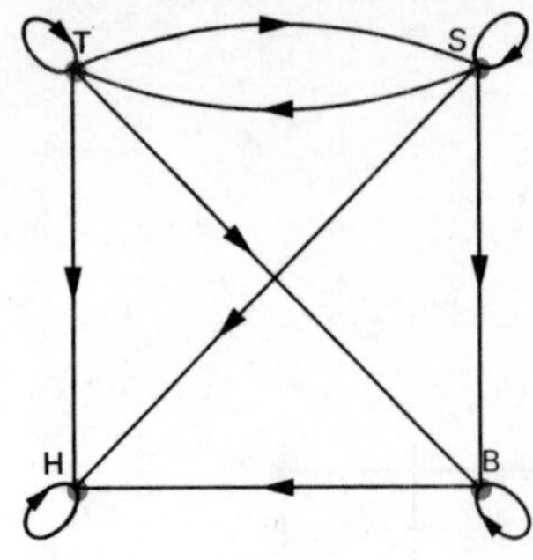

Figure 11·4 (a) and (b)

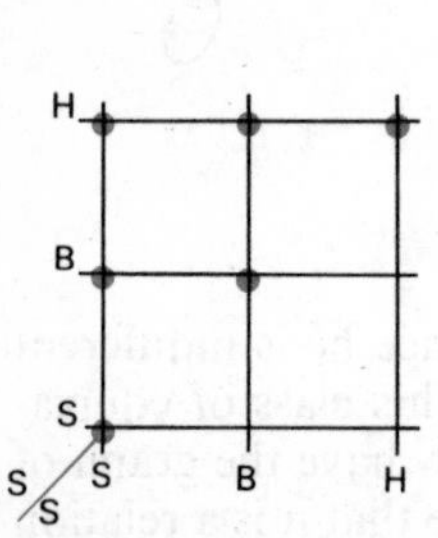

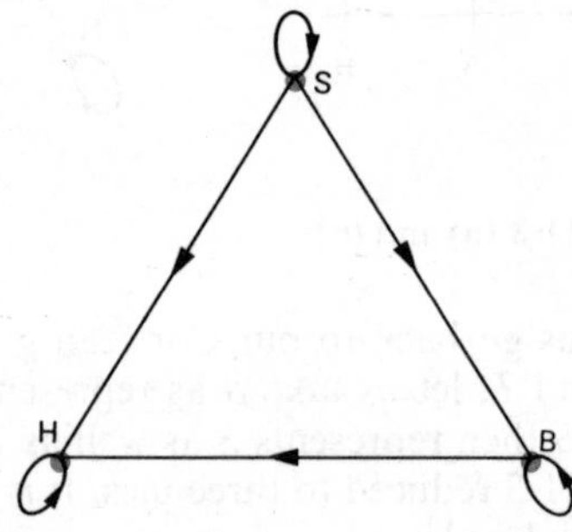

Figure 11·5 (a) and (b)

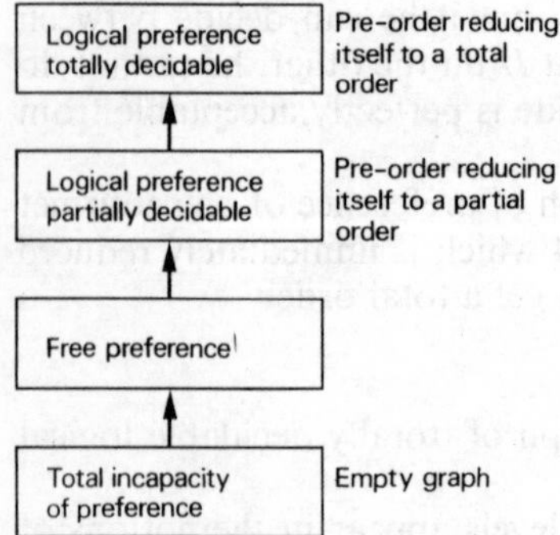

Figure 11·6

We could consider a few particular cases, of a commonplace kind which belong, like the others, to the proposed classifications.

Thus, if all the elements are indifferent to one another, the graph will be reduced to one point; it will be totally decidable for the class of single equivalence. This leads me to remind the reader that the notion of decidability concerns the classes of equivalence and not their component elements.

The examples demonstrated explain many behaviours. Free preference requires no logic, it is what is often called irrational, emotional behaviour with complete or partial lack of transitivity. The partially decidable logical preference represents a higher level; facing certain situations, one will be able to decide; facing other situations it will be impossible to decide. In conclusion final preference, at last introducing a total order, allows the perfect decision.

Thus, in a society where all behaviour would be an act of (totally decidable) logical preference, there would be no freedom left, everything would be determined. Action would become automatic. Such societies do exist (cell systems, bees, ants). On the other hand man prides himself on the fact that his behaviour is not merely logical. The graph of preference of an intelligent, developed man must be free, but some sub-graphs of this graph must be totally decidable, where it is acceptable to his code of ethics.

As I have stressed many times, what is important is to distinguish in every situation whether the structure of the preferences is free or logical. Here are some other simple examples.

Example 1. A young man sets himself four fundamental objectives:

A to marry a pretty girl.

B to get a good job.

C to own a comfortable house.

D to have a sports car.

The conditions are supposed to be such that it is possible for the young man to reach several objectives at the same time. The achievement of one objective will be noted as (*A*). The achievement

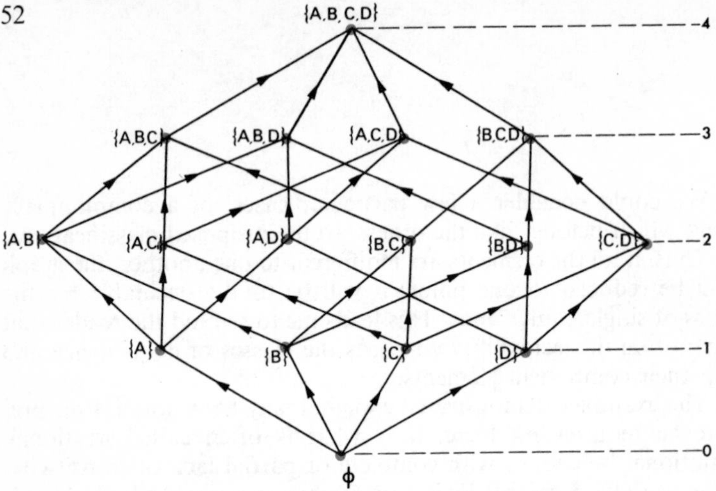

Figure 11·7

of two objectives will be (A, C) etc. The achievement of no objective will be noted as ϕ. The young man declares that the following rule represents the rule of his intentions. If one objective includes another one, the first one will be preferred to the second, thus:

$$(A, C, D) \succ (A, C)$$
$$(C) \succ \phi$$
$$(A, B, C, D) \succ (B, C)$$

From this rule let us build up the graph of preferences of this young man. In the diagram (figure 11·7), to avoid drawing too many arrowed sections, I have left out the reflexive loops and the arrowed sections which should form the objectives, when one of them includes another one, and when there is more than one objective missing in the second in relation to the first one; thus the arrowed section between (C) and (B, C, D) has not been drawn. The preference graph thus obtained is the graph of a pre-order, which is a partial order. It is to be noted that for each pair of objectives (simple or compound) there correspond: one objective which includes each of them and one objective which is included in both of them; to be more precise, to every pair of objectives O_1 and O_2 there corresponds an objective O_3 which is formed by the objectives included in O_1, and/or in O_2, and also an objective

O_4 which is formed by the objectives common to both O_1 and O_2. This particular structure has been given the name of 'lattice'; in our example it is a 'Boolean' lattice.

If we study the Boolean lattice in figure 11·7 we can see that on this graph it is possible to determine the levels, 0, 1, 2, 3, 4. (Note that the elements of these levels do not form classes of equivalence.) Between objectives of the same level, the choice is not decidable; between those of different levels it is the same, unless one includes the other, in which case the preference is given. Thus in this Boolean lattice we see 'chains' or 'sequences' of objectives appear:

$$\phi \prec (A) \prec (A, D) \prec (A, C, D) \prec (A, B, C, D)$$
$$\phi \prec (B) \prec (B, C) \prec (A, B, C) \prec (A, B, C, D)$$

They represent the sequential attainment, step by step, and in a certain order, of all the objectives. The young man could not say, from this (partially decidable) graph of logical preference, which chain he prefers. To transform this graph into a graph of (totally decidable) logical preference it would be necessary to introduce a total order of preference at each level, for instance:

$$(D) \prec (C) \prec (B) \prec (A)$$
$$(C, D) \prec (B, D) \prec (D, C) \prec (A, B) \prec (A, C) \prec (A, D)$$
$$(A, C, D) \prec (B, C, D) \prec (A, B, C) \prec (A, B, D)$$

Note that if the young man gives himself $(C) \prec (B)$, he can very well adopt $(A, B) \prec (A, C)$. The addition of a common objective, simple or compound, to each of the objectives can change the order of preference. This is not in the least paradoxical.

Unfortunately we do not have here the necessary space to study other interesting characteristics of these structures, my aim being limited to showing the interest of modern mathematics in problems of decision, but later on I shall take up certain conclusions again and develop them at greater length.

Example 2. The theory that we have developed in the present paragraph constitutes, in fact, a pedagogical introduction to the modern theory of economic preference put forward by Pareto, who was mainly concerned with the ideas necessary to make individual economic choice coherent. I have simply extended the economic aspects to the more general aspects of action (political action, military action), which are not necessarily economic.

The manner of exposition that I shall adopt is inspired by the one I found in the excellent book by Dehem.[12] The study of individual choice was first conceived as one of calculation of utilities, or satisfactions considered to be measurable. These were the hypotheses used by certain economists: Jevons,[15] Walras,[24] Edgeworth,[13] Marshall;[17] the latter adopted, as a unit of measurement of the utility of an object, the marginal utility of money (utility of an additional unit of money for a given person). This concept was derived from Bentham's analysis of pleasure and pain; he put it in an intuitive form, and as such it did not stand up to the mathematical formulation of Pareto. The latter demonstrated that a pre-order relationship permitted us to obtain an order, according to the procedure that I indicated at the start of this paragraph.

A consumer with definite tastes has at his disposal over a certain period of time an income I. The consumable assets $a_1, a_2, \ldots, a_n$ are available to him in quantities $x_1, x_2, \ldots, x_n$, at the respective prices $p_1, p_2, \ldots, p_n$.

If, for the sake of simplicity, the savings are supposed to be nil, what quantities $x_1, x_2, \ldots, x_n$ will be preferred to the others?

According to Pareto, and conforming to what we have considered in the case of a totally decidable logical preference, the consumer is assumed to be able to express his preferences. These will refer to all the pairs of sets $(x_1, x_2, \ldots, x_n)$ and $(x_1', x_2', \ldots, x_n')$. Asked about his preferences, the subject is supposed to express one of the three following judgments:

$(x_1, x_2, \ldots, x_n)$ is preferred to $(x_1', x_2', \ldots, x_n')$
$(x_1', x_2', \ldots, x_n')$ is preferred to $(x_1, x_2, \ldots, x_n)$
$(x_1, x_2, \ldots, x_n)$ and $(x_1', x_2', \ldots, x_n')$ are indifferent.

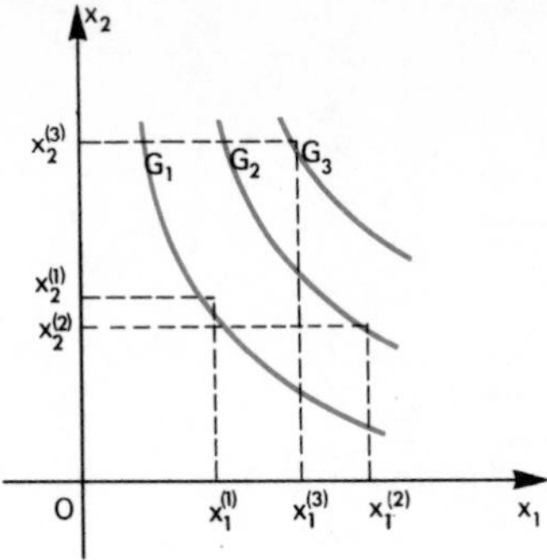

Figure 11·8

Thus, between the possible sets such as $(x_1, x_2, \ldots, x_n)$ there does exist a relation of pre-order.

Let us consider simplifying the case in which the set of assets contains two assets a_1 and a_2. Conforming to my explanation at the beginning of this paragraph, the first step is to group the assortments which are indifferent to each other; thus classes of equivalence are formed.

In figure 11·8 curves are the classes of equivalence in consideration. All the assortments (x_1, x_2) belonging to the same curve are supposed equivalent. These curves are called 'indifference curves' and evidently cannot intersect. As it has been supposed that any one assortment is comparable to another, there exists therefore a total order between classes of equivalence.

In making x_1 and x_2 vary from a point (x_1, x_2) i.e. so as to maintain the subjective equivalence to (x_1, x_2) the sets equivalent to (x_1, x_2) can be identified. If the assets a_1, a_2 were perfectly divisible, the compensatory variations could be infinitesimal and we would then have to consider in a continuous fashion the passage of a class (i.e. of the curve) to a neighbouring class.

It cannot be established that indifference curves are convex, but it usually follows from a very likely hypothesis based on the psychological analysis of a consumer.

Economists determine 'a marginal rate of substitution' which is given by the variation of x_2 as a function of x_1. When the rate of variation is taken over an infinitely small interval it gives the slope of the indifference curve. From these indifference curves, and when

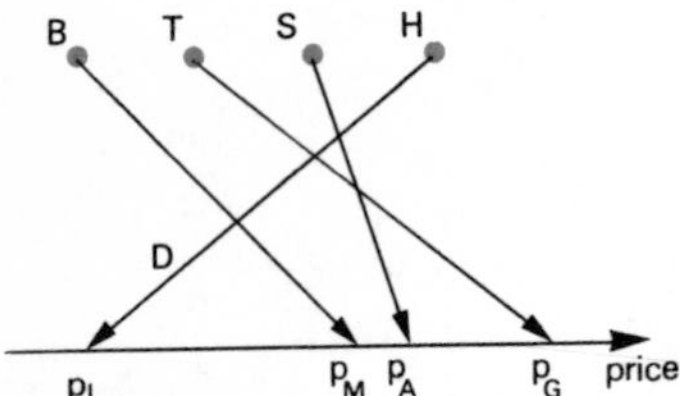

Figure 11·9

assortments of more than two assets are in question, from these equivalence surfaces, the economist has at his disposal a mathematical basis on which to build a rational theory of the behaviour of the consumer.

Preference function. We have just seen that only the case of a graph of (totally decidable) logical preference, i.e. a graph giving a total order of equivalence classes (indifference) allowed us to determine a preference order for all the elements. Obviously this is not always the case. A fundamental way of obtaining a total order consists in introducing a 'value function'.

Let us suppose that the pie-lover, incapable of deciding according to his own preference of taste, decides to rely on prices and choose the cheapest. Supposing that the prices are given according to the schedule of figure 11·9. He would then choose the hare pie. Another pie-lover, who might be very snobbish, would opt for the most expensive pie and finally choose the thrush pie. A function such as the one in figure 11·9 is called a 'preference function'. More generally speaking, if we take a set of objectives $\mathbf{X} = (x_1, x_2, \ldots, x_n \ldots)$ and if we are capable of making each objective x correspond with a value belonging to a set of numerical values, continuous or discontinuous, we introduce a 'preference function' or 'value function' which enables us then to place the objectives according to a total order. If the set $\mathbf{X}$ is not countable we introduce in the

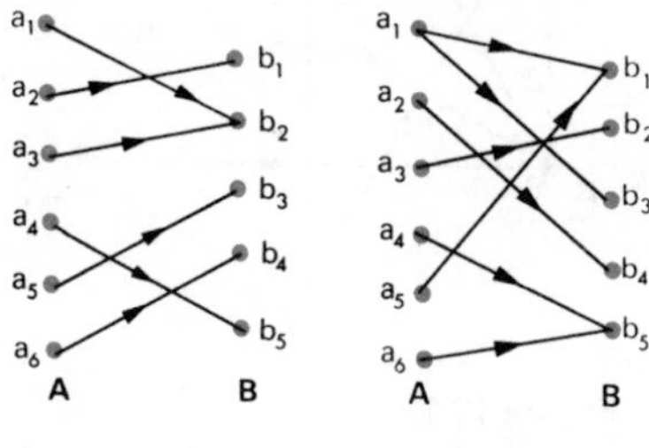

Figure 11·10 Figure 11·11

same way, if it is possible, a preference function which lets us determine completely ordered classes of equivalence.

May I remind the reader that the word 'function' must be taken in the very precise meaning given by mathematicians. Correspondence between two sets A and B is a function of **A** in **B** if: to an element of **A** corresponds one and only one element of **B**. Thus figure 11·10 represents a function, but figure 11·11 does not. (An element of **A**, say a_1 exists, to which two elements of **B**, say b_1 and b_2 correspond.) When a function exists between two sets we write, calling x an element of **A** and y an element of **B**: $x \xrightarrow{f} y$, $x \rightarrow y$ or more commonly $y = f(x)$.

To associate a value function to a set of objectives is one of the most difficult problems of the science of action; the methods used finally amount to the introduction of a 'measure' of the set of objectives. But, all sets are not easily measurable, we are far from having a 'metrics' at our disposal, for the phenomenon considered in praxeology – a 'metrics' such as distance in kinematics, energy in dynamics, wave length in electronics, etc. In human sciences the way of measuring is arbitrary; the choice of the preference function is an essential act of will, a higher form of freedom, a freedom often delicate and difficult to exercise.

Criterion of decision. If for a set of objectives a graph of completely ordered logical preference, or a value function exists, then we can

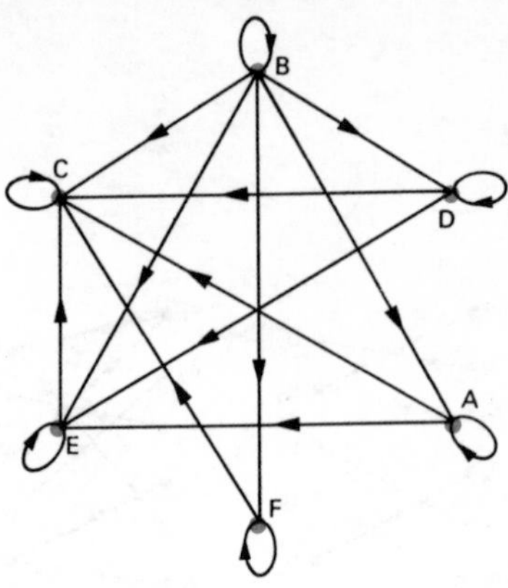

Figure 12·1

say that this set possesses a 'criterion of decision'.

Let us give some examples of sets of objectives to which we can suggest the following criteria.

1 For a firm wanting to invest in different economic fields, a criterion acceptable by the Board of Directors can be the maximisation of yearly income, supposing this income to be a known function of the investments.

2 It is proposed to build a motorway between two important urban centres, a great number of possible routes existing on the map. The minimisation of the total cost of landscaping work and expropriation can be used as a criterion.

3 Someone is to be chosen for a post from a set of candidates. A preference function will generally be adopted in which the coefficients given to each quality required for this post will appear. We shall then choose the candidate for whom the preference function takes the highest value.

4 A military commander has available a certain number of bombers and plans to attack an enemy railway centre. From all the possible formations which can be taken by the bomber aircraft within the space and time of this attack, he will choose the one that will be capable of destroying the greatest number of enemy installations which will take a long time to replace. He can also take different value functions: for example, a criterion relative to his losses.

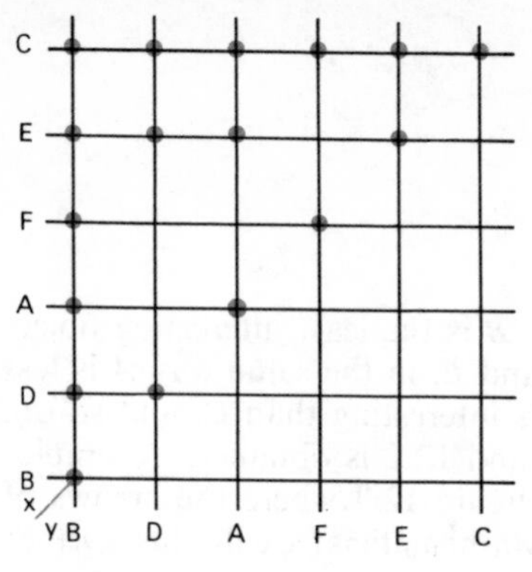

Figure 12·2

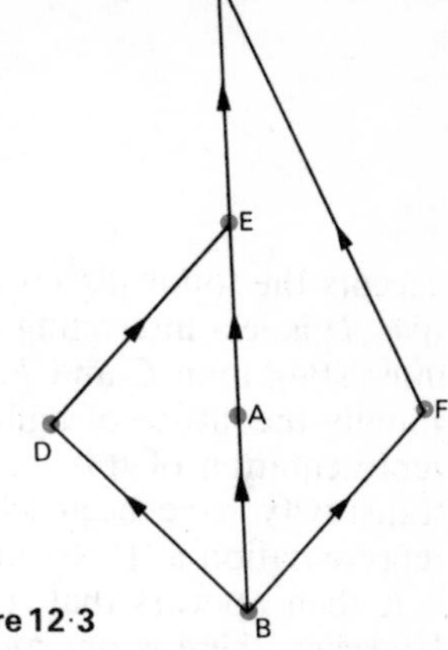

Figure 12·3

The choice of a criterion of decision, be it to build a preference graph or a preference function, requires not only a profound investigation of the problem itself, but also an analysis of the man or the group having the power of decision. We shall see how, in certain cases, mathematics can help to build a criterion of decision.

12 Lattices and vector spaces

Before we show the various methods which are most widely used to build valid criteria, we shall review, after those already examined in the previous paragraphs, some other interesting structures of partially ordered sets with which we shall try to associate preference functions.

Lattices. The problem of the young candidate for marriage (§11 – figure 11·7) gave us an instance of a lattice of objectives.

The notion of lattices belongs to the general theory of ordered sets. If the set of objectives is partially ordered and if, for any pair of objectives, we can find one objective which is preferred or of equal merit to them and one objective to which they are preferred or of equal merit, this set has the structure of a lattice.

Let us take the following example: the management of a firm and the choice between six objectives *A*, *B*, *C*, *D*, *E* and *F*. After a long and animated discussion the Board of Directors finally accepts the following conclusions. *B* is the least interesting objective, *D* is less interesting than *C* and *E*, in the same way *A* is less interesting than *C* and *E*, *E* is less interesting than *C*, and so on. Finally the lattice of figures 12·1 and 12·2 is obtained. A simpler representation of this is given in figure 12·3 where the arrows of transitivity have been left out. Mathematicians call this sort of representation a 'Hasse diagram'.

It then appears that it is a set of partially ordered objectives. However, there is one and only one objective which is preferable to all others, and one and only one objective to which all others are preferred. Thus the Board of Directors is going to choose *C*. Failing *C* they could, without argument, choose *E*. Failing *E*, no comparison could be possible between *D*, *A* and *F*. In the case of a complete order, there would always have been a possibility of comparison between the remaining objectives after eliminating some of them.

If the set of objectives considered is finite, there is always, in the case of a lattice, an objective which is preferred to all others, and an objective to which all others are preferable. One is called 'maximum', the other 'minimum', or vice-versa. If a lattice concerns a non-finite set of objectives, it does not necessarily possess a maximum and/or a minimum.

The whole theory of optimisation which we are going to discuss rests on the notion of lattices. Of course in such an elementary book as this, we cannot give a complete account of the theory of this concept. Nor can we investigate in detail the great many important properties which are concerned with it. The subject is nevertheless one of the most exciting in mathematics.

Vectors: vector lattices. Let us suppose that the considered set is made up of objectives characterised by pairs of numbers which can be 1, 2 or 3. This set would be:

$$\mathbf{O} = \{ (1,1), (1,2), (1,3), (2,1), (2,2), (2,3), (3,1), (3,2), (3,3) \}$$

[Equation 12.1]

An objective (A_i, B_i) will be preferred to an objective (A_j, B_j) if

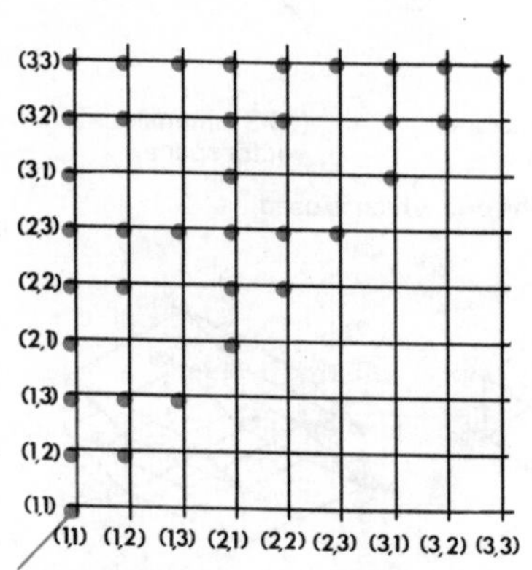

Figure 12·4

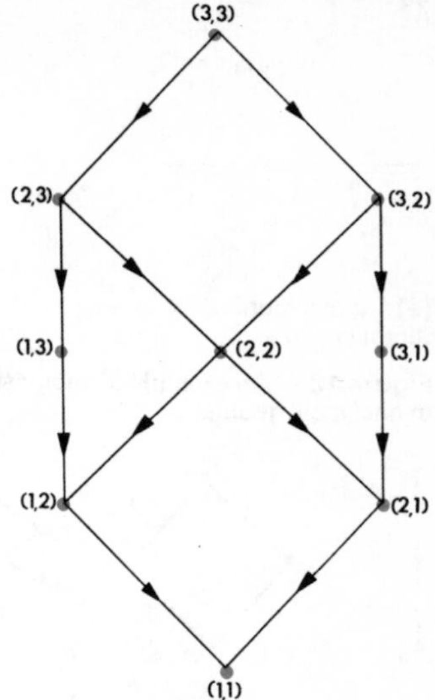

Figure 12·5

the numbers of (A_i, B_i) are higher or equal to the corresponding numbers of (A_j, B_j) with at least one higher number in the latter case. Thus (3, 1) is preferred to (2, 1), (5, 2) is preferred to (1, 2), (2, 3) is not comparable to (3, 1). We obtain in this way a lattice figure 12·4, 12·5 which constitutes a vector lattice (figure 12·5 gives the Hasse diagram of the lattice).

More generally speaking, let us consider an ordered sequence of elements $(A_i, B_j, ..., M_r)$ in which A_i belongs to a completely ordered set **A**, B_j belongs to a completely ordered set **B**, and M_r to a completely ordered set **M**. Such a sequence will be called a 'vector'. If we take as a rule of preference: any vector $(A_{i1}, B_{j1}, \dots M_{r1})$ is preferred to any vector $(A_{i2}, B_{j2}, \dots, M_{r2})$ if $A_{i1} > A_{i2}$ or $A_{i1} = A_{i2}$; $B_{j1} > B_{j2}$ or $B_{j1} = B_{j2}$; $M_{r1} > M_{r2}$ or $M_{r1} = M_{r2}$ with at least one element compared to his homologue for which we do not have an equality which will be stated as $(A_{i1}, B_{j1}, \dots, M_{r1})$ dominates $(A_{i2}, B_{j2}, \dots, M_{r2})$; we shall have constructed a vector lattice. The sets **A**, **B**, ..., **M** can possibly be identical.

Vector space, module. Among the vector lattices are considered very often those formed from real numbers or again those which are formed from binary numbers.

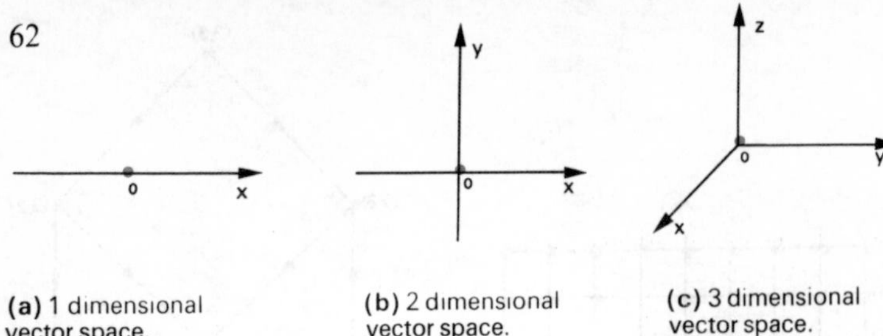

(a) 1 dimensional vector space.

(b) 2 dimensional vector space.

(c) 3 dimensional vector space.

Figure 12·6 An example of vector space, the one which is used in analytical geometry.

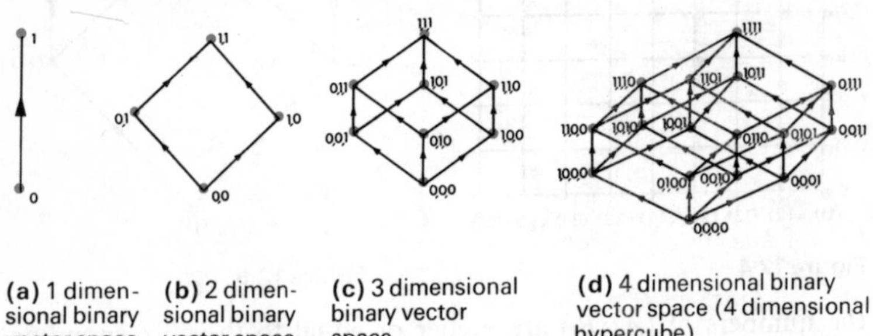

(a) 1 dimensional binary vector space.

(b) 2 dimensional binary vector space.

(c) 3 dimensional binary vector space.

(d) 4 dimensional binary vector space (4 dimensional hypercube).

Figure 12·7 Another example of vector space—a case of binary numbers (Boolean lattice). The drawings represent the Hasse diagrams of the lattices.

These vector lattices constitute what are called 'vector spaces'. If the considered vectors possess *r* elements it is said that the space is *r* dimensional. The vector lattice built with signed whole numbers (... −3, −2, −1, 0, 1, 2, 3 ...) constitutes what is called a 'modulus'. Vector spaces or moduli can be built with the use of other sets.

In human sciences these two vector spaces and the above-mentioned modules are those which are most often considered, although certain problems exist where other vector spaces or modules are referred to.

Lexicographical vector lattice. This is another type of lattice which is reducible to a total order, for instance the one used in a dictionary (whence its name).

The vector $(A_1, B_1, C_1, \ldots, M_1)$ will be preferred (that is to say

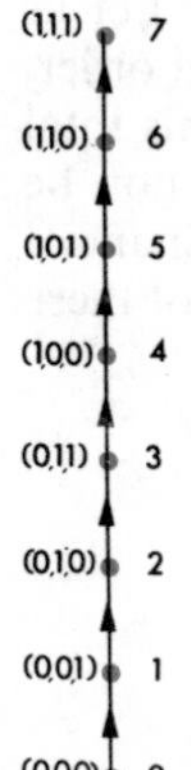

Figure 12·8
Hasse diagram of 3-dimensional lexicographical vector lattice.

will dominate) the vector (A_2, B_2, C_2, ..., M_2) if the first r elements (starting arbitrarily from the left) of the two vectors are equal, but the $(r + 1)$th element of the first is bigger (if it concerns numbers) or higher in the order (if it concerns letters) than the second (r could be zero).

Thus we obtain a vector lattice which constitutes a total order. In that way (3, 5, 7, 2, 5) is preferred to (3, 5, 7, 1, 9); (R, M, N) is preferred to (R, S, B); in this last case the chosen order gives preference to A over all the other letters, to B over those left when A is taken away and so on. For instance, the decimal coding system is lexicographical. 3, 5, 7, 2, 5 is higher than 3, 5, 7, 1, 9. In figure 12·8 a three dimensional lexicographical lattice is represented; it is formed by the first eight numbers written in binary coding.

The lexicographical is one of the methods most used to work out classifications, but is not, or very seldom, applicable to cases of choice or preference in problems of decision. Let us all the same consider a small example. A girl wonders how to choose between her suitors. She is interested in their physical appearance, their health, their education, and their financial circumstances. Let us suppose that she places these qualities in the following total order, in which the first is the one most preferred and so on. (This total order reflects a form of worldly-wisdom which might not be accepted by another girl.) (a) Education, (b) health, (c) financial circumstances, (d) physical appearance. Then for each one of these qualities she adopts a scale (total order):

Education	3 – very good
	2 – good
	1 – bad
Health	3 – very good
	2 – good
	1 – bad
Financial circumstances	5 – very rich
	4 – rich
	3 – well off
	2 – of modest means
	1 – poor
Physical appearance	4 – very handsome
	3 – handsome
	2 – unattractive
	1 – ugly

According to the lexicographical criterion, this girl would prefer (2, 2, 4, 1) to (1, 2, 3, 3). But I imagine that this method is very artificial, and that some girls might, for instance, prefer a little less education and a little more wealth. It is then that the use of a metrics or weighting might solve some problems of selecting objectives. Let us note, though, that love remains a sphere where free preferences occur, and this in spite of attempts – luckily as yet unsuccessful – to use match-making machines.

Linear vector space. Let us suppose that, on top of being a vector space, the set $\mathbf{O}$ of objectives is such that (1st) for each objective whose components are numbers, the multiplication of an objective by a real number determines a new objective which is part of $\mathbf{O}$ (2nd) it is possible to add two vectors to form a third one whose elements are constituted by the sum of corresponding elements; the result of which gives an objective which is part of $\mathbf{O}$.

It is said in that case that the set of objectives $\mathbf{O}$ is a 'linear vector space'.

Let us give some explanations of a more mathematical nature. We postulate that for all the objectives belonging to $\mathbf{O}$ being a real number:

$\lambda\,(a_1, a_2, ..., a_r) = (\lambda a_1, \lambda a_2, ..., \lambda a_r)$ is part of $\mathbf{O}$
[Equation 12.2]

$(a_1, a_2, ..., a_r) + (b_1, b_2, ..., b_r) = (a_1 + b_1, a_2 + b_2, ..., a_r + b_r)$ is part of $\mathbf{O}$
[Equation 12.3]

To make these slightly abstract formulas more easily understood, let us give a concrete example.

A firm considers promoting sales in three districts *I*, *II*, and *III*. It has unlimited capital which it can invest in each district. An objective will be constituted by a three-dimensional vector whose number will represent the investments in each district.

Thus (a_I, a_{II}, a_{III}) will represent the objective: to invest a_I in *I*, a_{II} in *II* and a_{III} in *III*. Of course these investments must be made of non-negative sums. ('Non-negative' should not be confused with 'positive'. The positive numbers do not include 0, whereas the non-negative numbers do include 0. This distinction is very important from the mathematical point of view.) The set of objectives will form a linear vector space (2). For example, if we suppose that these investments are expressed in millions:

$3\,(4, 5, 8) = (12, 15, 24)$ [Equation 12.4]

$(2, 8, 3) + (0, 2, 9) = (2, 10, 12)$ [Equation 12.5]

Of course, such problems are subject to restrictions, for instance a limitation of overall capital.

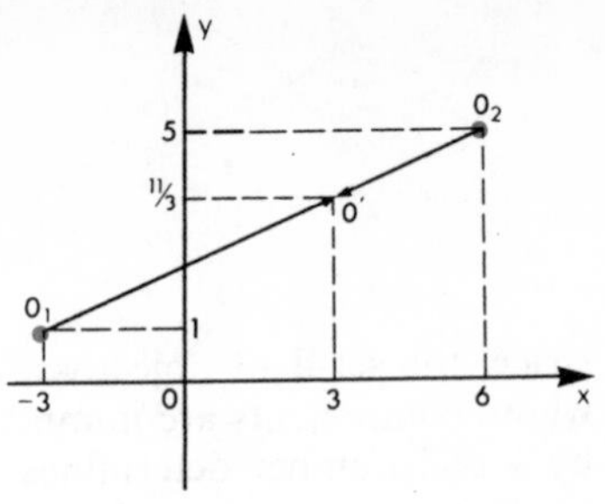

Figure 12·9

Convex weighting: convex body. This notion is perhaps a little theoretical but it is indispensable for the study of the problems we are interested in. Therefore we are going to make a special pedagogical effort.

Let us suppose that a set of objectives forms a linear vector space. Let us form the hypothesis that this space has two dimensions. Let us say there are two objectives O_1, O_2:

$O_1 = (-3, 1)$ [Equation 12.6]
and O_2 $(6, 5)$ [Equation 12.7]

and two non-negative numbers λ_1 and λ_2 the sum of which is equal to 1, for instance $\lambda_1 = \frac{1}{3}$ and $\lambda_2 = \frac{2}{3}$. Let us define the objective O' as follows:

$$\begin{aligned} O' &= \lambda_1 O_1 + \lambda_2 O_2 \\ &= \frac{1}{3}(-3, 1) + \frac{2}{3}(6, 5) \\ &= (3, \frac{11}{3}) \end{aligned}$$ [Equation 12.8]

On figure 12·9 we join the points O_1 and O_2 representing the corresponding objectives.

We then ascertain that the point O' representing the objective obtained by equation 12.8 is situated on the straight line which passes through O_1 and O_2 and is placed between O_1 and O_2.

This property is very easily demonstrated. If we took two numbers such that we would not have at the same time $\lambda_1 \geqslant 0$, $\lambda_2 \geqslant 0$ and $\lambda_1 \times \lambda_2 = 1$, the property considered would no longer be verified.

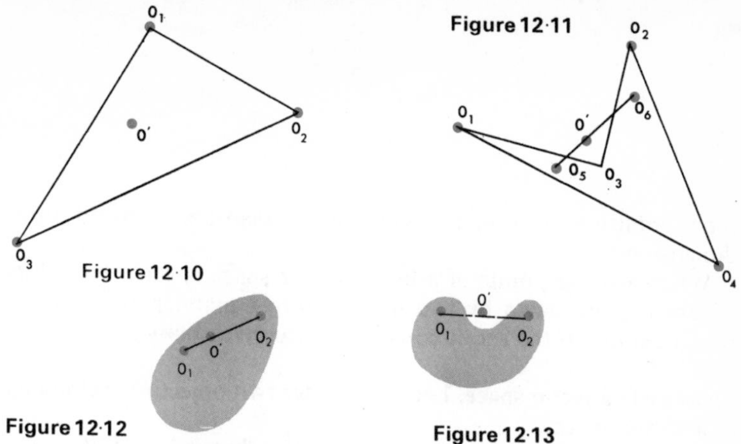

Figure 12·10

Figure 12·11

Figure 12·12

Figure 12·13

We have produced a convex weighting of two objectives.

Now let us take three objectives O_1, O_2, O_3, and three numbers λ_1, λ_2 and λ_3, non-negative and of a sum equal to 1. Then the objective $O' = \lambda_1, O_1 + \lambda_2, O_2 + \lambda_3, O_3$ will be situated within or on the sides of the triangle O_1, O_2, O_3 (figure 12·10), but if we take four objectives O_1, O_2, O_3, O_4, it is not certain that for a certain weighting λ_1, λ_2, λ_3, λ_4 (non-negative numbers which add up to 1) the weighted objective, $O' = \lambda_1 \, O_1 + \lambda_2 \, O_2 + \lambda_3 \, O_3 + \lambda_4 \, O_4$ will be within the quadrilateral O_1, O_2, O_3, O_4. We have represented in figure 12·11 a quadrilateral O_1, O_2, O_3, O_4 and a point O' obtained by such a convex weighting that O' is not inside the quadrilateral. This will lead us to distinguish between two sorts of sets of objectives, those which are 'convex' and those which are 'non-convex'.

For the former all convex weighting of any number of objectives gives a weighted objective which always belongs to the given set of objectives. For the latter this does not always prove true. The weighted objective can be outside the set of objectives.

In graphical terms, this may be translated in the following way: a figure representing a set of objectives is convex if any straight line joining any two points within the set lies completely within it. Compare figure 12·12 (convex) with figure 12·13 (non-convex). This applies to open as well as closed surfaces.

All we have shown and explained for two-dimensional objectives, can be generalised for r dimensional objectives, but, of course, a representation by a figure will not be realisable beyond three dimensions.

When a set of points of a linear vector space is such that all its weighted points, two by two in any convex manner, form points which belong to the set, it constitutes a 'convex body'.

Measure in a vector space. Let us consider two objectives belonging to a vector space.

If these two objectives are comparable, that is to say if one is equal to the other, or if one dominates the other, we can content ourselves with the result and choose according to the preference ascertained. This is not generally so. An effective means of making a choice consists in introducing a 'metrics' or 'measure' in the vector space.

In analytical geometry or in vector analysis for instance, the 'norm' of a vector is introduced, that is to say the sum of the squares of the components of the vector, or better still, the length which is the square root of the norm. One can in this way compare two otherwise non-comparable vectors by saying that one is larger than the other. In the theory of probability the mathematical expectation is a measure calculated from a known distribution. Other ways to define a measure exist.

In the problems presented by the search for criteria which best represent intentions, it is sometimes possible, in order to compare objectives expressed as vectors, to introduce a 'metrics' or measure. It is then possible to compare any one vector with any other by means of this measure, which is nothing more than a function of the components of the vector. To a certain vector will correspond one value of the function and one only.

This value function can take various forms: linear function, convex linear function (convex weighting), quadratic function and so on. We shall find such functions in almost all the problems of optimising economy and operational research. They most often constitute the criterion used to decide which compound or elementary objective will be chosen.

In certain problems of decision, the objectives are located in non-linear vector spaces (for instance when values are in whole numbers); or again, because rules different from equations 12.2 and 12.3 are introduced and determine other types of spaces, it is also possible to adopt a value function which allows a numerical selection of objectives. We shall not deal here with the more profound aspects of the corresponding theories, but shall study only the methods more generally used.

13 Ordinal selection or numerical selection

Most of the time the nature of the problems studied by human sciences require criteria occurring in numerical form, whereas the first analysis of preferences would lead us to adopt a partially ordered relationship. We then have to find a means of transposing a partially ordered structure into a value function. No general method is at present known, the few methods put forward by some being vigorously opposed by others (see for example, the works of P. Massé,[18, 25] and M. Allais.[9] The question remains a tricky one.

To begin with, we shall present several axioms which will allow us to build up a certain logical structure. We shall then give a concrete example and after that show the reasons why some people refuse one of these axioms.

Axiom I To each objective O_i a non-negative number $v(O_i)$ can be made to correspond.

Axiom II If O_j is preferred to O_i, then $v(O_j) > v(O_i)$; if O_i and O_j are indifferent, then $v(O_j) = v(O_i)$.

Axiom III If $v(O_i)$ corresponds to O_i and $v(O_j)$ to O_j, then $v(O_i) + v(O_j)$ corresponds to the set formed by the objectives O_i and O_j.

These axioms call immediately for corollaries.

Corollary I If O_i is preferred to O_j and O_j to O_k, then the set of objectives including O_i and O_j is preferred to O_k.

Corollary II If the set of objectives formed by O_i and O_j is indifferent with O_j, then $v(O_i) = 0$.

Before going any further let us examine Axiom III more closely by going back to the example of figure 11·7. According to Axiom I we can suppose that we have the following correspondence:

$(A, C) \rightarrow 3$
$(A, D) \rightarrow 5$ [Equation 13.1]

According to Axiom III we should have:

$(A, C, D) \rightarrow 3 + 5 = 8$ [Equation 13.2]

Now let us consider objectives (A, C) and (D); the number 8 corresponding to the set of objectives (A, C, D) and the number 5 corresponding to (A, C) we conclude from this that the number 3 corresponds to (D). Thus, 3 corresponds both to (A, D) and to (D); according to Corollary II, the number which corresponds to (A) must therefore be 0. We could manage in this way to demonstrate that zero must correspond not only to (A), but also to (B), to (C), to (D). This is a paradox. What happens now?

(A, C) and (A, D) are not independent: these non-elementary objectives have a common part which is the elementary objective A. In figure 13·1 we give a more general representation of this notion of independence.

All the criticism of the numerical system of Axiom I, II and III results from this notion of independence.

If the nature of the objectives to which this system of axioms is applied enables us to verify the independence of elements within each pair, we can build up a logical structure, but the range of the method is then limited to very elementary or very particular cases.

We can use instead a system of axioms which is perfect from the logical point of view, where the set of objectives forms a Boolean lattice such as in figure 11·7. The structure is then the same as the one which allows us to put the intuitive idea of probability into an axiomatic form.

Let us show in one example only, that of figure 11·7, how by correctly modifying Axioms I and II, we can give a value to all the objectives of the lattice if we give values to the elementary objectives.

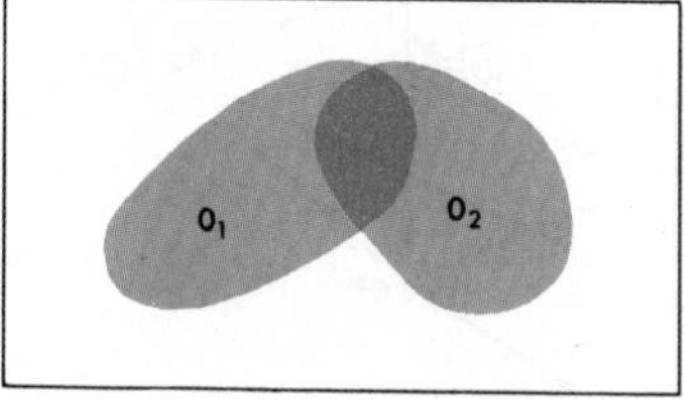

Objectives O_1 and O_2 are not independent.

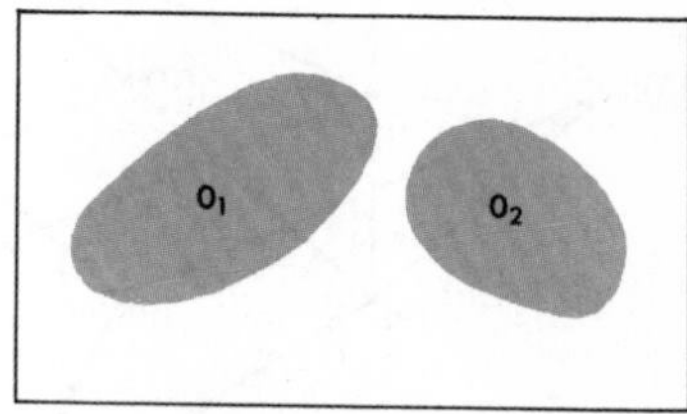

Objectives O_1 and O_2 are independent.

Figure 13·1 (a) and (b)

Borel's five axioms. For those readers who have a good mathematical knowledge, here are the five axioms corresponding to the Boolean lattice; they are those which the mathematician Borel introduced into the theory of probability.

Let **E** be a reference set of objectives and Δ such a family that $\Delta \in P(\mathbf{E})$ where $P(\mathbf{E})$ is the set of all subsets of $(\mathbf{E})$; we suppose that Δ necessarily includes **E**.

Axiom I $\forall \mathbf{A} \in \Delta,\ C_E\mathbf{A} \in \Delta$
Axiom II $\forall \mathbf{A}, \forall \mathbf{B} \in \Delta : \mathbf{A} \cup \mathbf{B} \in \Delta$
Axiom III Let $v(\mathbf{A})$ be the value of $\mathbf{A}$: $\forall \mathbf{A} \in \Delta,\ v(\mathbf{A}) \geqslant 0$
Axiom IV $\mathbf{A} \wedge \mathbf{B} = \phi \Rightarrow v(\mathbf{A} \cup \mathbf{B}) = v(\mathbf{A}) + v(\mathbf{B})$
Axiom V $v(\mathbf{E}) = 1$

If it is a problem of infinite sets of objectives, Axioms *II* and *IV* will be replaced by Axioms *IIa* and *IVa*:

Axiom IIa For any enumerable sequence of objectives: $\mathbf{A}_1, \mathbf{A}_2, \ldots, \mathbf{A}_n \ldots$:

$$\mathbf{A}_1, \mathbf{A}_2, \ldots, \mathbf{A}_n, \ldots \in \Delta \Rightarrow \bigcup_{k=1}^{\infty} \mathbf{A}_k \in \Delta$$

Axiom IVa For $A_1, A_2, \ldots, A_n \ldots \in \Delta$
if $A_i \wedge A_j = \phi,\ \forall i, j\ (i \neq j)$

$$\text{then } v\left(\bigcup_{k=1}^{\infty} A_k\right) = \sum_{k=1}^{\infty} v(A_k)$$

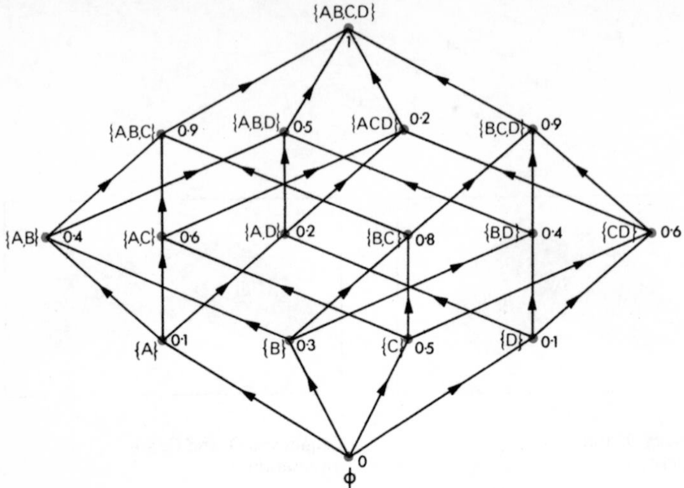

Figure 13·2

Axiom Ia To each elementary objective O_i, a non-negative number $v(O_i)$ can be made to correspond in such a way that, $v(O_1) + v(O_2) + \ldots + v(O_r) = 1$ if there are r elementary objectives.

Axiom IIIa $v(O_i \cup O_j) = v(O_i) + v(O_j) - v(O_i \cap O_j)$ corresponds to the value of the objective formed by the set of all the elementary objectives existing in O_i, in O_j or in both; $v(O_i \cap O_j)$ being the value of the whole of the elementary objectives existing in both O_i and O_j.

Let us use the example of figure 11·7, repeated in figure 13·2 and on which we have marked values. Let us suppose that the young man has given the following values to the elementary objectives A, B, C and D which are independent:

$$v(A) = 0{\cdot}1;\ v(B) = 0{\cdot}3$$
$$v(C) = 0{\cdot}5;\ v(D) = 0{\cdot}1$$

Then, following Axiom *Ia*, *II* and *IIIa*, we shall have

$$v(A, B) = v(A) + v(B) - v(A \cap B) = 0{\cdot}1 + 0{\cdot}3 - 0 = 0{\cdot}4$$
$$v(A, C) = v(A) + v(C) - v(A \cap C) = 0{\cdot}1 + 0{\cdot}5 - 0 = 0{\cdot}6$$
$$v(A, D) = v(A) + v(D) - v(A \cap D) = 0{\cdot}1 + 0{\cdot}1 - 0 = 0{\cdot}2$$

....

$$\begin{aligned} v(A, B, C) &= v(A, B) + v(B, C) - v((A, B)\cap(B, C)) \\ &= v(A, B) + v(B, C) - v(B) \\ &= 0{\cdot}4 + 0{\cdot}8 - 0{\cdot}3 = 0{\cdot}9 \qquad \text{[Equation 13.3]} \end{aligned}$$

$$\begin{aligned} v(A, B, C, D) &= v(A, B, C) + v(A, B, D) - v(A, B, C)\cap(A, B, D) \\ &= v(A, B, C) + v(A, B, D) - v(A, B) \\ &= 0{\cdot}9 + 0{\cdot}5 - 0{\cdot}4 = 1 \end{aligned}$$

Thus, all the objectives will have a numerical value and it will then be possible to compare them with each other where they were not previously comparable. For instance, (A, C) will be preferred to (A, B, D), (A, C) to (B, D) and so on. In the scale of values we shall have:

$$\begin{array}{l} \underset{1}{(A, B, C, D)},\ \underset{0\cdot9}{(A, B, C)} \text{ or } \underset{0\cdot9}{(B, C, D)},\ \underset{0\cdot8}{(B, C)},\ \underset{0\cdot7}{(A, C, D)},\ \underset{0\cdot6}{(A, C)} \\ \text{or } \underset{0\cdot6}{(C, D)},\ \underset{0\cdot5}{(A, B, D)} \text{ or } \underset{0\cdot5}{(C)},\ \underset{0\cdot4}{(B, D)} \text{ or } \underset{0\cdot4}{(A, B)},\ \underset{0\cdot3}{(B)},\ \underset{0\cdot2}{(A, D)},\ \underset{0\cdot1}{(A)} \\ \text{or } \underset{0\cdot1}{(D)},\ \underset{0-}{\phi} \end{array}$$

[Equation 13.4]

We again find a complete ordering but if the method we have used is perfectly logical and can satisfy the most fastidious mathematician, it nevertheless remains true that the values given to the elementary objectives by the young man can be very arguable even to the young man himself. However, after arbitrarily giving such values or 'weights' to his elementary objectives and after determining the values corresponding to each of the objectives of the lattice, he can carry out some corrections. These would ensure that his intentions would be reproduced in the best way possible by the whole of the values in the lattice. The device of translating from order to weighting that we shall describe later meets this need for adjustment. Before describing it, we shall point out that, under one condition, it is possible to give *a priori* values to compound objectives.

For a mathematician, the condition is that the objectives on which a value has been previously set constitute a basis producing a sub-lattice.

The objectives not belonging to this sub-lattice will all then have zero value. Everything is constructed as if it concerned a family which is probabilisable in the meaning of Borel, and into which a basis of probability is introduced. The idea of an 'event' is replaced here by 'objective'. As for the axiomatic ideas of probability, the reader may care to refer to [56].

Example of a method which enables us to obtain a convex weighting from a complete order of preference. (Method due to R. L. Ackoff and C. W. Churchman.[11])

Let there be n objectives $O_1, O_2, \ldots, O_n$ of which we take an order of preference which is, for instance,

$$O_1 \succ O_2 \succ, \ldots, \succ O_{n-1} \succ O_n$$

We shall obtain a convex weighting by working as follows:

A. Give O_1 the value $v(O_1) = 1 \cdot 00$ and to each one of the other objectives a value which seems appropriate and such that $v(O_j) < v(O_i)$ if $j < i$.

B. Compare O_1 to the set of objectives $O_2, O_3, \ldots, O_n$.

B1. If O_1 is preferred to $O_2, O_3, \ldots, O_n$ adjust $v(O_1)$ if necessary so that

$$v(O_1) > v(O_2) + v(O_3) + \ldots + v(O_n) \qquad \text{[Equation 13.5]}$$

The aim of this operation is to retain the relative values of $O_2, O_3, \ldots, O_n$. Pass then to operation C.

B2. If O_1 and the set $O_2, O_3, \ldots, O_n$ are considered as being indifferent, adjust $v(O_2)$ so that

$$v(O_1) = v(O_2) + v(O_3) + \ldots + v(O_n) \qquad \text{[Equation 13.6]}$$

Then pass to C.

B3. If the set $O_2, O_3, \ldots, O_n$ is preferred to O_1, adjust $v(O_1)$ if necessary so that

$$v(O_1) < v(O_2) + v(O_3) + \ldots + v(O_n) \qquad \text{[Equation 13.7]}$$

Then pass to B3.1.

B3.1. Compare O_1 to the set $O_2, O_3, \ldots, O_{n-1}$.

B3.1.1. If O_1 is preferred to the set $O_2, O_3, \ldots, O_{n-1}$, adjust if necessary the values so that

$$v(O_1) > v(O_2) + v(O_3) + \ldots + v(O_{n-1}) \qquad \text{[Equation 13.8]}$$

Then pass to C.

B3.1.2. If O_1 and the set $O_2, O_3, \ldots, O_{n-1}$ are indifferent, rectify the values if necessary so that

$$v(O_1) = v(O_2) + v(O_3) + \ldots v(O_{n-1}) \qquad \text{[Equation 13.9]}$$

Then pass to C.

B3.1.3. If the set $O_2, O_3, \ldots, O_{n-1}$ is preferred to O_1, rectify the values if necessary so that

$$v(O_1) < v(O_2) + v(O_3) + \ldots + v(O_{n-1}) \qquad \text{[Equation 13.10]}$$

Then pass to B3.2.

B3.2. Compare O_1 to the set $O_2, O_3, \ldots, O_{n-2}$ until the comparisons between O_1 and the set $O_2, \ldots O_3$ is finished. Then pass on to C.

C. Compare O_2 to the set $O_3, O_4, \ldots, O_n$ and operate as in B.

D. Carry on until the comparison of O_{n-2} and the set O_{n-1}, O_n is finished.

E. Divide each $v(O_i)$ thus obtained by the sum $v(O_1) + v(O_2) + \ldots + v(O_n)$.

It should be emphasised that the weighting thus obtained would have to be completely recalculated if an objective were to be added to or taken away from the set. Moreover, such a weighting, if accepted, must be modified later if opinions change. Finally, as soon as the number of objectives becomes large such a process becomes too complicated to operate.

A note on the choice of examples. The reader may wonder why the various examples presented in this chapter are artificial and far removed from the serious concerns of the businessman. Most of the mathematicians, psychologists, sociologists, or economists responsible for much of the progress in the spheres of decision-making in human actions, agree that we are still quite a long way from having at our disposal systems of axioms which enable us to deal rigorously with real cases, on the scale of business enterprises and beyond, at the level of political decisions. But they also agree that the problem is more one of inculcating a scientific mental attitude than of inducing new thought processes. We know, however, a number of actual cases where identical methods, or near enough to those that we have just described, have been satisfactorily made use of. Churchman, Ackoff and Arnoff[11] give some examples, which unfortunately are too long to be described in an introductory book such as this. I myself[16] have shown how a regional index of wealth in rural districts (poor and rich – search for a poverty index – weighting of values) could be established. This could be done from statistics of distribution, taken from the files, and a convex weighting which was, in fact, calculated from relations of arbitrary order could be dealt with according to the method recommended by Ackoff and Churchman. It is in order to forestall justified criticisms that I have chosen only artificial examples. Elsewhere in the book, on the other hand, where the growing elements of the future science of action are given in more detail and can be made direct use of, I shall present more practical and possibly more convincing examples.

The following example, then, will once again be very elementary.

Example: An examination panel intends to determine the coefficients of four tests, A, B, C, D. A preliminary discussion between members of the panel has led them to adopt an order of importance of the tests as follows:

$$O_1 = C,\ O_2 = A,\ O_3 = D,\ O_4 = B$$

The following values have been assigned:

$$v(O_1) = 1,\ v(O_2) = 0{\cdot}7,\ v(O_3) = 0{\cdot}5,\ v(O_4) = 0{\cdot}2$$

[Equation 13.11]

which gives, for a convex weighting

$$K_1 = \frac{10}{24},\ K_2 = \frac{7}{24},\ K_3 = \frac{5}{24},\ K_4 = \frac{2}{24}$$ [Equation 13.12]

The panel then decides to improve this weighting so that the intentions of its members are better represented.

Comparing O_1 to the set O_2, O_3, O_4 it is decided that O_2, O_3, O_4 is preferable to O_1. $v(O_1)$ is then compared to $v(O_2) + v(O_3) + v(O_4)$, that is, 1 to 1·4. The value of $v(O_2)$, $v(O_3)$ or $v(O_4)$ will not be changed. $v(O_1)$ is then compared to $v(O_2) + v(O_3)$ and it is decided that O_1 appears $1 < 1{\cdot}2$; preferable to (O_2, O_3) but it is therefore necessary to modify one or more values. $v(O_1)$ is increased from 1 to 1·3, thus we have $v(O_1) > v(O_2) + v(O_3)$ and $v(O_1) < v(O_2) + v(O_3) + v(O_4)$. This adjustment gives us therefore:

$$v(O_1) = 1{\cdot}3,\ v(O_2) = 0{\cdot}7,\ v(O_3) = 0{\cdot}5,\ v(O_4) = 0.2$$

[Equation 13.13]

whence

$$K_1 = \frac{13}{27},\ K_2 = \frac{7}{27},\ K_3 = \frac{5}{27},\ K_4 = \frac{2}{27}$$ [Equation 13.14]

It is then decided, on comparing O_2 with O_3, O_4, that the latter is to be preferred to the former. Since, at the moment, $v(O_2)$ and $v(O_3, O_4)$ have the same value (0·7), $v(O_2)$ must be decreased and, in consequence, so must $v(O_1)$.

Let us make $v(O_1) = 1{\cdot}2$ and $v(O_2) = 0{\cdot}6$. This does not alter the previous order, and we now satisfy the new relationship. We have, after this adjustment:

$$v(O_1) = 1{\cdot}2,\ v(O_2) = 0{\cdot}6,\ v(O_3) = 0{\cdot}5,\ v(O_4) = 0{\cdot}2$$

[Equation 13.15]

No further adjustments are needed and the convex weighting accepted by the panel will be:

$$K_1 = \frac{12}{25},\ K_2 = \frac{6}{25},\ K_3 = \frac{5}{25},\ K_4 = \frac{2}{25}$$ [Equation 13.16]

Finally, the panel thinks it would be easier to take 40 as a sum of the points. An easy conversion gives us:

$$K_1' = \frac{12 \times 40}{25} \simeq 19, \; K_2' = \frac{6 \times 40}{25} \simeq 10$$

$$K_3' = \frac{5 \times 40}{25} = 8, \;\; K_4' = \frac{2 \times 40}{25} \simeq 3 \qquad \text{[Equation 13.17]}$$

In problems of this sort, since the choice belongs to several persons, there may be arguments within the group. In most cases it is agreed that the majority decision will prevail, but other processes, which are more or less democratic, can be admitted or imposed.

When the final adjustment has been carried out, one may possibly be led, after the chosen weighting has been applied to a particular population, to make a new adjustment, taking into account the results previously obtained (Condorcet effect). Condorcet was interested in the modification *a posteriori* of the preferences of an assembly. A domain connected with the science of action, the Theory of Committees and Elections, would have merited some attention in this book, but, lacking space, I have not touched on it. The reader could profitably consult D. Black's *The Theory of Committees and Elections*, Cambridge University Press, 1958.

14 Search for optimal solutions: examples: singleness of the value function

We have seen that the selection of objectives, from the point of view of satisfying intentions, resulted in the search for a complete ordering over the set or a part of the set of objectives. (In the latter case, we suppose that this part includes *a priori* the preferred objective or objectives.)

A sure way to obtain a complete ordering consists in introducing a value function, that is to say in giving a numerical value to each objective, and then in calculating the whole set of the values taken by the function. Logically, in this case, the preferred objective can only be the greatest possible value (maximum) or the smallest possible value (minimum), according to the nature of the problem.

We say then that we proceed to an 'optimisation'.

The search for the minimum or for the maximum of a function is one of the most important general problems of mathematics. From Huyghens to Poincaré by way of Rayleigh, Hamilton, Lagrange, Gauss and recently Pontryagin, Dantzig, Kantorovitch, Bellman, to name but a few, a great many important works have been published on optimisation of numerical functions.

Generally speaking, the problems of optimisation arise in the following manner, in the study of actual cases.

Construction of a model or mathematical representation of the considered phenomenon.

Specification of the problem, and particularly working up specifications of the set of solutions.

Statement of the criteria and choice of a value function.

Search for the optimal solution or solutions for this value function.

Possible study of variations of the optimal solution or solutions in relation to parameters which could not be introduced in the value function (parametric programming).

Possible study of *K*-optimal solutions, that is to say solutions finding their place in the order of the value function in the vicinity of and after the optimal solution.

Possible modification of the chosen value function and reconsideration of the model.

Example 1. This concerns the construction of a motorway between town *A* and town *E*, passing through urban centres *B*, *C* and *D*. Between each town or urban centre various sections can be built (figure 14·1); the problem to be solved by the committee responsible for public works is to know which criterion to choose for determining the best route.

The problem set includes relatively few possible objectives: here they are simply ways from *A* to *E*. To define this clearly, the sections which can be built are represented by lines separating the possible passage points. Thus in *B* there are three possible passage

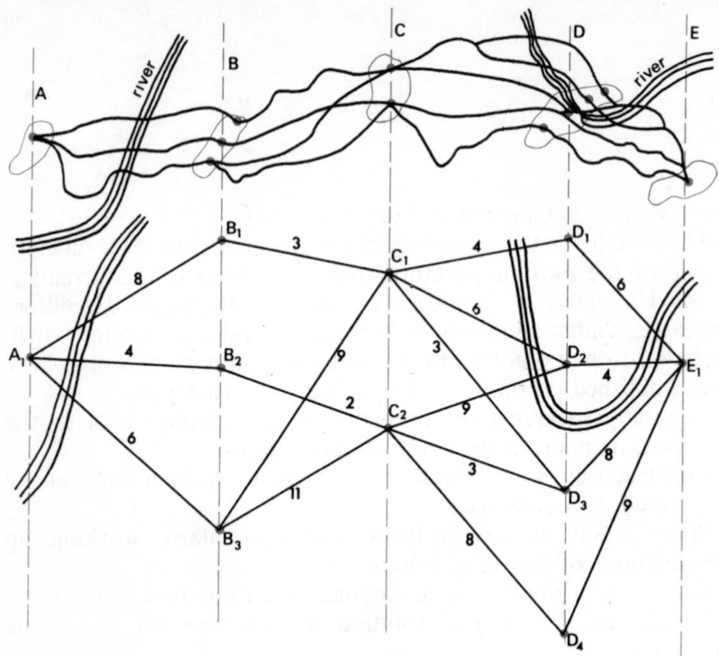

Figure 14·1

points, B_1, B_2, B_3; in C there are two, C_1 and C_2; in D there are four, D_1, D_2, D_3, D_4.

The enumeration of all the possible routes from A to E is easy in the present case, in view of the simplicity of the problem set. There are twelve distinct routes possible, which are shown in the second column of table 4.

The different factors, calculable or not, which emerge in a problem of this nature are: the technological costs of production, the costs of expropriation, the delays in execution, the influence on the economy of the region, and so on. It is very likely that the Public Works Committee will be subjected to various pressures, as certain towns crossed by the motorway may have a stake in seeing the project scrapped, since the motorway might divert the flow of traffic from the commercial centre and redirect it elsewhere. Suppose, for instance, that the main trade in a town is the sale of local souvenirs to motorists, the building of a motorway would affect well-established interests. In short, the choice of a criterion is not easy in this kind of problem.

The Public Works Committee will probably decide to take as the main criterion the total cost (technology and expropriation) of each proposed route. The costs of each section having been estimated and marked in figure 14·1, this calculation will be made by adding the relevant figures together and the results are entered in the third column of table 4.

Table 4 Possible routes from *A* to *E*.

No.	Possible route	Cost
1	A_1, B_1, C_1, D_1, E_1	21
2	A_1, B_1, C_1, D_2, E_1	21
3	A_1, B_1, C_1, D_3, E_1	22
4	A_1, B_2, C_2, D_2, E_1	19
5	A_1, B_2, C_2, D_3, E_1	17
6	A_1, B_2, C_2, D_4, E_1	23
7	A_1, B_3, C_1, D_1, E_1	25
8	A_1, B_3, C_1, D_2, E_1	25
9	A_1, B_3, C_1, D_3, E_1	26
10	A_1, B_3, C_2, D_2, E_1	30
11	A_1, B_3, C_2, D_3, E_1	28
12	A_1, B_3, C_2, D_4, E_1	34

It appears from this point of view that the best route is the least expensive one, i.e. (A_1, B_2, C_2, D_3, E_1) for which the result is 17. The criterion chosen has enabled us to find a total order between the routes, i.e.:

5, 4, 1 and 2, 3, 6, 7 and 8, 9, 10, 11, 12 [Equation 14.2]

Let us suppose that after a more detailed study of route 5 it is noticed that the length of some of the work would not allow the motorway to be brought into service within the prescribed time and that, in spite of the extra cost, it would be better to take route 4 which would require more landscaping, more expensive but more rapidly carried out. Yet again, because the mayor of one of the towns through which the motorway passes has a good deal of political influence, it is possible in the end that route 2, more expensive even than 5 and 4, will be accepted. However, the knowledge of the optimal solution enables us to realise that keeping within the time limits would add 2 to the cost and that the next electoral success of the mayor of *B* would increase the total cost by 2 more.

The search for the optimal cost is important, for it enables us to study the extra cost of non-optimal choices. In the very simplified problem which we have just studied, and which is a picture on a smaller scale of actual problems of the same kind, it seems that the criterion chosen is incontestable, but when we examine the routes of roads and railways we must agree that this criterion of total cost has not been chosen, sufficiently powerful pressure-groups having used their influence at a suitable time so that the results of analysis have been disregarded.

Example 2. A company manufactures two kinds of equipment intended for the same use, an equipment *A* of a high quality, and an equipment *B* of an ordinary quality.

Each unit of *A* requires twice as much time for execution as one unit of *B* on a certain machine. By means of this machine it is impossible to produce in one day more than a thousand units of *B*.

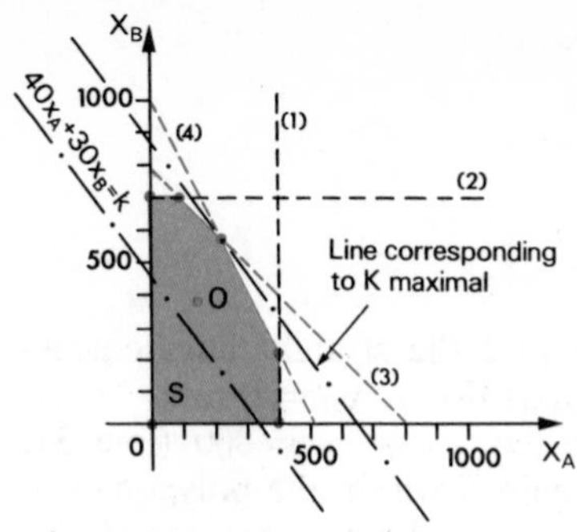

Figure 14·2

The supply of the main raw material for the production of equipment of type A or of type B, is limited; it does not allow the production of more than eight hundred pieces of equipment, be they of type A or type B or both. On the other hand, type A requires a special material of which only four hundred units are available per day. Type B requires another special material of which only seven hundred units are available per day.

Before trying to find which criterion can be accepted for selecting the daily quantities to be manufactured, let us see what is the nature of the objective in this case.

An objective is here constituted by a 'production vector', say (x_A, x_B), where x_A represents the daily production of A and x_B the daily production of B. Let us first look for the domain S of the possible objectives.

The quantities to be produced of A and B cannot be negative; they must take positive or zero values in a domain S which we shall calculate.

Let us write therefore first:

$$x_A \geqslant 0$$
$$x_B \geqslant 0 \qquad \text{[Equation 14.3]}$$

The above stated limitations set us:

$$\begin{aligned} x_A &\leqslant 400 \quad (1)\\ x_B &\leqslant 700 \quad (2)\\ x_A + x_B &\leqslant 800 \quad (3)\\ 2x_A + x_B &\leqslant 1000 \quad (4) \end{aligned} \qquad \text{[Equation 14.4]}$$

It is then easy to build the domain S where the possible objectives can be found. We draw, in figure 14·2 the straight lines corresponding to the equations $x_A = 0$ (axis Ox_B); $x_B = 0$ (axis Ox_A); $x_A = 400$ (line 1); $x_B = 700$ (line 2); $x_A + x_B = 800$ (line 3); $2x_A + x_B = 1000$ (line 4). The domain S within the polygon thus drawn, including the perimeter, holds all the possible objectives.

It will be noted that this polygon is convex because of the nature of the relations [Equation 14.4]. Thus 400,200 being a possible objective, as well as 200,500, then:

$(x_A, x_B) = \lambda_1 (400{,}200) + \lambda_2 (200{,}500) = (\lambda_1 (400) + \lambda_2 (200), \lambda_1 (200) + \lambda_2 (500))$ is also a possible objective if $\lambda_1 \geqslant 0$, $\lambda_2 \geqslant 0$, $\lambda_1 + \lambda_2 = 1$ [Equation 14.5]

Any convex weighting of possible objectives gives a possible objective; in the representation given by means of the diagram $x_A\, Ox_B$, the weighted objective is always on the section of line which joins the two given objectives. This note will come in useful later on.

Among all the possible objectives, which is the best? In other words, which is the best production vector?

To find an answer to that let us examine various criteria which can occur in the form of a value function.

Let us call $F(x_A, x_B)$ the value function chosen. Let us suppose that we take as a criterion the total profit, knowing that the profit on A is 40 per unit and the benefit on B is 30 per unit. The value function is then:

$$F_1(x_A, x_B) = 40x_A + 30x_B \qquad \text{[Equation 14.6]}$$

Naturally we shall look for the maximum of $F_1(x_A, x_B)$. In the present very simple case it is easy to find this maximum. Whatever the possible objective (x_A, x_B) chosen, there always will be a straight line $40x_A + 30x_B = K$ which will pass through the point representing the objective, and the further the straight line will move away from the origin 0 while keeping the same slope while it does so, the higher will be the value K represented by the points on it.

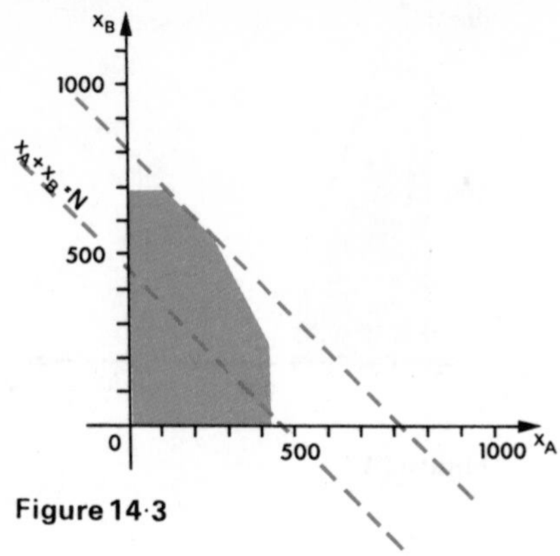

Figure 14·3

The straight line cannot be moved outwards beyond the position where it no longer has a common point with the domain S of the possible objectives. This will happen for the objective corresponding to the point where the lines (3) and (4) intersect, say:

$$x_A + x_B = 800$$
$$2x_A + x_B = 1000 \qquad \text{[Equation 14.7]}$$

which gives $x_A = 200$, $x_B = 600$, whence the optimal objective (200,600) which gives a maximal profit:

$$F_1(200,600) = (40)\,(200) + (30)\,(600) = 26{,}000 \qquad \text{[Equation 14.8]}$$

We could also adopt another criterion, the quantity of manufactured equipment, without worrying about the profit. Suppose

$$F_2(x_A, x_B) = x_A + x_B \qquad \text{[Equation 14.9]}$$

Of course, according to this criterion we will also have to try and find the maximum of $F_2(x_A, x_B)$. Working as previously we see from figure 14·3 that the maximum of $F_2(x_A, x_B)$ will now occur for $(x_A, x_B) = (100{,}700)$ and $(x_A, x_B) = (200{,}600)$. The straight line $x_A + x_B = N$ being parallel to the straight line $x_A + x_B = 800$. We then have $N = 800$. This time we have two optimal objectives (100,700) and (200,600) and by virtue of the property of convexity, any objective such that

$$(x_A, x_B) = \lambda_1(100{,}700) + \lambda_2(200{,}600)$$
$$= (100\lambda_1 + 200\lambda_2,\ 700\lambda_1 + 600\lambda_2) \qquad \text{[Equation 14.10]}$$

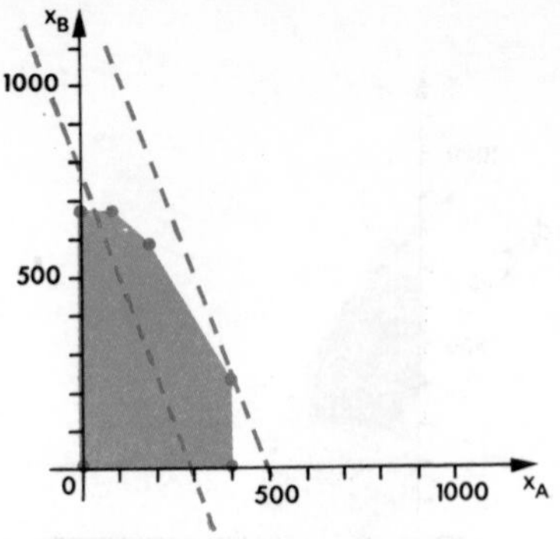

Figure 14·4

is also an optimal objective, a point on the line which joins the two extreme points.

If we compare the results obtained by taking $F_1(x_A, x_B)$ on the one hand, and $F_2(x_A, x_B)$ on the other, we obtain in each case the same optimal objective (200,600). Does therefore finding the maximum of profit and the maximum of production come to the same thing?

With the numbers that we have chosen, this is true. Let us take other numbers for the profit, say, 40 for *A* and 15 for *B*. We then have as value function:

$$F_3(x_A, x_B) = 40x_A + 15x_B \qquad \text{[Equation 14.11]}$$

Working as before we obtain (figure 14·4) the following result: The optimal objective corresponds to the intersection of the straight lines (1) and (4) where

$$x_A = 400$$
$$2x_A + x_B = 1000$$

that is to say $(x_A, x_B) = (400{,}200)$. For these values of the unit profit, the choice of a criterion F_2 leads to a very different result from the criterion F_3.

A little later we shall come back to this important question.

Let us now see if other criteria could reasonably be used in the same problem.

Can we choose, for instance, as a criterion the total cost $F_4(x_A, x_B)$ of manufacture, supposing that the unit costs of *A* and of *B* are given, and then look for the minimum of the total cost? It would

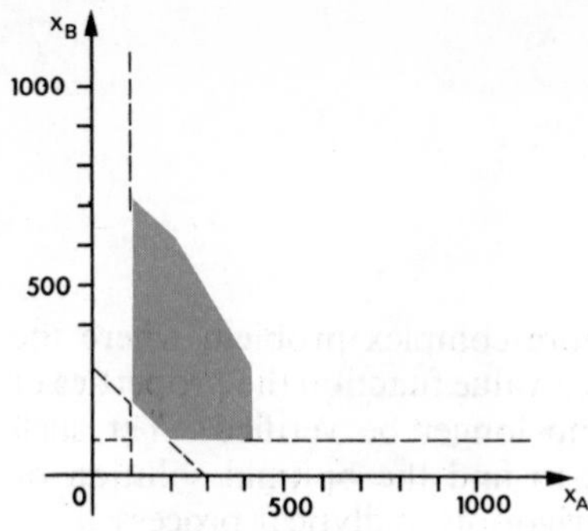

Figure 14·5

not be rational because, as we can easily see in studying the domain S of possible objectives, the minimum of $F_4(x_A, x_B)$ corresponds to 0, no production! The nature of specified restrictions in this problem does not allow us to search for a minimum which has a meaning from the point of view of business management. But, if we were to introduce other restrictions, for instance to produce at least a given quantity of units of A or of B, for example to set:

$$x_A \geqslant 100$$
$$x_B \geqslant 100$$
$$x_A + x_B \geqslant 300 \qquad \text{[Equation 14.12]}$$

we should then obtain the domain of figure 14·5 where it appears that the calculation of a minimum cost could have a meaning.

The value function can take other aspects.

Let us suppose that the unit profits are not constant, for instance:

$$\gamma_A = 40 \quad 0 \leqslant x_A < 500$$
$$= 50 \quad x_A \geqslant 500$$
$$\gamma_B = 30 \quad 0 \leqslant x_B < 500$$
$$= 40 \quad x_B \geqslant 500 \qquad \text{[Equation 14.13]}$$

Where γ_A is the unit cost of A and γ_B the unit cost of B, the value function would thus become:

$$F_5(x_A, x_B) = 40x_A + 30x_B \quad x_A < 500, x_B < 500$$
$$= 50x_A + 30x_B \quad x_A \geqslant 500, x_B < 500$$
$$= 40x_A + 40x_B \quad x_A < 500, x_B \geqslant 500$$
$$= 50x_A + 40x_B \quad x_A \geqslant 500, x_B \geqslant 500$$
$$\text{[Equation 14.14]}$$

We shall not deal with this more complex problem where the value function is not linear (for such value function the properties of equations 12.2 and 12.3 would no longer be verified). Yet such problems exist and it is possible to find the optimal solution or solutions for some of them by a rigorous analytical process.

Example 3. We consider a given operation to instal a machine for manufacturing a certain article. This operation calls for an investment of $I_0 = 500$, and yearly operating cost $e_0 = 65$, these being constant (these maintenance expenses are intended to ensure the indefinite running of the machine).

To this given operation O_0 we try to compare two other operations, O_1 and O_2, requiring a greater initial capital but with lower operating costs.

If, using the same notation as before, we put

For O_1: $I_1 = 600$, $e_1 = 50$
For O_2: $I_2 = 800$, $e_2 = 25$ [Equation 14.15]

Various criteria can be proposed to compare O_1 and O_2 to O_0; we shall study two of them.

The expenses from the initial date occur under the form of a vector with an infinity of elements.

O_0: $V_0 = (500,65,65,65...)$ [Equation 14.17]
O_1: $V_1 = (600,50,50,50...)$ [Equation 14.18]
O_2: $V_2 = (800,25,25,25...)$ [Equation 14.19]

Let us notice first that if one of the vectors dominated the two others, i.e. if all its elements were lower than the corresponding elements of the other vectors, in view of the nature of this problem, the preference would be given to the operation represented by this vector; but this is not so.

Since no vector dominates the others, we cannot find a total or even partial order between the vectors. Let us consider then the total expenses. They are all infinite and therefore no direct comparison can be made between them.

$$O_0\colon S_0 = 500 + 65 + 65 + 65 + \ldots + = \infty \quad \text{[Equation 14.20]}$$
$$O_1\colon S_1 = 600 + 50 + 50 + 50 + \ldots + = \infty \quad \text{[Equation 14.21]}$$
$$O_2\colon S_2 = 800 + 25 + 25 + 25 + \ldots + = \infty \quad \text{[Equation 14.22]}$$

One of the means of comparing these expenses is by reducing them to 'present values' by assigning to each future expense a positive multiplier less than unity. Let us suppose that an interest rate of r is valid for the future and that we ignore inflation, the present values will then take the following form:

$$D = I + \frac{e}{1+r} + \frac{e}{(1+r)^2} + \frac{e}{(1+r)^3} + \ldots \quad \text{[Equation 14.23]}$$

It is easy to show that

$$\frac{1}{1+r} + \frac{1}{(1+r)^2} + \frac{1}{(1+r)^3} + \ldots = \frac{1}{r} \quad \text{[Equation 14.24]}$$

therefore

$$D = I + \frac{e}{r} \quad \text{[Equation 14.25]}$$

Let us suppose that the interest rate is 10 per cent. We shall have to compare the various expenses.

$$O_0\colon D_0 = 500 + \frac{65}{0{\cdot}10} = 500 + 650 = 1150 \quad \text{[Equation 14.26]}$$
$$O_1\colon D_1 = 600 + \frac{50}{0{\cdot}10} = 600 + 500 = 1100 \quad \text{[Equation 14.27]}$$
$$O_2\colon D_2 = 800 + \frac{25}{0{\cdot}10} = 800 + 250 = 1050 \quad \text{[Equation 14.28]}$$

With such a criterion it then appears that:

$$D_0 > D_1 > D_2; \quad \text{[Equation 14.29]}$$

and O_2 will be preferred to O_1, and O_1 to O_0.

Under a capitalist régime, the criterion of present value is generally adopted in investment problems, but we can consider others. Thus, some Soviet economists recommend the use of a criterion which does not resort to the interest rate, but is based on the 'recovery period' of the invested capital in relation to the capital of reference. Various authors, and in particular Massé,[18] have shown that in fact this is only the indirect introduction of an interest rate. However, the two criteria, that of the present value and that of the recovery period, can lead to different choices.

Let us first explain to the reader what the recovery period consists of. Consider the datum operation O_0 to which correspond I_0 and e_0, then the operation O_1 to which correspond I_1 and e_1. The 'recovery period' of O_1 will be given by:

$$T_1 = \frac{I_1 - I_0}{e_0 - e_1} \qquad \text{[Equation 14.30]}$$

We obviously suppose that $I_1 > I_0$ and $e_1 < e_0$, otherwise the problem set would have no meaning.

If we consider now another operation O_2 to which correspond I_2 and e_2 and for which:

$$T_2 = \frac{I_2 - I_0}{e_0 - e_2} \qquad \text{[Equation 14.31]}$$

with $I_2 > I_0$ and $e_2 < e_0$ we shall prefer the operation for which we have the smallest recovery period.

Going back to the numerical example; we have

$$T_1 = \frac{I_1 - I_0}{e_0 - e_1} = \frac{600 - 500}{65 - 50} = \frac{100}{15} = 6\tfrac{2}{3} = 6 \text{ years } 8 \text{ months} \qquad \text{[Equation 14.32]}$$

$$T_2 = \frac{I_2 - I_0}{e_0 - e_1} = \frac{800 - 500}{65 - 25} = \frac{300}{40} = 7\tfrac{1}{2} = 7 \text{ years } 6 \text{ months} \qquad \text{[Equation 14.33]}$$

Thus $T_2 > T_1$ and O_1 is preferred to O_2 with O_0 taken as a datum.

Therefore, if we take the first criterion (present value) O_2 is preferred to O_1 and if we take the second (recovery period) O_1 is preferred to O_2. With different values for I_i and e_i, we could make the two criteria agree, but this example was designed to show the importance which should be put on the choice of a criterion in investment problems, as in all economic problems. Also suggested for these investment problems, according to their size, their structures, and the accepted principles of political economy, are various other criteria (depreciation, cost price, etc.). See references [18, 25, 9].

Singleness of the value function. The examples just described have brought to the fore the fact that generally we are not faced with one criterion only, and that the criteria considered can give results whose numerical values do not put the objectives in the same order of preference.

It is now time to introduce a general principle:

If we take a criterion in the shape of a value function to be optimised, this function shall be one only. In other words, we must not try to optimise several functions at the same time.

Intentions such as:

To try to find for one's next holiday the least expensive hotel and the one which gives the best food;

To marry the prettiest and richest heiress in town;

To optimise both a production rate and the profit of this production;

To destroy the maximum number of enemy targets while losing the minimum of aircraft;

are not necessarily coherent and must not be formulated in this way. On the other hand the following intentions are correctly expressed:

To try to find, among hotels charging a certain price, the one offering the best food;

To marry the prettiest girl having at least some prospects of coming into money;

To optimise a profit of production for a rate equal to or higher than a given rate;

To destroy the maximum number of enemy factories with a fixed number of aircraft.

Let us now see the very simplified mathematical aspects of the singleness of the value function to be optimised.

Let there be five objectives A, B, C, D, E and two value functions $V_1(X)$ and $V_2(X)$ constituting two criteria.

Suppose that we have, for the value function, $V_1(X)$:

$$V_1(B) < V_1(A) < V_1(C) < V_1(D) < V_1(E) \quad \text{[Equation 14.34]}$$

and with value function $V_2(X)$:

$$V_2(C) < V_2(A) < V_2(D) < V_2(B) < V_2(E) \quad \text{[Equation 14.35]}$$

Suppose also that for each of the value functions a minimum is sought; with $V_1(X)$ the optimal objective is B, with $V_2(X)$ the optimal objective is C, there is no concordance between the results given by $V_1(X)$ and $V_2(X)$.

For one value function to be considered as equivalent to another, from the optimisation point of view, it must give to objectives that it measures the same complete ordering. Even if the optimal objective obtained by means of each of the two functions is the same, the two functions cannot be merged. For this, the preference order should be the same in both cases. This is very important, because very often it is not only the knowledge of the optimal objective which is important, but also the sensitivity around this optimal objective. Thus, considering the value function $V_1(X)$ and $V_2(X)$ and the results (equations 14.34 and 14.35) we shall have:

	$V_1(X)$	$V_2(X)$	
objective 1 – optimal	B	C	
2 – optimal	A	A	
3 – optimal	C	D	
4 – optimal	D	B	
5 – optimal	E	E	[Equation 14.36]

The search for kth best objectives is important in many problems of decision. Mathematicians and economists are beginning to concern themselves closely with such questions. To see how some difficulties arise, let us go back to our little example including five objectives.

Suppose we have found the following numerical values:

	A	B	C	D	E	
$V_1(X)$	110	105	125	140	164	
$V_2(X)$	54	68	53	60	74	[Equation 14.37]

we shall have:

$$\frac{V_1(A) - V_1(B)}{V_1(B)} = \frac{110 - 105}{105} = \frac{5}{105} \quad \text{[Equation 14.38]}$$

$$\frac{V_2(A) - V_2(C)}{V_2(C)} = \frac{54 - 53}{53} = \frac{1}{53} \quad \text{[Equation 14.39]}$$

These quantities measure the relative sensitivity when we go from the 1-optimal objective to the 2-optimal objective. Since they are relatively small, we can be led to choose A which is 2-optimal but is so in relation to both $V_1(X)$ and $V_2(X)$.

In the case where objectives are determined by sets of continuous values, the previous notes are still valid. Thus, let us consider two value functions $V_1(X)$ and $V_2(X)$ (relative to the same variable X) which constitute the objectives. Let us suppose that the curves representing these functions are those which are shown on figure 14·6 where we have:

$$\text{Max } V_1(X) = V_1(a) \quad \text{[Equation 14.40]}$$

$$\text{Max } V_2(X) = V_2(b) \quad \text{[Equation 14.41]}$$

In the interval $]ab[$, $V_1(X)$ decreases while $V_2(X)$ increases.

If the optimum corresponds to the same value of the objective, we have:

$$\text{Max } V_1(X) = V_1(a) \quad \text{[Equation 14.42]}$$

$$\text{Max } V_2(X) = V_2(a) \quad \text{[Equation 14.43]}$$

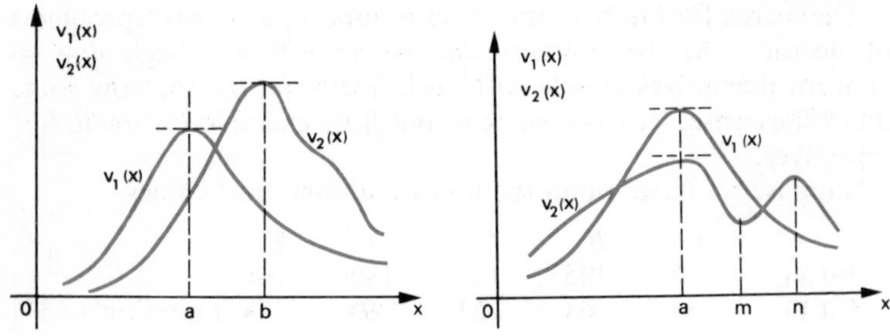

Figure 14·6 **Figure 14·7**

An interval can also exist, for which functions vary the other way round (see interval $]mn[$ in figure 14·7).

What we have just noted in the case of objectives described by means of only one variable, can be extended to the cases where the objectives are described by vectors, for example production vectors, flows of material transported, investments spread, efforts of social promotion assigned to underdeveloped regions, installation of defence devices, stocks, distribution of charity funds, etc.

Although in nearly every language there are proverbs which warn against trying to do two things at once, as in the English 'to run after two hares', there still remains an incalculable number of people around us who quite happily do just that.

15 Horizon of action

In the following sections we shall study the influence, obviously of prime importance, of the level of information that is received from moment to moment, about future states of nature. But several questions of a general character are worth looking into right away.

For this reason I shall introduce a notion 'the horizon of action', which will cover more general cases – what the economists call the 'economic horizon'. It concerns the span of time from some initial date, over which the action is contemplated. This horizon can be finite or indefinitely extended, and the intention is, within this interval of time, to take the best decision or decisions depending on the chosen criteria.

Within this horizon, the degree of knowledge and the quality of information that one can possess are very variable: some states and/or values of the future can be known with virtual certainty; others can be expressed in probabilistic terms, while others are still uncertain *a priori*.

The problems set by the action are dominated by difficulties in gathering information. This information is obtained from past events (historic analysis of situations, statistical analysis of state and/or values), or again, introduced in hypotheses about the structures being built, and such information is generally expensive. Therefore one should also estimate its cost, a delicate operation which is seldom precise.

These considerations will bring us, a little later in this book, to the notions of learning and adaptation.

One should also bear in mind that the criteria chosen can themselves be voluntarily modified by the information, or by the results themselves, as already mentioned at the end of section 13 (Condorcet effect).

Let us now ask the following question: How can we compare objectives corresponding to different horizons of action? We are now touching on the problem of comparing short-term, long-term, or even medium-term aims, if one can give a sufficiently precise meaning to these adjectives: short, long or medium.

The processes of comparison are far from being universal, and those used in the Enterprise Economy (amortisation, present values, to quote only the most common) are *a priori* rejected by some, and advocated by others.

It is at the level of the behaviour of the individual or that of the attitude of the group that one should first place this choice of horizon of action, or again the time-span of the criteria of action.

Let us try to bring out the elements affecting the choice of a horizon.

Physiological influence. The age of the individual, or its distribution in the group, evidently has an influence in this choice. An old and childless man will generally have short-term aims, a family man's plans will be bound up with the future of his family, for at least a generation, i.e. about twenty years. The attitude of a government assured of a certain stability or the attitude of the chairman of an economically sound firm would not at all be the same if the hope of survival of the system or of the organisation were far less secure.

Influence of temperament. To choose one's own horizon of action is, in the end, a fundamental freedom of each individual. Some would rather spend their money immediately, on comforts and amusements, others would rather make a long-term investment, for instance, planting a forest. Let us beware of the grave consequences of warping this fundamental freedom by publicity or political propaganda; a well balanced nation, a well balanced family, and even the individual, must tend towards a diversity of attitudes in the choice of a horizon of action.

Transforming a whole populace into pressurised consumers, to satisfy and gratify influential groups, without bothering to build enough schools, can be as bad as sacrificing consumer goods entirely for the sake of equipment. The object of planning, when it is conscientiously carried out, is to produce a *balance* which suits the temperament of the country or the group.

Influence of the evolving environment. Technological progress is mainly responsible for limiting the validity of hypotheses on the evolution of future states. Its influence on the time taken to define objectives will become greater and greater. Fashion, be it about ladies' hats, cars, furniture or whatever, is another factor which should not be ignored in the choice of a horizon of action. For those who are able, wisdom leads to the creation of progress rather than the mere acceptance of it.

16 Can ethics provide us with a system of measurement?

I need hardly tell the reader that I have no acceptable answer to give to this question. This said, we must show the extent of the problem which, presented in all sorts of different forms, is the fundamental one of the human sciences.

As long as the size of the systems allowed the setting up – in a relatively explicit way, as a result of reflection or discussion – of rules of life and action arising from morality, whether revealed or constructed, then the definition of the world, its laws, its principles, and its traditional criteria, did not require any processes of comparison or measurement. If people felt charitable, their gift to the poor at the church door sufficed, in part anyway, to satisfy their instincts in a material sense. If they had to make a political choice, the parties and their organisers presented them with forceful ideas, capable of expression in simple terms, though possibly of varying degrees of sincerity. The building of a road or railway here rather than there, simply meant discussion and tactics between pressure groups. Choosing a style of living (when this was possible) was simply a book-keeping operation in which each person was able to state his claims clearly enough. Unintentionally placing on others the risks one accepted for oneself did not then require any kind of notion of mathematical expectation. Finally, knowledge of good and evil remained one of the main facts of life. If psychological or social tragedies occurred, they were at least understandable.

In the age of the flexible world, when everything is being reappraised in less than a generation, when sociological context, social mystiques, philosophical ideas, individual and mass psychology have lost even a temporary stability, what measuring instruments can we use that will also be acceptable to the other members of our social group? In fact, in this era of continuous technological progress we are not in complete agreement amongst ourselves. Psychologists in all scientifically developed countries know of innumerable cases in which the moral problem may be the same but for which it becomes almost impossible to keep the same ethical approach. If we are driving along in our motorcar, the moral attitude we adopt excludes or puts off the idea of limiting our speed. But let us become pedestrians for a few moments in the same street and we switch from this attitude to another one which sees other motorists as careless people who are forever driving too fast.

In the name of liberty, it is not advisable to let the police exercise too much control, and yet we are indignant if even one thief escapes detection. The freedom of the press must be jealously guarded, but abuses of this freedom might well call for severe limitations on it.

In these circumstances, how can we suppose it possible to evolve, from ethics, measures and suitable value functions acceptable to all? It is a vital problem, but one which is neglected by the majority of people living in affluent countries, in spite of their evolution; and it is because of such neglect that these countries are accused of being selfish and imperialistic. Aid to underdeveloped countries is an instance of charitable intentions, of moral and material assistance motivated by ethics, without a suitable measure being found for comparing needs and sharing out the aid. There would probably be a complete change in the relations between rich and poor if the affluent peoples came to an agreement among themselves to apportion their contributions according to a norm they could all follow. A utopia perhaps, but then it would be a serious matter if this agreement were not brought about, for we would be thrown into a hopeless muddle, into the most dangerous kind of muddle, rich and poor alike. It is one of the gravest problems of our time. If a science of action had been sufficiently developed, if the possibility of universal standardisation had not been dismissed as mere fancy (it would have involved a lengthy study of our moral code and the manner in which we apply it) we should not be surrounded by so much suffering and indifference. It would not be a matter of universal standardisation in all things, but simply for clearly defined and recognisable situations, where the measures agreed on would be acceptable to all, and would even be introduced as short-term measures if such were necessary.

Without a numerical transposition, the best of intentions can bring developments which will be the very opposite of what was sought.

Logic and a concern for human relationships should be the two basic ingredients of human nature, the latter giving us the good intentions which the former allows us to put into practice.

3 The search for an optimal policy

17 Introduction

In this chapter we shall study how models are built and optimised, which are set by their hypotheses in a future which is certain.

According to these hypotheses, a well-defined state of nature corresponds to each set of variables whose values can be fixed. In the scientific literature of our time, this domain is often called 'theory of programs'. The limited aims of this book preclude us from doing more than scratch the surface of this subject. An abundant literature exists on it. The chosen examples will need only elementary mathematical knowledge, but the actual problems are often very complex and require long discussion as well as numerical treatment by computers.

An optimal policy is a set of values decided for certain variables which we control, but generally it constitutes only a reference set. If a program concerns future situations, these will develop during the elaboration of the decisions and within the horizon of action. In spite of this the programs, in so far as they provide a base to work from, are useful and sometimes indispensable to the man of action.

18 Construction of a deterministic model: plans and programs

The model of a 'phenomenon of organisation' is called 'deterministic' when the hypotheses behind the model are such that its uncontrollable variables are all of known magnitudes.

Among the variables which occur in the model, some are controllable, that is to say, constrained by the will of the decision-maker within a specified field of values. Others are not so.

In such a case, the model is generally called a 'plan' or 'program of action' or again in more scientific language a 'praxeogram'. A value function is chosen, and the decision-maker makes his choice between the possible values to be given to the variables which he controls, this in such a way that the chosen value function is

Table 5

	P_1	P_2	P_3
A_1	C_{11}	C_{12}	C_{13}
A_2	C_{21}	C_{22}	C_{23}

optimal. Of course a system of deterministic hypotheses is not always true to reality, because many variables not controlled by the decision-maker can be uncertain; in a plan or a program they are supposed, however, to be fixed and known.

To build a program (we shall use this word for preference) we should first examine the nature of the organisation, so as to identify those factors, controllable or uncontrollable, which have a significant effect upon its evolution. We then concern ourselves with the causal relationships, or to be more exact, with functional relationships which exist between these factors so as to take into account all the restrictions affecting them.

An example will show what a 'program' consists of.

A company manufactures three articles, P_1, P_2 and P_3 which it can dispose of in two separate economic sectors or regions, A_1 and A_2. The profits realised are given in table 5.

When the profits were calculated, they were found to be affected by the different transport costs and the relative advantages of the contracts with the customers, as well as by other expenses as between the different regions.

The unit profit was found to vary only slightly with the quantity sold; in other words the profit on the whole of the articles of a certain type sold in the same region was in simple proportion to the quantity sold. (In other commercial situations this state of affairs does not necessarily hold.)

Let X_{ij} be the quantity of articles P_i sold during one season in region A_j. With the above hypothesis the total profit will be:

$$Z = C_{11}X_{11} + C_{12}X_{12} + C_{13}X_{13} + C_{21}X_{21} + C_{22}X_{22} + C_{23}X_{23}$$
[Equation 18.1]

the production and marketing of these articles are subject to various restrictions.

First, the nature of the manufactured articles does not allow them to be stocked from one season to the corresponding season of the following year. It is therefore important not to manufacture surplus stocks or their cost price, after allowing for the clearance price, will have to be included as deduction from the overall profit.

Let the demand for each article in each market or district be known, with d_{ij} representing the demand for article P_i in district A_j. We shall then have:

$$X_{11} \leqslant d_{11},\ X_{12} \leqslant d_{12},\ X_{13} \leqslant d_{13},$$
$$X_{21} \leqslant d_{21},\ X_{22} \leqslant d_{22},\ X_{23} \leqslant d_{23}$$
[Equation 18.2]

The production of one item P_3 requires a manufactured part made by a sub-contractor whose production, during the period of manufacture, is limited to n_3 units. We then have:

$$X_{13} + X_{23} \leqslant n_3$$
[Equation 18.3]

In the firm itself, the articles P_1, P_2, P_3 must be processed on a certain machine, whose capacity is limited by its availability time T. Let t_1, t_2, t_3 be the respective processing times of articles P_1, P_2, P_3 on this machine, we shall have another restriction:

$$t_1(X_{11} + X_{21}) + t_2(X_{12} + X_{22}) + t_3(X_{13} + X_{23}) \leqslant T$$
[Equation 18.4]

In problems of this kind other restrictions may appear. Let us suppose, for instance, that the sale of P_2 depends on the sale of P_1 in district A_1, the particular conditions after selling agreements being as follows:

$$X_{12} = kX_{11}$$
[Equation 18.5]

that is:

$$X_{11} - \frac{1}{k}X_{12} = 0 \qquad \text{[Equation 18.6]}$$

We can again suppose that the article P_1, because of commercial agreements, must be delivered in quantities each in excess of some stipulated minimum, M for example:

$$X_{11} \geqslant M_{11},\ X_{21} \geqslant M_{21} \qquad \text{[Equation 18.7]}$$

On examining the restrictions (equations 18.2 and 18.7) we find that they have a general characteristic: all the variables occur to the first power in the formulas. They are said to be *linear* restrictions. It is the same with the profit function (equation 18.1) which is a 'linear function'. By putting together all the formulas (equation 18.1 to equation 18.7) and defining the value function to be optimised as the total profit (equation 18.1), we arrive at a mathematical model of production, which is a 'linear program'.

$$(\text{Max})\ Z = C_{11}X_{11} + C_{12}X_{12} + C_{13}X_{13} + C_{21}X_{21} + C_{22}X_{22} + C_{23}X_{23} \qquad \text{[Equation 18.9]}$$

$$M_{11} \leqslant X_{11} \leqslant d_{11} \qquad \text{[Equation 18.10]}$$
$$0 \leqslant X_{12} \leqslant d_{12} \qquad \text{[Equation 18.11]}$$
$$0 \leqslant X_{13} \leqslant d_{13} \qquad \text{[Equation 18.12]}$$
$$M_{21} \leqslant X_{21} \leqslant d_{21} \qquad \text{[Equation 18.13]}$$
$$0 \leqslant X_{22} \leqslant d_{22} \qquad \text{[Equation 18.14]}$$
$$0 \leqslant X_{23} \leqslant d_{23} \qquad \text{[Equation 18.15]}$$
$$X_{13} + X_{23} \leqslant N_3, \qquad \text{[Equation 18.16]}$$
$$t_1(X_{11} + X_{21}) + t_2(X_{12} + X_{22}) + t_3(X_{13} + X_{23}) \leqslant T \qquad \text{[Equation 18.17]}$$
$$X_{11} - \frac{1}{k}X_{12} = 0 \qquad \text{[Equation 18.18]}$$

Solving such a linear program consists in finding a set of six numbers X^*_{11}, X^*_{12}, X^*_{13}, X^*_{21}, X^*_{22}, X^*_{23} which would satisfy the nine restrictions (equations 18.10 to 18.18) and would make the value function (equation 18.9) maximal. Of course, if the model is badly constructed, if the values such as the d_{ij}, n_i, t_i, T, k, are badly chosen, the program may not have a solution at all. On the other hand a linear program can possess several optimal solutions, all giving the same value of Z.

More generally, a linear program will have the following shape:

$$\text{(Opt) } Z = C_1X_1 + C_2X_2 + \dots + C_nX_n$$
$$A_{11}X_1 + A_{12}X_2 + \dots + A_{1n}X_n \Leftrightarrow B_1$$
$$A_{21}X_1 + A_{22}X_2 + \dots + A_{2n}X_n \Leftrightarrow B_2 \qquad \text{[Equation 18.19]}$$
$$\dots\dots\dots\dots\dots\dots \qquad \dots\dots\dots \qquad \dots$$
$$A_{m1}X_1 + A_{m2}X_2 + \dots + A_{mn}X_n \Leftrightarrow B_m \qquad \text{[Equation 18.20]}$$

where the signs $\Leftrightarrow$ will be replaced, according to the nature of the problem by signs $\geqslant$, $=$ or $\leqslant$. The variables X_i will all be non-negative, i.e. positive or zero. As for the coefficients C_j, A_{ij} and B_i, they will be, according to the nature of the problem, negative, zero or positive.

Over the last twenty-seven years, following the work of Kantorovitch[37] and Dantzig,[31] the theory of linear programs has formed the subject of several thousands of articles and at least a hundred specialised books. The real problems of business economy which can be represented by such models very often contain scores or even hundreds of variables and they have to be solved with the aid of computers. Many variations of the main method of solution, called the 'Simplex Method' have been evolved. The reader is referred to the bibliography for this chapter.

I have given in section 14 two numerical examples with two variables only. In this case, the solution as we have seen, can be easily obtained by a geometrical method.

The nature of some problems does not lend itself to a linear model. For instance, when the value function is quadratic, i.e.:

$$Z = C_{11}X_1^2 + C_{22}X_2^2 + \dots + C_{nn}X_n^2$$
$$+ C_{12}X_1X_2 + \dots + C_{n-1,n}X_{n-1}X_n$$
$$+ D_1X_1 + D_2X_2 + \dots + D_nX_n \qquad \text{[Equation 18.21]}$$

the restrictions being linear or not depending on the problem. The solution of these programs is slightly more difficult; but algorithms which give the optimal solution are known.[28]

Another type of program concerns variables which, because of the nature of the problem, can only take integer values, as 0, 1, 2, 3, 4. Several methods are known for solving such problems, but unfortunately in our present state of knowledge, even the largest computers cannot complete the calculations required within a reasonable time if the number of variables is more than about ten.

Among the linear programs, let us look at certain particular forms. First comes what is called 'a transportation program'. M factories and N warehouses are being considered; the factory i has a_i of a product available, while at the warehouse j there is a demand b_j for this product. The cost of transport from the factory i to the warehouse j is C_{ij}. If we suppose that the product is the same for all the factories and warehouses, we shall have the following linear program, where X_{ij} is the quantity transported from i to j and the minimal cost z is being sought:

$$\begin{aligned}(\text{Min})\ Z = {} & C_{11}X_{11} + C_{12}X_{12} + \ldots + C_{1N} \\ & + C_{21}X_{21} + C_{22}X_{22} + \ldots + C_{2N}X_{2N} \\ & \ldots\ldots\ldots\ldots\ldots\ldots\ldots\ldots \\ & + C_{M1}X_{M1} + C_{M2}X_{M2} + \ldots + C_{MN}X_{MN}\end{aligned} \quad \text{[Equation 18.22]}$$

$$\begin{aligned} & X_{11} + X_{12} + \ldots + X_{1N} = a_1, \; X_{11} + X_{21} + \ldots + X_{M1} = b_1 \\ & X_{21} + X_{22} + \ldots + X_{2N} = a_2, \; X_{12} + X_{22} + \ldots + X_{M2} = b_2 \\ & \ldots\ldots\ldots\ldots \quad \ldots\ldots\ldots\ldots \quad \ldots\ldots\ldots\ldots \quad \ldots\ldots\ldots\ldots \\ & X_{M1} + X_{M2} + \ldots + X_{MN} = a_M, \; X_{1N} + X_{2N} + \ldots + X_{MN} = b_N \\ & a_1 + a_2 + \ldots + a_M = b_1 + b_2 + \ldots + b_n \end{aligned} \quad \text{[Equation 18.23]}$$

In spite of its apparent difficulty this model can be solved far more easily than an ordinary linear program (the stepping-stone method, see [5]).

Another problem of transport arises when we propose to find the maximal flow of material passing through a network whose

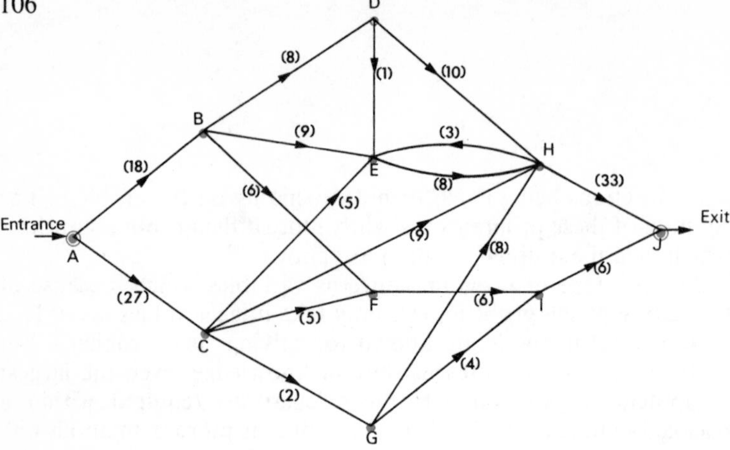

Figure 18·1

channels have limited capacity. Such problems arise in phenomena of transfer or of transport, whether they concern products, vehicles, individuals or even abstract concepts.

A method due to Fulkerson (see [5]) allows us to find the set of flows which have to go through each of the channels (called arcs) so that not one of these flows increases beyond the capacity imposed in the channel considered, and so that the overall flow passing through the whole network is maximal.

This method has been generalised where many entrances and exits are considered. In figure 18·1 we give an example of a problem of flow in a network. The question is to transport from A to J a maximal total flow, the quantities between brackets representing capacities.

In figure 18·2 we show the solution of such a problem (the numbers between brackets give the value of each flow). This gives the maximum of the total flow from A to J as equal to 33. Following the chain-dotted line shown on the picture we can see that all the channels cut by it are saturated if they go from left to right of the line, or zero if they go in the opposite direction. It is therefore impossible to increase the total flow crossing the whole of the arcs met by the chain-dotted line. This flow is therefore maximal.

Another kind of problem consists in the making of connexions or channels between the points of distribution of a product. The

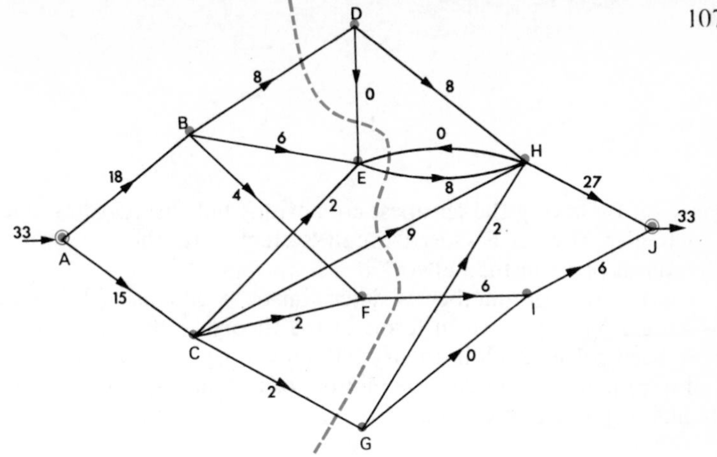

Figure 18·2

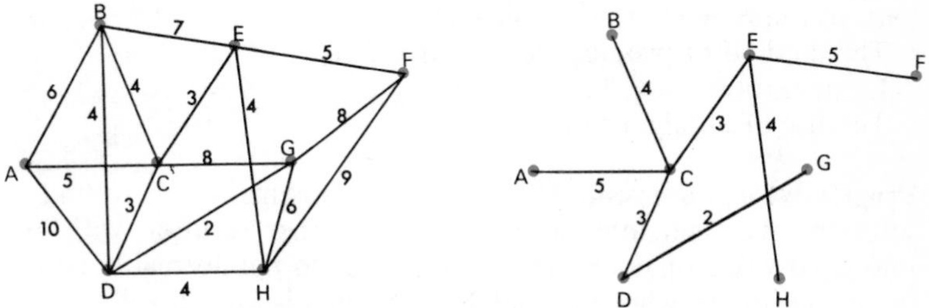

Figure 18·3

Figure 18·4

cost of each connexion is known. We propose to find a network of non-directional connexions, the total cost of which is minimal, while making it a necessary condition that the resulting network does not contain any closed circuit. Figure 18·3 gives an example of possible connexions and figure 18·4 gives the optimal network for which we have a total cost of 26. A very simple method from Kruskal (see [5]) allows the optimal network or networks (for there may be several) to be calculated. This method can be summed up as follows: begin with the connexion whose cost is the lowest, carry on by taking the cheapest connexions but disregarding ones which give rise to a closed-circuit system with the connexions already in place in the network.

There is a large number of deterministic problems of this kind which can be expressed in terms of the theory of programs. They have been solved both in theory – thanks to rigorous algorithms – and in practice, in spite of the number of parameters they contain, thanks to the use of computers.

19 Optimisation of a program

The three main methods used to optimise a program or, failing that, to improve a known policy are:

The method of progressive improvement;
Enumeration;
The use of an algorithm.

Progressive improvement. The first step in this method is to find a solution. We then look for a way to another solution with an improved value function. This corresponds to the normal habit of the businessman who does not have at his disposal a sufficiently precise model. It is also the attitude of the mathematician when the state of knowledge at the time does not allow a systematic search for the optimal solution. This is the method of research and discovery to which the greatest scientists, from Leonardo da Vinci to Henri Poincaré, had recourse and which the able businessman is constantly re-inventing in new forms. It relies not on rigour but on the combination of experience and partial analysis of the known factors.

The progressive improvement of the value function is not necessarily achieved by a repeated procedure, but by a study of the results obtained and the search for a better solution. This *modus operandi* does not always lead to the optimal solution. Very often we content ourselves with the progressive improvement of the solutions found without being able to prove or even to estimate

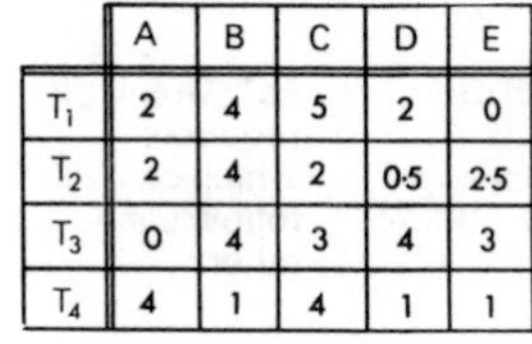

	A	B	C	D	E
T_1	2	4	5	2	0
T_2	2	4	2	0·5	2·5
T_3	0	4	3	4	3
T_4	4	1	4	1	1

Figure 19·1

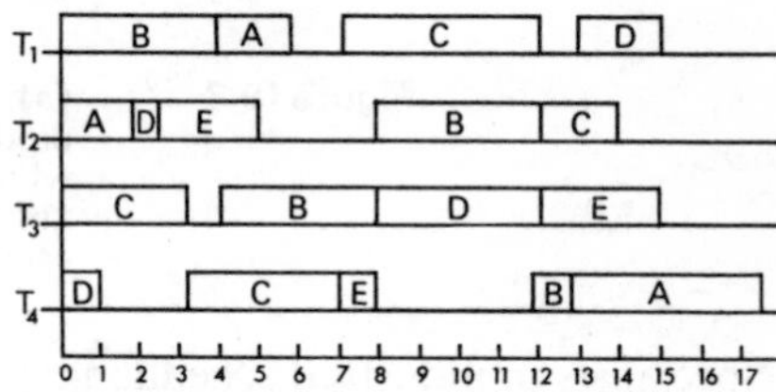

Figure 19·2

intuitively that the optimum has been reached. Of course some familiarity with the kind of problem being considered allows us to reach a 'good' solution more quickly, or even to go further. It is a victory for professional 'know-how', for acquired experience. Not having a method which gives the optimum with strict exactness, it is difficult to see how we can work differently. It is the method used by people who have no scientific training, or perhaps who do not know a comprehensive algorithm or an enumeration procedure.

An example of a problem of progressive optimisation is given by the search for a best sequence of p products on m machine-tools or similar problems: time-tables of occupation of school buildings, simultaneous treatment of information in a computer, etc. We know the processing time of product P_j on machine M_i, and we set certain restrictions: non-simultaneity of operations on the same product or on the same machine, certain operative orders, for example. We often take the minimisation of idle time as a criterion, and then look for the sequence which corresponds to the minimum idle time. Although we know the theoretical solutions to this kind of problem, in practice for $p > 2$ and any m, or the converse, the rigorous treatment of this optimisation by hand or electronically, leads to unacceptably long calculation times.

It must be noted that in these combinatorial problems, the enumeration of all the solutions in order to find the best one, leads to calculations of astronomical proportions.

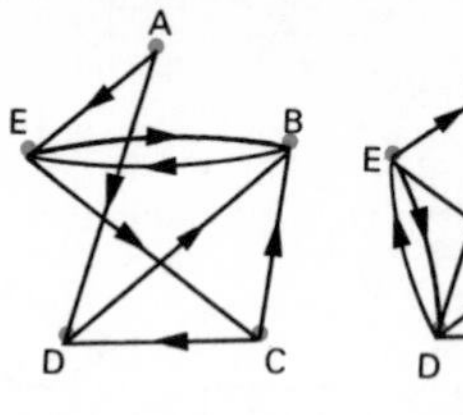

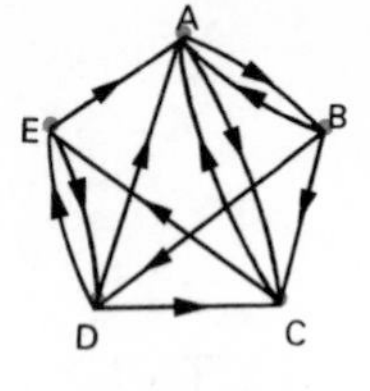

Figure 19·3 (a) Graph of products which must not follow each other. (b) Graph of products which can follow each other.

Specialists in industrial scheduling work differently. They search for a solution, then improve this solution step by step considering two or three products at a time and carrying out suitable permutations. This manner of operating seldom leads to the optimal solution or solutions, but we are satisfied with the partial result. Figures 19·1 and 19·2 give a small example where $p = 5$ and $m = 4$ with which the reader can practise.

Enumeration. This method deals basically with combinatorial problems; by means of a suitable method we enumerate where possible all the solutions, or again we enumerate a sub-set of solutions knowing that it contains the optimal solution or solutions.

An example of the method of combinatorial enumeration is given by the 'Latin multiplication'. It will be introduced in a technological application, but it can be used in many other problems.

We propose to pass five products A, B, C, D, E through a pipe line. The nature of these products is such that some can pass through after others without trouble, since the one product is not seriously polluted by the other; for other products, there may be restrictions.

Let us suppose that the restriction against passing a product Y after a product X is represented by an arrow directed from X to Y. We thus obtain a graph like the one in figure 19·3. The problem consists in finding which sequences formed with the five products do not infringe any restriction. Hence D, E, A, B, C is a sequence which constitutes a solution of the problem, but B, C, D, A, E or C, E, B, A, D are not solutions. It is easy to see that there are 120 sequences, and we propose to enumerate all the sequences which constitute solutions. With five products there are 5.4.3.2.1 = 120 sequences. With ten products there would be 10.9.8.7.6.5.4.3. 2.1 = 3,628,800. With a hundred we would go beyond the supposed number of atoms in the universe (if we accept the numbers given by some scientists). We then understand how useful it is to have at out disposal a method which allows the enumeration of the solutions, provided that their number is appreciably smaller than the number of the sequences or permutations existing in theory and which may or may not be solutions.

From the graph in figure 19·3(a) let us draw the graph in figure 19·3(b) quite simply by putting an arrow into figure 19·3(b) if it does not appear in figure 19·3(a) and *vice versa.* A solution will then be constituted by a sequence of five letters, not containing the same letter twice, but containing all the letters on figure 19·3(b). This represents a path starting from a point and giving access to all the other points by following the arrows without passing more than once through the same point. An enumeration of all the solutions requires a systematic method.

Let us draw up the double-entry table (1) of figure 19·4, and if an arrow appears in the graph of figure 19·3(b) put the corresponding pair in the table (1). Thus, an arrow *DC* appears in the graph and we have put *D*, *C* in the table at the intersection of row *D* and column *C*. From table (1) we make table (2) by removing the left-hand number of each pair of letters. This done, we form table (3) by observing the following rule: We put into cell *ij* of table (3) all the sequences within which no letter is repeated obtained by considering successively cell *i*1 of line *i* of (1) and cell 1*j* of column *j* of (2). Next follows cell *i*2 of line *i* of (1) and cell 2*j* of column *j* of (2) ... cell *in* of line *i* of (1) and cell *nj* of column *j* of (2). Table (3) thus obtained gives all the sequences comprising three products and satisfying all the conditions. By working in the same way with tables (3) and (2) we obtain table (4) which gives all the sequences comprising four products. By continuing with (4) and (2) we get table (5) giving all the sequences comprising five products and satisfying all the conditions. In order to make the assimilation of this method easier, figure 19·5 shows

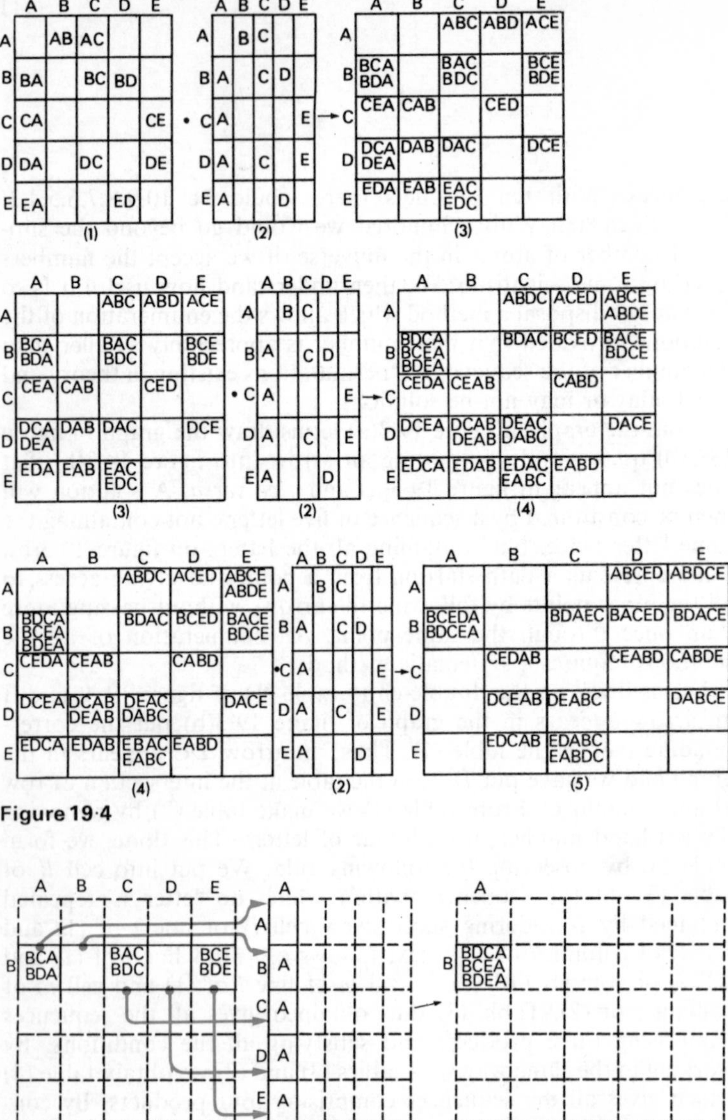

Figure 19·4

Figure 19·5

how we have obtained cell *B*, *A* of table (4). To the sequence *B*, *C*, *A* nothing can be added, nor to *B*, *D*. *A*; *A* could be added to *B*, *A*, *C* but there would be repetition; to *B*, *D*, *C*, *A* can be added, which gives *B*, *D*, *C*, *A* which we put into cell *B*, *A* of (4); *A* can be added to *B*, *C*, *E* and also to *B*, *D*, *E*: thus we have *B*, *C*, *E*, *A* and *B*, *D*, *E*, *A* which we put into (4).

Finally, there are 16 sequences which satisfy the conditions and constitute the solutions:

(*A*, *B*, *C*, *E*, *D*) (*A*, *B*, *D*, *C*, *E*) (*B*, *C*, *E*, *D*, *A*) (*B*, *D*, *C*, *E*, *A*)
(*B*, *D*, *E*, *A*, *C*) (*B*, *A*, *C*, *E*, *D*) (*B*, *D*, *A*, *C*, *E*) (*C*, *E*, *D*, *A*, *B*)
(*C*, *E*, *A*, *B*, *D*) (*C*, *A*, *B*, *D*, *E*) (*D*, *C*, *E*, *A*, *B*) (*D*, *E*, *A*, *B*, *C*)
(*D*, *A*, *B*, *C*, *E*) (*E*, *D*, *C*, *A*, *B*) (*E*, *D*, *A*, *B*, *C*) (*E*, *A*, *B*, *D*, *C*)

In this problem an economic aspect could be associated with the technological statement. For instance a value function might be applied to the set of sequences. Then, from the enumeration we could pass to the optimisation by ranking all the sequences in order of value.

Generally the procedure to be used must allow us to avoid enumeration of all the sequences or permutations, and step by step, or by certain short cuts, must allow us to obtain the sequences which constitute the solution of the problem. The 'Latin multiplication' which we have used possesses these properties. It can be applied after suitable modification to various other combinatorial problems.

Algorithm. This word, let us remember, comes neither from Latin nor from Greek, but from the name of the famous Arab mathematician Al Khovaresmi, a word which has been distorted under the influence of the Greek *arithmos* (number). An algorithm is a method of calculation.

To give the reader an idea of how a program is optimised when we make use of an algorithm, I shall refer to the one which allows the optimal solution of a linear program to be calculated. I do not have enough space to demonstrate the general method here (see [5], for instance), and furthermore, to avoid going too far in developing abstract theories, i.e. beyond the limits imposed by an introductory work, I shall present this algorithm in a numerical example.

Let us attempt to find the optimal solution to the following linear program:

$$\begin{aligned} &(\text{Max})\ Z = 2X_1 - 3X_2 + X_3 \\ &X_1 - X_2 + 3X_3 \leqslant 6 \\ &2X_1 + X_2 + 4X_3 \leqslant 2 \quad \text{with} \begin{cases} X_1 \geqslant 0 \\ X_2 \geqslant 0 \\ X_3 \geqslant 0 \end{cases} \\ &2X_1 + 5X_2 \leqslant 1 \end{aligned}$$

[Equation 19.1]

For this we shall first introduce 'slack' variables U_1, U_2 and U_3 representing the differences between the members of the left-hand side and the members of the right-hand side of the inequalities. These variables will also be such that $U_1 \geqslant 0$, $U_2 \geqslant 0$ and $U_3 \geqslant 0$. Let us then present the problem in the following manner:

$$\begin{aligned} &(1)\ X_1 - X_2 + 3X_3 + (U_1) = 6 && 6 \div 1 = 6 \\ &(2)\ 2X_1 + X_2 + 4X_3 + (U_2) = 2 && 2 \div 2 = 1 \\ &(3)\ 2X_1^* + 5X_2 + (U_3) = 1 && 1 \div 2 = 0{\cdot}5 \\ &(4)\ 2X_1 - 3X_2 + X_3 = Z \end{aligned}$$

[Equation 19.2]

There is a first solution $X_1 = X_2 = X_3 = 0$, $U_1 = 6$, $U_2 = 2$, $U_3 = 1$, with $Z = 0$. Let us try to increase Z. For this purpose we should replace one of the bracketed variables by another one, so that in the new solution there is no variable with a negative value. Dantzig has established that we must (1) look for the coefficients of the left-hand side numbers of Z and choose from them the variable with the higher positive coefficient, (2) establish the ratio, equation by equation, between the value of the right hand number of the equation and the coefficient of the selected variable. We then choose the equation for which this ratio is the lowest among the positive ratios.

The variable whose coefficient has the highest value in Z is X_1 for which the coefficient is 2. Now let us calculate the ratio of each element of the right-hand side number to the corresponding coefficient of X_1. We have: line (1) $6 \div 1 = 6$, line (2) $2 \div 2 = 1$, line (3) $1 \div 2 = 0{\cdot}5$. Thus the lowest positive ratio is 0·5 and line (3) will therefore be selected. Let us put an asterisk against the variable X_1 in (3). We now transform the equations in a simple manner so that a new solution appears.

Divide line (3) by 2, to give us line (3)′ of the following system of equations (equation 19.3). Now multiply (3)′ by −1 and let us add this equation to (1) to give (1)′.

$$
\begin{array}{llr}
(1)' \; -\frac{7}{2}X_2 + 3X_3 + (U_1) - \frac{1}{2}U_3 = \frac{11}{2} & & \frac{11}{2} \div 3 = \frac{11}{6} \\
(2)' \; -4X_2 + 4X_3^* + (U_2) \quad - U_3 = 1 \leftarrow & & 1 \div 4 = \frac{1}{4} \\
(3)'\,(X_1) + \frac{5}{2}X_2 \qquad\qquad + \frac{1}{2}U_3 = \frac{1}{2} & & \frac{1}{2} \div 0 = \infty \\
(4)' \; -8X_2 + X_3 \qquad\qquad - U_3 = Z - 1 & & \\
\qquad\qquad\quad\;\; \uparrow & &
\end{array}
$$

[Equation 19.3]

Multiply (3)′ by −2 and add this equation to (2) to give (2)′. Multiply (3)′ by −2 and add this equation to (4) to give (4)′. The system of equations (equation 19.3) gives a new solution:

$$X_2 = X_3 = U_3 = 0,\; X_1 = \frac{1}{2},\; U_1 = \frac{11}{2},\; U_2 = 1 \text{ with } Z = 1.$$

Starting again with the system of equations (equation 19.3) we do the same as with the set (equation 19.2). Let us examine the coefficients of the variables in the left member of (4)′. The variable with the highest positive coefficient is X_3: line (1): $\frac{11}{2} \div 3 = \frac{11}{6}$, line (2): $1 \div 4 = \frac{1}{4}$, line (3): $\frac{1}{2} \div 0 = \infty$. The lowest ratio among the positive ratios is $\frac{1}{4}$, so we put an asterisk against X_3 in line (2)′.

Now divide (2)′ by 4, which gives line (2)′′ in the system (equation 19.4).

$$(1)'' \quad -\frac{5}{2}X_2 + (U_1) - \frac{3}{4}U_2 + \frac{1}{4}U_3 = \frac{19}{4}$$
$$(2)'' \quad -X_2 + (X_3) + \frac{1}{4}U_2 - \frac{1}{4}U_3 = \frac{1}{4}$$
$$(3)'' \quad (X_1) + \frac{5}{2}X_2 \qquad + \frac{1}{2}U_3 = \frac{1}{2}$$
$$(4)'' \quad -7X_2 \qquad -\frac{1}{4}U_2 - \frac{3}{4}U_3 = Z - \frac{5}{4} \qquad \text{[Equation 19.4]}$$

Multiply (2)′′ by −3 and add this equation to (1)′, to give (1)′′. Since (3)′ does not contain X_3, so we put (3)′ in equation 19.4 and call it (3)′′. By multiplying (2)′′ by −1 and adding this equation to (4)′, we get (4)′′. The system of equations (equation 19·4) gives a new solution: $X_2 = U_2 = U_3 = 0$, $X_1 = \frac{1}{2}$, $X_3 = \frac{1}{4}$, $U_1 = \frac{19}{4}$ with $Z = \frac{5}{4}$.

Now the coefficients of the variables in the left-hand side of (4)′′ are all negative. Dantzig has established that in this case the optimum was reached, thus the solution

$$X_1 = \frac{1}{2},\ X_2 = 0,\ X_3 = \frac{1}{4} \qquad \text{[Equation 19.5]}$$

for which we have the 'slack' variables: $U_1 = \frac{19}{4}$, $U_2 = 0$, $U_3 = 0$ gives the maximal value to Z which is then $\frac{5}{4}$.

An optimising algorithm must lead with absolute exactness and with a finite number of stages to the optimal solution or solutions. This is the case for the Simplex Method.

20 Inadequacies of rigorous models: sub-optimisation: sensitivity – parametric analysis: optimal solution as a datum

Sub-optimisation. Economic and social mechanisms, of which a program gives a representation, are often more complex in reality than in a model. These programs must be considered as more or less precise diagrams of the real world. In fact a business or administrative system is only part of a larger system, which itself is again only a part of a still greater one. In building the deterministic model, we should include the effects of the environment of the system represented in the restrictions. But this is not always easy or even possible. For instance, the model representing the production and stocks of a company manufacturing motor-cars will not easily be able to take into consideration the variations resulting from the frequent desire of customers to forgo a new car in favour of a good holiday. In the model representing a program for locating the route of a motorway the effect on the economy of the regions or towns to be crossed or by-passed cannot easily be included. If we are obliged, in constructing a program, to take into account only a part of a well specified organisation, then we say that we are doing a 'sub-optimisation'. Consider a system broken down into several parts or 'sub-systems'. The optimal solution for each sub-system does not necessarily agree with the optimum for the system as a whole. Moreover, a mathematical study confirms this intuitive conclusion, which has repercussions in human society. The choice of 'level of sub-optimisation' appears to be a very delicate one to make. If the system whose model is built is too small, this model is in great danger of presenting a solution which will be optimal for the model only, the exogenous variables which were not taken into account then intervening in reality; if the model is too large the details will perhaps be needlessly sacrificed. Such difficulties are constantly being met by planners at the national level. They are asking themselves such questions as: is it better to develop regional economies separately or concentrate on the economy of the country as a whole? Quite often serious crises have arisen because of a badly chosen set of dimensions. The wiser course is to begin by using a model of parts or components of the system, then to enlarge the model by correctly grouping certain parts, but this process of 'aggregation' is not easy to handle.

Sensitivity – parametric analysis. Having established a program and obtained the optimal solution or solutions, a very important question often asked is: how near to the optimum are the next-best solutions? To express the sensitivity of a value function around a solution, economists have introduced a very useful notion, the notion of 'marginal cost'. For instance, in a linear program we have seen that the optimal solution, if it is the only one, corresponds to a vertex of the convex polyhedron determined by the linear restrictions. If we pass from the solution corresponding to the optimal vertex, to the solutions corresponding to the nearby vertices, we shall then have the 'marginal cost' of changing the solution by varying the value function.

Let us take the numerical example given in equation 19.1. We saw that the optimal solution corresponded to $X_1 = \frac{1}{2}$, $X_3 = \frac{1}{4}$, $U_1 = \frac{19}{4}$, $X_2 = U_2 = U_3 = 0, Z = \frac{5}{4}$. In line (4)'' of equation 19.4 the values $-7, -\frac{1}{4}, -\frac{3}{4}$ give the variations per unit of the corresponding variables when we pass from this optimal solution to the solution on the neighbouring vertices of the polyhedron.

The notion of 'marginal cost' proves to be very useful in discussing the problems of business management.

One of the most serious criticisms made of the methods of building and using the linear programs was that it gave an optimal solution about whose stability we had little information when a modification of the uncontrollable parameters occurred.

A device frequently used to overcome this criticism, consists in varying the parameters of the value function. We study then the evolution of the optimum when one or several parameters introduced in this function, or even in the restrictions, develop. In figure 20·1, I have presented a linear program with three variables and four restrictions. If the value function Z is replaced by function Z_1, the optimum previously placed in F passes into I.

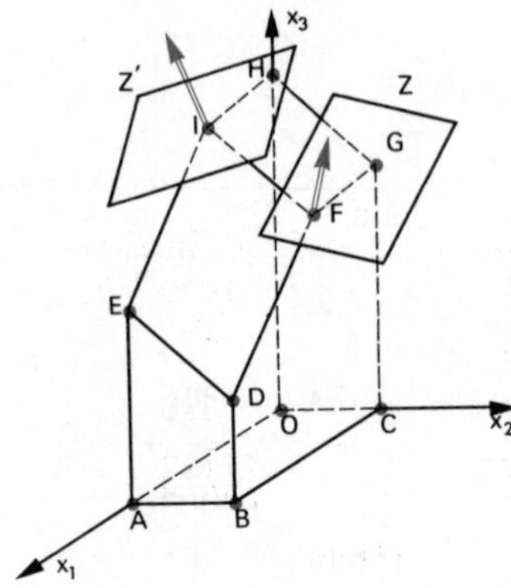

Figure 20·1

Now let us see, in looking at a small industrial problem, how we use this method called parametric programming.

A firm can manufacture, on an automatic machine working forty-five hours per week, three articles P_1, P_2, P_3. The article P_1 gives a net profit of 4, P_2 a net profit of 12 and P_3 a net profit of 3. In one hour the machine can produce 50 of P_1, 25 of P_2 or 75 of P_3. The possible sales for the week under consideration are limited to 1000 of P_1, 500 of P_2 and 1500 of P_3. To these restrictions we add $X_1 + 2X_2 + 2X_3 \leqslant 4000$, which concerns the stock capacity. This linear program will then be written as follows:

$$(\text{Max})\ Z = 4X_1 + 12X_2 + 3X_3$$
$$0 \leqslant X_1 \leqslant 1000,\ 0 \leqslant X_2 \leqslant 500,\ 0 \leqslant X_3 \leqslant 1500$$
$$\frac{X_1}{50} + \frac{X_2}{25} + \frac{X_3}{75} \leqslant 45,\ X_1 + 2X_2 + 2X_3 \leqslant 4000$$

[Equation 20.1]

where X_1, X_2, X_3 are the quantities manufactured.

Table 6

λ	-1		$-\frac{5}{8}$		$\frac{1}{8}$		$+\infty$
C_1	0		1·5		4·5		$+\infty$
X_1		0		375		1000	
X_2		500		500		500	
X_3		1500		1312·5		375	
Max Z		10500		11437·5 $+1500\lambda$		11125 $+4000\lambda$	
			10500		11625		

Let us suppose now that the information about the profit on product P_1 is rather vague because its sale price is subject to unforeseeable fluctuations of the market. We put $C_1 = 4(1 + \lambda)$ where λ is a parameter which can take any value from -1 to $+\infty$ (of course in practice such wide fluctuations would not be considered, only limited intervals). The value function then becomes:

$$\text{Max } Z = 4(1 + \lambda)X_1 + 12X_2 + 3X_3 \qquad \text{[Equation 20.2]}$$

In these conditions how will the optimal solution develop when λ varies? For lack of space, the algorithm itself is omitted here, but the result is presented in the following table 6.

Parametric programming permits a problem to be discussed and decisions taken, when some parameters are uncertain. In other cases the parameter or parameters with an uncertain value appear in the right-hand side of the restrictions, or again in the coefficients or functions (linear or not) of the left-hand side of the restrictions. Parametric programming is appreciably more difficult in the latter case and we only know how to do it for a few simple cases.

Optimal solution as a datum. Of course, in the long run a deterministic model of a business system constitutes no more than a guide for action. Between the time the program is made up and the time it is fed into the computer to obtain the optimal solution or solutions, certain variables over which we have no control may have changed; furthermore, it is not always possible to incorporate certain sociological or psychological effects in the model. This point has already been stressed several times. The optimal solution must be considered as a datum, the 'best theoretical road', from which future circumstances will very likely divert us. But then the cost of a change of solution, in regard to the value function adopted, can be estimated.

We shall see in chapter 6, when we study dynamic models, that the correct attitude lies in keeping the chosen model constantly under review, taking into account the information which the future might bring. Yet the period of anticipation and the frequency of readjustment constitute evaluations whose justification poses quite a number of awkward questions.

4 Dealing with chance

21 Introduction

The theory of probabilities linked with the theory of statistics could well be symbolised by the mask of Janus, the King of Latium, who looked to the past in order to foresee the future. Of all the concepts born of reflection and research over the last three hundred years, these appear to be the most important of all. We shall first consider the distinction between random events and uncertain events. We shall then see how, in problems demanding decisions, criteria derived from mathematical expectation and in some cases from measurement of risk, can be adopted and lead to problems of optimisation. Although very many models are built from probabilistic concepts and analytical methods, in other cases the simulation of chance can be extremely helpful by artificially imitating real facts. It is in this way that the 'Monte Carlo method' has assumed an important place in methods of business management, just as it has done in physics.

As usual the examples will be very simple so as to be easily understood by all.

22 Intuitive notion of probability

The word chance is often used in an incorrect sense where its meaning is confused with the meaning of uncertain occurrence. We should use the word 'chance' only when we are able to link a 'probability' with the event being considered. If we meet one of our friends in the street and we say, 'This is a chance meeting', this suggests that we knew such a meeting was on the cards; what we should say is, 'I had no idea that I would meet you'. Of course, in everyday life and in normal speech the misuse of the word 'chance' does not cause much difficulty. It is a different matter when we turn to the study of phenomena in organisations.

We shall say that an elementary phenomenon is 'random' or 'subject to chance' if the stages it can go through are known to have probabilities. For example, throwing a 5 on a die; emission of n particles during one second by a given radioactive element; flow of more than K cars per minute at a given time on a given day of the week, along a given motorway; future death at the age of 73 of any member of a statistically-known population. It should be noted that the Ancients used to call chance *stochos*, i.e. the goal or target to be reached, and the goddess of chance was Automatia. It was from the first works of Pascal on the theory of so-called games of 'chance' that the intuitive notion of chance was determined with sufficient clarity for it to be used. For some decades, after the works of Borel and Kolmogorov, the theory of probabilities has rested on undeniably axiomatic bases.

Let us recall the two points of view, intuitive and axiomatic.

Consider the following problem about a six-faced die. If the die is thrown 600 times, how many times will the 5 come up? Intuitively we shall accept that it will come up a hundred times or a number near to a hundred. If you have the right to throw the die only once, we shall accept intuitively that there is one chance in six of the 5 coming up. More generally let us suppose a phenomenon which can occur in N mutually independent ways, all supposedly equiprobable. If among these N states, n are considered as being favourable, the intuitive notion of probability allows us to say positively that the occurrence of a favourable state has a probability n/N, and this will be confirmed by experience if N is sufficiently large.

The axiomatic theory gives us a different view of the situation. From the theory of sets we define certain sets which may be expressed in terms of probability, that is to say, made to correspond to numbers which are either zero or positive and less than or equal to one, while obeying well-defined rules within a structure which is that of the lattices. (See for instance [56].)

When we construct a model of a business system in which chance has its place, it is generally by making the hypothesis that the frequencies studied in the past will be found again, unchanged in some future period, or again that the mathematical relations, having led to estimations of probabilities, will remain valid during this period.

In applications of the theory of probabilities, a particularly difficult point is the acceptance of these hypotheses. The improvements made over several decades through statistical methods, allow us to project frequencies from the past into the future fairly correctly. The important place taken by these methods, in business management, in econometrics, in operational research, in quality control, is one of the fundamental aspects in the evolution of processes of preparing decisions.

23 Behaviour in the face of chance

Consider the following three lotteries:

Lottery A	**Lottery B**	**Lottery C**
4000 tickets are sold at 2F each.	4000 tickets at 2F each.	4000 tickets at 2F each.
It is possible to win		
1 prize of 1000F	3 prizes of 1000F	20 prizes of 100F
30 prizes of 100F	10 prizes of 100F	200 prizes of 10F

Suppose first of all that these three lotteries are offered each week to a subscriber who pays two francs only per week, to buy one lottery ticket. Then let us consider the behaviour of various subscribers. A subscriber who understands the theory of probabilities: since he can gamble every week, he will estimate the mathematical expectation of winning:

$$\textbf{Lottery A}: (1000)\left(\frac{1}{4000}\right) + (100)\left(\frac{30}{4000}\right) = 1\text{F}$$

$$\textbf{Lottery B}: (1000)\left(\frac{3}{4000}\right) + (100)\left(\frac{10}{4000}\right) = 1\text{F}$$

$$\textbf{Lottery C}: (100)\left(\frac{20}{4000}\right) + (10)\left(\frac{200}{4000}\right) = 1\text{F}$$

His conclusion is that it does not matter which lottery he buys a ticket for, and also that these lotteries are not fair, since for two francs he is offered a mathematical expectation of one franc.

Rationally we should refuse to take part in a lottery with such poor returns, but if he is wealthy enough to throw away his money on such amusements, he may do so for the fun of it.

All lotteries and particularly the so-called 'national' lotteries which exist in most countries all over the world, capitalist, neo-capitalist, neo-socialist, or socialist, amount to the same thing: they are booby-traps, and for a mathematician constitute a 'direct tax on human stupidity'. They are a form of artificial adventure taking the place of action.

Perhaps this indictment by mathematicians is a little too damning. Some subscribers to these lotteries think along different lines. They feel incapable of acquiring, either through their work or through their savings, the amount of money which the prizes represent, and they accept the unfair gamble in the hope of winning and then stopping – (but *would* they stop?). Let us look at some criteria, so as to demonstrate the different attitudes.

To have the maximum chance of winning a big prize of a thousand francs: lottery **B** will be chosen.

To have the maximum chance of winning any prize: choose **C**.

For the hope of a big prize and of a consolation prize: choose **A**.

Let us now suppose that the three previous lotteries are replaced by the following ones:

Lottery A′	**Lottery B′**	**Lottery C′**
4000 tickets at 2F	4000 tickets at 2F	4000 tickets at 2F
1 prize of 1000F	3 prizes of 1000F	20 prizes of 100F
400 prizes of 10F	10 prizes of 100F	100 prizes of 10F

mathematical expectation:

$$\mathbf{A}': (1000)\left(\frac{1}{4000}\right) + (10)\left(\frac{400}{4000}\right) = 1{\cdot}25\text{F}$$

$$\mathbf{B}': (1000)\left(\frac{3}{4000}\right) + (100)\left(\frac{10}{4000}\right) = 1\text{F}$$

$$\mathbf{C}': (100)\left(\frac{20}{4000}\right) + (10)\left(\frac{100}{4000}\right) = 0{\cdot}75\text{F}$$

Let us look again at the considerations previously explained, taking into account these new terms. A subscriber who knew the theory of probabilities and gambled two francs per week, would choose **A**′. With tests other than mathematical expectation:

To have the maximum chance to win a big prize: **B**′.

To have the maximum chance to win a medium prize: **A**′.

To win a big prize and have a reasonable mathematical expectation of gain, hesitation between **A**′ and **B**′.

To be especially interested in a prize of 100F: **C**′.

Now let us imagine that the customer has the right to gamble only once and on only one of the lotteries. In this case the mathematician would no longer give valid arguments for **A**′ to be chosen because of the value of mathematical expectation. When a random phenomenon is not repetitive, mathematical expectation has only an indicative value.

This lottery example can be generalised. The duration of a human life in the western world is about sixty-five years. In the face of certain random events, men in this part of the world behave in a way which often removes them from the criterion of mathematical expectation. Suppose that, like Methuselah, they have an average life of (say) six hundred years: they would, in their wisdom, far more frequently choose the criterion of mathematical expectation, but though the average duration of the life of men has been increasing from generation to generation for some decades, thanks to progress in medicine, the business systems are affected more and more by internal or external actions impossible to foresee, and these systems become less repetitive. One must therefore be very careful in using the criterion of mathematical expectation.

When a random phenomenon follows a law where one or many variables are involved, so that the law of probability does not vary with time, this phenomenon or this law is called 'stationary' and 'non-stationary' in the opposite case. It is vital to recognise this fact in any study based on the theory of probabilities. We shall note that the physical, biological, random phenomena, or more generally, the natural phenomena, are often stationary when they are isolated; it is a different matter for phenomena in which man intervenes. But it could be said that meteorology does not allow us to draw up stationary laws, or if so, only rarely, and some habits of consumers are almost invariable in time. We can also accept that mechanical failures or waiting periods call for stationary laws. On these important questions, references which can be consulted are: [45], [47], [48], [55] and [56].

Let us, however, proceed to examples of industrial management.

24 The use and misuse of mathematical expectation in industrial management

Let us examine a few practical problems simplified so as to make them readily understandable.

Example 1. In ordering a machine-tool of a special type it is necessary to order a certain expensive accessory. The machine has an expected life span of five years. If an accessory is bought at the same time as the machine, it costs ten units; if the accessory existing on the machine is damaged, it must be replaced by a new one. In this case we consider two hypotheses: a spare accessory is in stock, bought at the same time as the machine, or it is not in stock, in which case one has to be made immediately; the cost of the accessory is then appreciably higher at thirty units. The accessories bought as spares when the machine is bought, but not used, are considered worthless after five years. A statistical survey of the deterioration of similar machines has allowed us to set up an hypothesis of a law of probability. It is given by the bottom line of figure 24·1. In these circumstances what stock must be carried?

The mathematical model will be very easy to build and I shall present it, not by means of formulas, but with the help of tables (figure 24·1).

First make out the table of cost for demands from 0 to 5 and stocks from 0 to 5. Thus, to the pair (2, 4) or stock 2 and demand 4, will correspond a cost of (2) (10) + (2) (30) = 80. The number

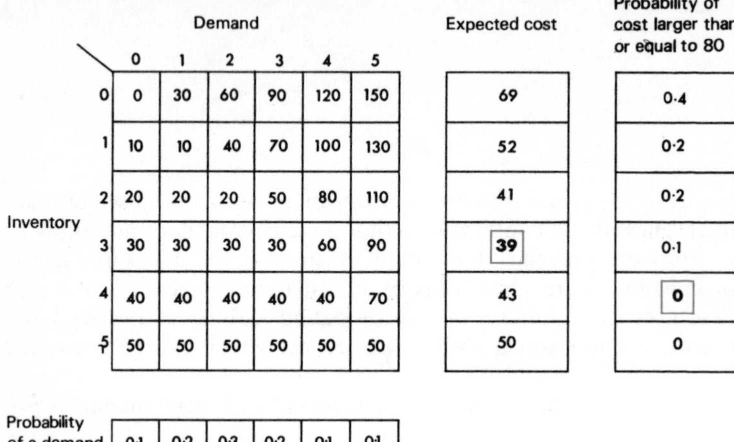

Inventory \ Demand	0	1	2	3	4	5	Expected cost	Probability of cost larger than or equal to 80
0	0	30	60	90	120	150	69	0·4
1	10	10	40	70	100	130	52	0·2
2	20	20	20	50	80	110	41	0·2
3	30	30	30	30	60	90	**39**	0·1
4	40	40	40	40	40	70	43	**0**
5	50	50	50	50	50	50	50	0
Probability of a demand	0·1	0·2	0·3	0·2	0·1	0·1		

Figure 24·1

80 will be carried in cell (2, 4) of the table. To the pair (3, 1) will correspond (3) (10) = 30.

In the problem considered, the non-repetitive characteristic of the random phenomenon is quite evident and only one machine is bought for five years. During those five years 0, 1, 2, 3, 4, or 5 parts will have to be changed. Can we accept without reservation the mathematical expectation? Certainly not.

Let us first calculate this mathematical expectation as given by figure 24·1. We see that the minimal value 39 of the mathematical expectation corresponds to a stock of 3. But in practice we can be led to use another criterion, for instance, to look for the stock giving the smallest probability of reaching or going beyond 80, an expense considered to be intolerable in such a problem. In another column given in figure 24·1 the probabilities of exceeding 80 have been given. It then appears that stocks of 4 or 5 are the ones which are satisfactory. In combining this criterion with the one of mathematical expectation (with an equal value of probability, choose the stock which gives the smallest value of mathematical expectation) we shall then decide to hold a stock of 4.

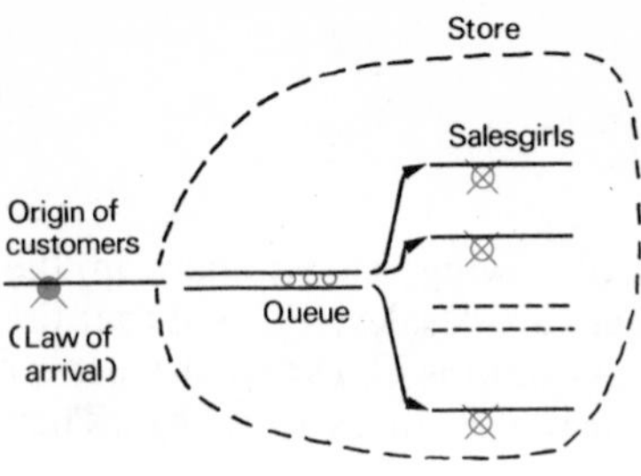

Figure 24·2

A misuse of the theory of probabilities would consist in taking the stock corresponding to the most frequent demands (highest probability 0·3); this stock is equal to 2, but costs would not be considered. Another attitude would consist in taking the mathematical expectation of the cost. We have seen that the optimum corresponds to 3; yet such an attitude can only be completely justified in the case of a phenomenon which is sufficiently repetitive. Finally, according to the economic aspects of the problem, another criterion could be chosen, and for a solution of an equal value for this criterion, we can fall back on a second, for example mathematical expectation.

Example 2. Another example deals with the number of salesgirls to be detailed for a department of a large store. Supposing that the law of probability of arrival of customers and the law of probability of duration of the sales assistants' duties are known and stationary, for the day of the week considered.

This is a random phenomenon belonging to an important class, the class of 'waiting lines' or 'queues', the theory of which has been very well developed and the object of many books, e.g. [57].

Let us suppose that the procedure for the customers is 'first come, first served'. From the two laws of probability specified above, we can, by accepting certain hypotheses on the nature of these laws, calculate the probability that there may be n customers in the department (waiting or actually being served).

Let us call p_n the probability of having n customers in the department. Let us suppose that there are S salesgirls, and that the hourly wage (before tax) of a sales assistant is C. Let us also accept as the cost of the patience of a customer an expense K_C, Then three solutions can occur:

$n < S$ some salesgirls are idle, no customer is waiting.
$n = S$ all the salesgirls are busy, no customer is waiting.
$n > S$ all salesgirls are busy, a queue of customers has formed.
[Equation 24.1]

Let us call $\Gamma(S)$ the total hourly cost of waiting for both the salesgirls and their customers. Hence:

$$\Gamma(S) = C(S-n) \quad 0 \leqslant n \leqslant S$$
$$= K_C(n-S) \quad S < n \qquad \text{[Equation 24.2]}$$

Let us suppose that the chosen criterion is the minimisation of the mathematical expectation of $\Gamma(S)$, or $\overline{\Gamma}(S)$. Hence:

$$\overline{\Gamma}(S) = C\sum_{n=0}^{S} (S-n)p_n + KC\sum_{n=S+1}^{\infty} (n-S)p_n \qquad \text{[Equation 24.3]}$$

The calculation of the minimum of $\overline{\Gamma}(S)$ in relation to S is a problem which is easy to solve. It is enough to try and find the integer S_0 such that $\overline{\Gamma}(S_0)$ is smaller than $\Gamma(S_0 + 1)$ and smaller than $\Gamma(S_0 - 1)$.

In many other problems of waiting, very different criteria can be chosen.

Another problem of waiting concerns the landing of aircraft at an airport. How many runways must be laid down? From the point of view of flight and landing security, the criterion should be to choose the smallest number of runways for which the probability of a given average waiting time will be lower than a certain given figure. A criterion of this kind will likewise be accepted for a casualty department in a hospital, or, for instance, a fire-brigade.

As can be seen, the criterion of optimisation of mathematical expectation is not always suitable.

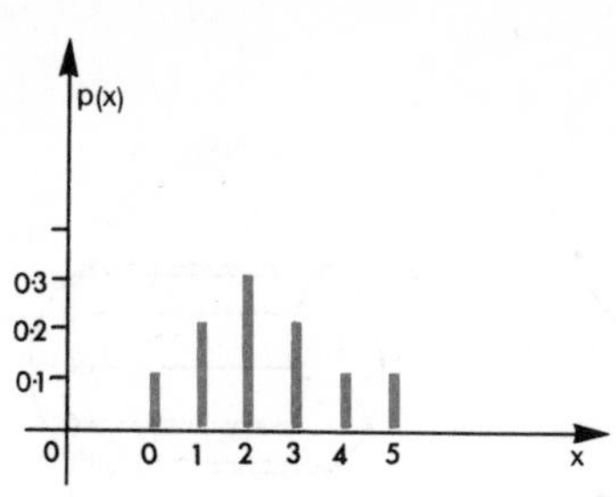

Figure 25·1

Figure 25·2

25 Generating chance artificially: the Monte Carlo method

In some complex problems several random variables appear. It is sometimes very difficult to build a suitable mathematical model for these problems, or again, the amount of calculation from these models is prohibitive. It is then possible to resort to simulation by the Monte Carlo method. What does this method consist of? Let us suppose that we have succeeded in determining the elementary relation between cause and effect of a phenomenon in which chance intervenes, without, however, having built the model. We therefore suppose that the laws of probability are known. According to processes described later in the book, artificial samples of random variables will be generated, i.e. sequences of values or states, the law of probability for each of which will correspond to that originally postulated for the variable considered. These samples are introduced into the elementary relations between cause and effect and the results are then studied by statistical methods.

Let us first see how chance may be artificially produced. Suppose that we have a random variable for which the law of probability is:

X	0	1	2	3	4	5
$p(X)$	0·1	0·2	0·3	0·2	0·1	0·1

(The histogram is shown in figure 25·1).

Now let us build a wheel of fortune divided into areas proportional to the probabilities $p(X)$ (figure 25·2).

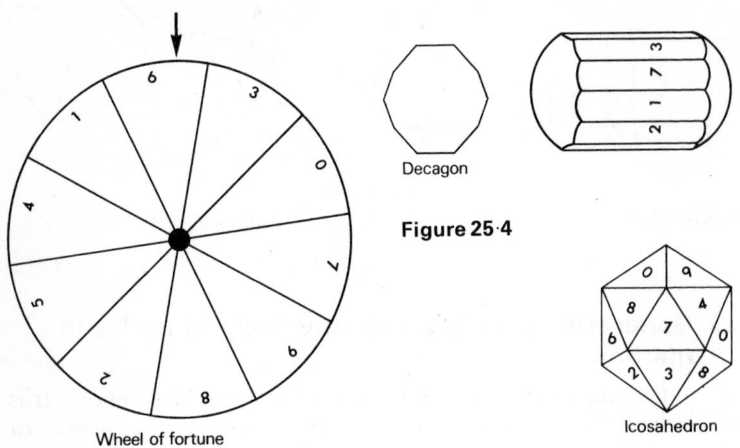

Figure 25·4

Figure 25·3

Figure 25·5

Spin this wheel sufficiently fast and each time it stops, note the result; we shall then obtain a sequence of integers from 0 to 5 (the variable of our example can only take these values). Here is what we might have obtained by spinning the wheel fifty times:

4, 0, 1, 2, 3, 2, 5, 2, 0, 0, 3, 1, 2, 2, 1, 2,
3, 5, 2, 3, 3, 1, 1, 3, 1, 1, 3, 5, 2, 2, 1, 0, 5,
3, 1, 4, 1, 2, 2, 4, 4, 0, 1, 2, 0, 2, 0, 2, 2, 2.

We find 7 noughts, 11 ones, 16 twos, 8 threes, 4 fours, 4 fives. The frequency with which the six numbers come up is a little different from the theoretical frequency, which would be, in the same order: 5, 10, 15, 10, 5, 5. Now, let us spin the wheel 500 times; we might find the following result: 49 noughts, 103 ones, 147 twos, 100 threes, 48 fours and 53 fives, whereas the theoretical frequency would give: 50, 100, 150, 100, 50, 50. By taking larger and larger samples we would find that relative frequencies would get nearer and nearer the theoretical law of probability. The sequences thus

x	p(x)	P(x)	n
0	0·1	0·1	{0}
1	0·2	0·3	{1,2}
2	0·3	0·6	{3,4,5}
3	0·2	0·8	{6,7}
4	0·1	0·9	{8}
5	0·1	0·1	{9}

Figure 25·6

obtained are called 'artificial samples' of the given law of probability.

Generally speaking, tables of 'random numbers' are used (see for instance [65]); they are formed by sequenoes of equiprobable integers from 0 to 9. They could be produced by a wheel of fortune, figure 25·3, by a regular decagonal prism, figure 25·4, or a regular icosahedron, figure 25·5. We prefer to produce them electronically, either from natural phenomena, the laws of probability of which are known, or by the use of certain properties of the integers from which algorithms for computers have been drawn.

These sequences of equiprobable integers, from 0 to 9 inclusive, allow us to produce samples of any law of probability. In figure 25·6, we show how to obtain an artificial sample of the law given in figure 25·1.

We make $\mathbf{N} = (0)$ correspond to $X = 0$

$\mathbf{N} = (1, 2)$ to $X = 1$

$\mathbf{N} = (3, 4, 5)$ to $X = 2$

$\mathbf{N} = (6, 7)$ $X = 3$

$\mathbf{N} = (8)$, $X = 4$

$\mathbf{N} = (9)$, $X = 5$

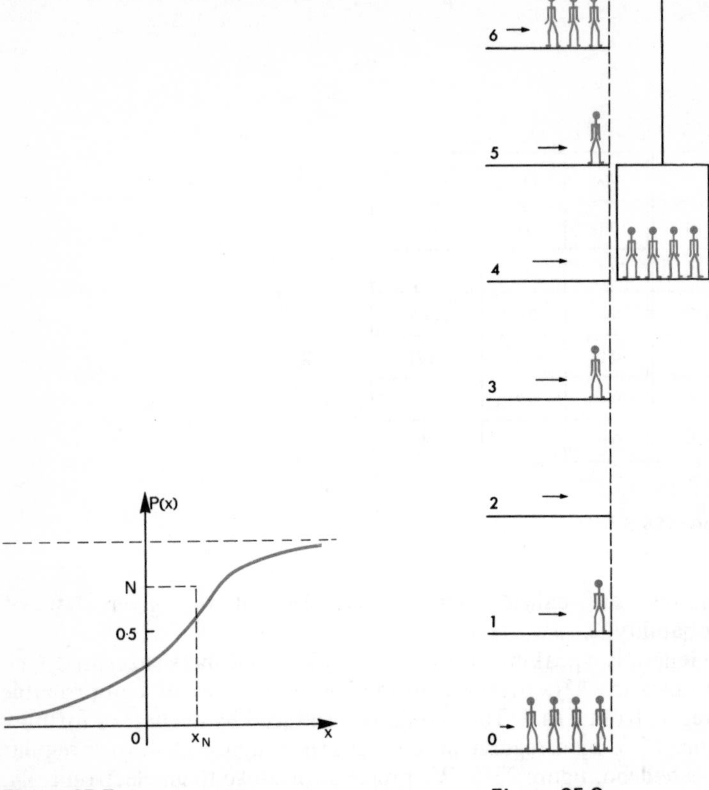

Figure 25·7

Figure 25·8

Thus, to a sample: 9, 5, 8, 5, 5, 3, 9, 2, 9, 3, 0, 6, 1, 2 ... will correspond the sequence: 5, 2, 4, 2, 2, 2, 5, 1, 5, 2, 0, 3, 1, 1, ...

The method is extended to the case of continuous random variables by considering the cumulative probability curve (figure 25·7). To any number $0 \leqslant N < 1$ will correspond a number X_N whose law of probability will be the given law, if the size of the sample is large enough.

This is only an outline of the so-called Monte Carlo theory and methods.

Let us now look at some of the possible applications of it in problems of decision.

I propose to study the waiting lines which could occur on the different floors of a skyscraper, outside the lifts, at different times of the day. This problem must be studied before the skyscraper is built, as it is practically impossible to add a new shaft afterwards if the existing ones prove inadequate. To simplify the picture, suppose that in our first hypothesis there is only one shaft (figure 25·8). For each floor, we shall adopt a law of arrival for the tenants of the building or for the visitors. This law is obviously not stationary and this must be taken into account. Artificial samples of all the variables representing arrivals and movements will be generated. After doing so (and it must be said that this is no easy matter), the time will be broken down into one-second intervals. For each second a record of travellers entering or leaving the lift will be made, bearing in mind rules which are rather complicated to describe: rules of summoning, of entering, of maximum load, of exit, etc. By means of a computer, suitably programmed, we can present a 'history' of the lift's activity for, shall we say, 10 minutes or more if necessary. But the computer can, in 'contracted time', 'relate' in this manner hundreds of 'histories' and we can, from these, estimate the waiting lines on various floors. If these lines are too long at certain peak hours, we shall decide whether it is necessary to recommend a second shaft. Another simulation with two shafts will be made, and if necessary with three. The simulation by the Monte Carlo method allows the construction of an 'artificial world' in which all sorts of experiments are possible.

5 Dealing with uncertainty

26 Introduction

In the theory of games of strategy we are concerned with the search for optimal strategies against an intelligent opponent (or several) or perhaps against nature.

Outlined by mathematicians of the seventeenth and eighteenth centuries (Cardan, Kepler, Galileo, Pascal, Waldegrave), its foundations were laid by Borel (in 1921) in an article which remains its starting point: 'La théorie du jeu et les équations intégrales à noyau symétrique gauche'. But we are indebted to J. von Neumann for the theory which has, for a quarter of a century, led to all sorts of discoveries of exceptional interest in econometrics, operational research, the study of competitive behaviour, and military strategy and tactics.

This theory deals in fact with the possibilities of decision offered when facing 'structured' uncertainty. In the ever more flexible world in which human phenomena take place, one may imagine how useful, even indispensable, this theory can be. The only cases in which it can be applied are very simple and elementary ones, but until it allows us to make calculated decisions in the structured uncertainty, it remains, meanwhile, in real cases, a reliable guide when deliberating the possible analysis of highly complex situations. When the theory of games of strategy allows us to tackle efficiently real problems of combat, duelling, competition and rivalry, then it will be possible to herald the dawn of a new era – that of the science of action.

27 Uncertainty and information

I have given in section 22 a definition of mathematical chance. Let us now see how uncertainty looks from the mathematical point of view.

Consider systems which can assume certain conditions, from the present instant t_0. We shall then designate certain degrees of knowledge:

1 *Non-structured uncertainty*	The states of the system are unknown at any time $t > t_0$.
2 *Structured uncertainty*	The states of the system are known, but we do not know what will be the state of the system at any time $t > t_0$.
3 *Chance*	The states of the system are known, as well as the laws of probability at any time $t > t_0$. If the laws do not vary with t, the chance is called 'stationary'; in the opposite case it is 'non stationary'.
4 *Certainty*	The states are known and we can describe the state in which the system will be at any time $t > t_0$.

We pass from one degree of knowledge to a higher one, from 1 to 2, from 2 to 3, from 3 to 4, through an increase in information. Thus, to pass from 1 to 2 the information is a 'specification'; from 2 to 3 it is a 'statistic'; from 3 to 4 it is a 'deterministic hypothesis'.

Let us study a few examples.

Non-structured uncertainty: the total number of vehicles on the roads of a county, the clientele of a shop, a battle where no situations can be specified.

Structured uncertainty: a battle in which possible outcomes can be stated, Brownian movement without statistical information, economic phenomena.

Chance: a wheel of chance, laws of genetics, mortality of human beings under certain conditions, radiation of particles.

Certainty: numerous macroscopic laws of physics, automatic production line supposedly without breakdowns, strikes or any other incidents, the position of the stars.

For many phenomena, however, uncertainty can be imperfectly structured. Randomness acceptable only for some domains or some variables, the others being uncertain; finally the determinist hypothesis may be only partially acceptable.

28 Games of strategy against nature

The notion of uncertainty is therefore less simple than is usually supposed. The uncertain can be structured or not. Just as we are unable to create chance except by means of devices directly or indirectly possessing the structure corresponding to the law or laws that we wish to originate, so neither can we theoretically create uncertainty with chance, even by multiplying arbitrarily, and by varying as much as possible the random laws of this chance; it is only possible to create a quasi-uncertainty. We shall now examine how to distinguish between structured uncertainty, structured quasi-uncertainty and chance. For this purpose we shall consider a game in which we have to take successive decisions in the face of unknown 'decisions' of nature.

Let us consider three urns U_1, U_2, U_3. A demon, whose behaviour is totally unknown, places in each of these urns a hundred balls of four colours C_1, C_2, C_3, C_4. He chooses for each one of the urns a proportion of colours r_1, r_2, r_3, r_4 where all numbers r_i are positive and $r_1 + r_2 + r_3 + r_4$ adds up to 100.

A player is asked to choose an urn and to draw a ball from it. We assume that he does not know what the demon has placed in the urns. After choosing urn U_i and drawing a ball C_j, he gets a prize A_{i_j} given by the table in figure 28·1. Thus, if the player chooses urn U_2 and draws a ball C_3 he receives 4. This represents one turn. After this turn, the demon changes as he pleases the proportions of colours in the urns. The player chooses an urn and takes out a ball; he receives a prize, again according to the table in figure 28·1. Let us suppose the game has a hundred turns under the same conditions: the demon changes the proportions, the player chooses an urn, draws a ball and receives a prize. Such a game is called 'a game of strategy against nature without information'. A convex weighting p_1, p_2, p_3 showing the relative frequencies of the

	C_1	C_2	C_3	C_4
U_1	4	2	0	1
U_2	2	3	4	0
U_3	5	0	2	3

Figure 28·1

choices of the player is called a 'mixed strategy'. The player is free to choose the strategy he likes best, he remains totally unaware of the demon's activities and *there is no diminution of his ignorance with each succeeding turn*. This is a structured uncertainty; we do not know what the results will be, but they will belong to the set: (C_1, C_2, C_3, C_4).

Let us demonstrate a case of less perfect uncertainty. Let us replace the demon by an opponent who works in the following way. He takes a table of random equiprobable integers from 0 to 9. From this table he chooses sequences of numbers of two figures such as:

32, 09, 48, 23

and he draws the convex weighting:

For C_1: $\dfrac{32}{32+9+48+23} = \dfrac{32}{112}$.

For C_2: $\dfrac{9}{112}$, for C_3: $\dfrac{48}{112}$ and for C_4: $\dfrac{23}{112}$.

(If he had found eight consecutive noughts in the sequence he would have taken the next sequence, and so on.) The opponent then puts into urn 1 in absolute secrecy, balls whose colours are distributed according to the frequencies nearest to $\dfrac{32}{112}$, $\dfrac{9}{112}$, $\dfrac{48}{112}$ and $\dfrac{23}{112}$. If he puts a hundred balls in urn 1, it will, for instance, be: $C_1 = 29$, $C_2 = 8$, $C_3 = 43$, $C_4 = 20$. In the same way he starts to put a hundred balls in urn 2 but with a sequence of equiprobable numbers taken from somewhere else in the table, and so on for urn 3.

This done, the player chooses an urn and draws a ball from the chosen urn, he receives a prize as in the table in figure 28·1. A hundred turns are taken in this way, the opponent altering the proportions after each turn.

This game is also a game against nature, but slightly different. There is very little information; the player only knows that a man has taken the place of the demon and that this man uses a procedure which he is aware of. The player, contrary to what we may think, is not in a situation where he fights against the uncertainty. If he plays not a hundred times, but thousands or billions of times under these conditions, he will realise that the relative frequencies of C_1, C_2, C_3, C_4 tend towards a law of probability which is known but which we shall not bother to calculate here, though by dint of repeating the turns, he could investigate this law.

In effect, as humans, we are unable to fabricate complete uncertainty: this fact is well known to cryptographers. In the procedure just described, however, we can talk of quasi-uncertainty; for samples of results of average size, no acceptable law of probability can be formulated. The opponent could also manufacture quasi-uncertainty by taking a large share of very different laws of probability from a list. He could draw one of these laws at random. Then, taking an artificial sample of the law obtained he would give the three urns this proportion, the player being unaware of how the opponent was working.

Now let us suppose that the opponent operates in another way. He extracts at random from a table of numbers four two-figure numbers giving a proportion of colours of the balls to be made; and, still in secret, but once and for all, he puts this same proportion into each of the three urns. The player chooses an urn, draws a ball and receives a prize according to the table in figure 28·1. The ball is put back into its urn, the opponent shakes up the balls and the player starts again until a hundred turns have been taken. This time the information on the strategy of nature will

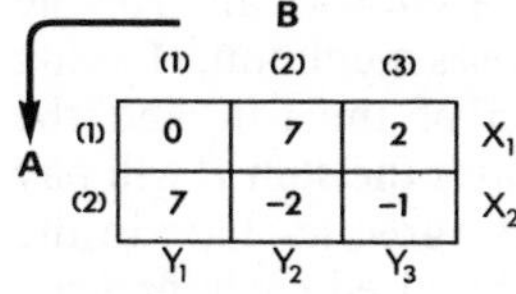

Figure 29·1

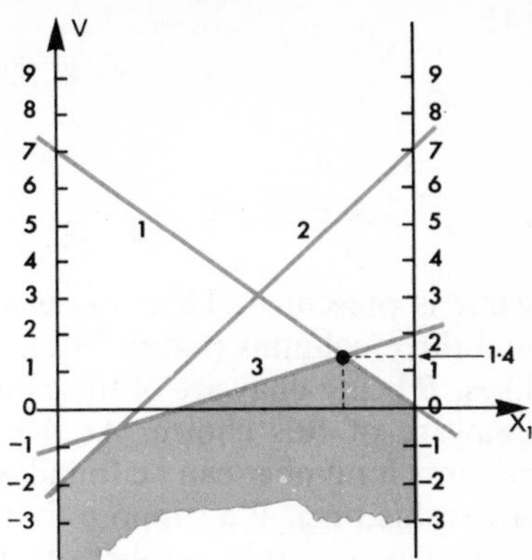

Figure 29·2

improve turn by turn, from the statistical point of view. This game is a game of strategy against nature with increasing statistical information. A variant consists in drawing the balls out exhaustively, i.e. without putting them back into the urn.

Let us pass on to another case and suppose that the opponent, after deciding the proportion of colours, the same for all the urns, gives the information to the player who now knows the strategy of nature. This time it will not be a game of strategy any more, but a decision in a random world. If the player can have a hundred turns, the criterion of maximal mathematical expectation of the prize should be adequate.

Finally, a more trivial example. The opponent draws a colour at random or decides on this colour, fills all the urns with this colour, and informs the player of everything he has done. The game of strategy is reduced to a decision in a determined universe.

29 Games of strategy against an intelligent opponent: the duel

We shall come back later on to the case of games of strategy against nature, so as to examine how some criteria can be envisaged. Before that we shall study a particular case which is very important, the case of 'the duel', or game of strategy against an intelligent opponent.

Let us consider then two players A and B, to whom the following game is presented. There exists a rectangular table with two rows and three columns (figure 29·1). The player *A* chooses any row he likes, *B* being unaware of this choice. *B* chooses a column, *A* being unaware of this choice. At the intersection of the row and the column, a number can be found which indicates the sum *B* will pay *A* for this turn. We suppose that the players agree to share in the same way a certain number of turns, say a hundred each, and the results will be declared at the end. Such a game is a 'duel without information', called by mathematicians a 'rectangular two-person zero-sum game'. This being so, we can study for *A* and for *B* various sorts of behaviour, but considering the description of this game, the behaviour of one or the other can be expressed as a fraction or weighting of each of the rows for *A*, or a fraction of each of the columns for *B* (the fractions adding up to 1 in each case). For instance, if a hundred turns are taken, *A* could choose row (1) 35 times, and row (2) 65 times. *B* could choose column (1) 20 times, column (2) 25 times and column (3) 55 times.

We shall call a player's 'strategy' a convex weighting of rows for *A* or columns for *B*. A strategy of *A* will therefore be a vector (X_1, X_2) where $X_1 \geqslant 0$, $X_2 \geqslant 0$, $X_1 + X_2 = 1$ and a strategy of *B* will be a vector (Y_1, Y_2, Y_3) when $Y_1 \geqslant 0$, $Y_2 \geqslant 0$, $Y_3 \geqslant 0$, $Y_1 + Y_2 + Y_3 = 1$, these strategies being the representations of choice of rows by *A* or choice of columns by *B*. Under these conditions, if *B* takes the vector (Y_1, Y_2, Y_3) when *A* chooses row (1), the mathematical expectation of the winnings per turn of *A* is:

row (1): $0.Y_1 + 7.Y_2 + 2.Y_3$ [Equation 29.1]

It can only be a mathematical expectation as *B* chooses a weighting unknown to *A*. The latter can only make the hypothesis that *B* has taken a vector. When *A* chooses row (2) the mathematical expectation of his winnings per turn is:

row (2): $7.Y_1 - 2.Y_2 - Y_3$ [Equation 29.2]

If *A* decides to take a vector (X_1, X_2) the mathematical expectation of his winnings per turn will be:

$$(X_1)(0.Y_1 + 7.Y_2 + 2Y_3) + X_2(7Y_1 - 2Y_2 - Y_3)$$
$$F = 7X_1Y_2 + 2X_1Y_3 + 7X_2Y_1 - 2X_2Y_2 - X_2Y_3$$

[Equation 29·3]

For instance, if $(X_1, X_2) = \left(\frac{7}{20}, \frac{13}{20}\right), (Y_1, Y_2, Y_3) = \left(\frac{4}{20}, \frac{5}{20}, \frac{11}{20}\right)$
The average winnings would be:

$$(7)\left(\frac{7}{20}\right)\ \frac{5}{20} + (2)\left(\frac{7}{20}\right)\left(\frac{11}{20}\right) + (7)\left(\frac{13}{20}\right)\left(\frac{4}{20}\right) +$$
$$(-2)\left(\frac{13}{20}\right)\left(\frac{5}{20}\right) + (-1)\left(\frac{13}{20}\right)\left(\frac{11}{20}\right)$$
$$F = \frac{245 + 154 + 364 - 130 - 143}{400} = \frac{490}{400} = 1{\cdot}225$$

[Equation 29.4]

Let us suppose then that *A* and *B* play a very great number of games of a hundred turns. By trying all sorts of strategies, they would discover in adapting themselves to the game that there must be a state of balance. We shall now show what such a balance is by stating one of the most famous theories of mathematics which we owe to Von Neumann and which Borel had previously suggested without a general demonstration. We shall again use the above numerical examples.

There exists for *A* a strategy (X_1^*, X_2^*) for which the mathematical expectation of its winnings per turn $F(X_1^*, X_2^*, Y_1, Y_2, Y_3)$ will be greater than or equal to a quantity V, which is unique and called 'value of the game'; this, whatever may be the strategy (Y_1, Y_2, Y_3) chosen by *B*. There exists for *B* a strategy (Y_1^*, Y_2^*, Y_3^*) for which the mathematical expectation of its losses per turn $F(X_1, X_2, Y_1^*, Y_2^*, Y_3^*)$ is less than or equal to the quantity V, the value of the game, this being the case whatever strategy (X_1, X_2) is chosen by *A*.

We should not be surprised at the asymmetry of the two propositions, which is due to the fact that the table of payments represents payments from B to A; with a table where rows became columns and *vice versa*, by changing the positive signs into negative ones and *vice versa*, we would have a table of payments of A to B and the above statement should be reversed as far as A and B are concerned.

We shall not prove this theorem (see reference [67] and [75]), but we shall state immediately that it is valid if A can choose from among m lines and B from among n columns, the table $m \times n$ holding any real, positive, negative or zero numbers.

According to the theorem we can therefore say that a quantity V exists such as:

column (1) $7X_2 \geqslant V$
column (2) $7X_1 - 2X_2 \geqslant V$
column (3) $2X_1 - X_2 \geqslant V$
$X_1 \geqslant 0,\ X_2 \geqslant 0,\ X_1 + X_2 = 1$ [Equation 29.5]

on the one hand, and on the other:

row (1) $7Y_2 + 2Y_3 \leqslant V$
row (2) $7Y_1 - 2Y_2 - Y_3 \leqslant V$
$Y_1 \geqslant 0,\ Y_2 \geqslant 0,\ Y_3 \geqslant 0,\ Y_1 + Y_2 + Y_3 = 1$
[Equation 29.6]

In the particular case of the 2×3 game considered, it is easy to determine (X_1^*, X_2^*) (Y_1^*, Y_2^*, Y_3^*) and V from these relations. For the general ease of games $m \times n$, the theory of linear programming is used (see [15] and [75]).

Here we shall calculate (X_1^*, X_2^*) and V from a simple graphic method. Let us consider the inequalities (1), (2) and (3) of equation 29.5. In each of them let us replace X_2 by $1 - X_1$, hence:

column (1) $V \leqslant 7 - 7X_1$
column (2) $V \leqslant 9X_1 - 2$
column (3) $V \leqslant 3X_1 - 1$ [Equation 29.7]

Now let us take a system of cartesian coordinates $X_1 0 V$ (figure 29·2) and draw the straight lines (1) $V = 7 - 7X_1$. (2) $V = 9X_1 - 2$. (3) $V = 3X_1 - 1$. Any point (X_1, V) within the shaded zone, constitutes a solution of the system of inequalities and this domain is obviously convex (see section 12). If player A chooses the solution corresponding to point $(X_1, V) = \left(\frac{4}{5}, \frac{7}{5}\right)$, i.e. the point of the domain for which we have the highest value of V, he will be assured of getting a mathematical computation of wins which will be at least equal to $\frac{7}{5} = 1{\cdot}4$. Since, to this point, corresponds $X_1 = \frac{4}{5}$, the value of X_2 associated to X_1 is $X_2 = 1 - X_1 = 1 - \frac{4}{5} = \frac{1}{5}$. Thus by choosing the strategy $(X_1^*, X_2^*) = \left(\frac{4}{5}, \frac{1}{5}\right)$, the player A is assured that his mathematical expectation of winnings will not be lower than 1·4, whatever the strategy chosen by B. This is a very important result, because, in this way, A is assured of a minimum below which his winnings cannot fall (we must insist on the fact that we are concerned here with the mathematical expectation of his winnings). For instance, if these wins are given by equation 29.3, let us see what happens for various strategies of B.

$$F = (7)\left(\frac{4}{5}\right)Y_2 + (2)\left(\frac{4}{5}\right)Y_3 + (7)\left(\frac{1}{5}\right)Y_1 - (2)\left(\frac{1}{5}\right)Y_2 - (1)$$

$$\left(\frac{1}{5}\right)Y_3$$

$$= \frac{7}{5}Y_1 + \frac{26}{5}Y_2 + \frac{7}{5}Y_3 \qquad \text{[Equation 29.8]}$$

Let us therefore see the effect of a few of B's strategies:

$$(Y_1, Y_2, Y_3) = (1, 0, 0):\ F = \frac{7}{5} = 1{\cdot}4$$
$$= (0, 1, 0):\ F = \frac{26}{5} = 5{\cdot}2$$
$$= (0, 0, 1):\ F = \frac{7}{5} = 1{\cdot}4$$
$$= (0, \frac{1}{2}, \frac{1}{2}):\ F = \frac{33}{10} = 3{\cdot}3$$
$$= (\frac{1}{3}, \frac{1}{3}, \frac{1}{3}):\ F = \frac{8}{3} = 2{\cdot}66$$
$$= (0, \frac{3}{4}, \frac{1}{4}):\ F = \frac{17}{4} = 4{\cdot}25 \qquad \text{[Equation 29.9]}$$

Which is the best strategy for B? A little more complicated calculation would show that the optimal strategy for B is $(Y_1^*, Y_2^*, Y_3^*) = \left(\frac{3}{10}, 0, \frac{7}{10}\right)$. Thus, if B chooses the strategy $\left(\frac{3}{10}, 0, \frac{7}{10}\right)$ he is assured that the mathematical expectation of his losses will not be higher than 1·4.

Now let us examine the same type of duel with, this time, the table of figure 29·3. A quick calculation shows that the best strategy for A is $(X_1^*, X_2^*) = (0, 1)$ and the best strategy for B is $(Y_1^*, Y_2^*, Y_3^*) = (1, 0, 0)$ for a value of the game $V = 2$.

Thus, A will always choose row (2) and B column (1), so as to behave, both of them, in the manner prescribed by Von Neumann's theorem. Having said that, let us suppose that A reasons as follows: I choose in each row a number corresponding to my minimal winnings, say -6 for row (1) and 2 for row (2); I next choose the row for which I find the highest minimal winnings, what is called in mathematics the 'maximin' (figure 29·4), thus, by choosing row (2), I am assured of winnings at least equal to 2. Let us suppose now that B reasons as follows: I choose in each column the number corresponding to my maximal losses, say 2 for column (1), 5 for

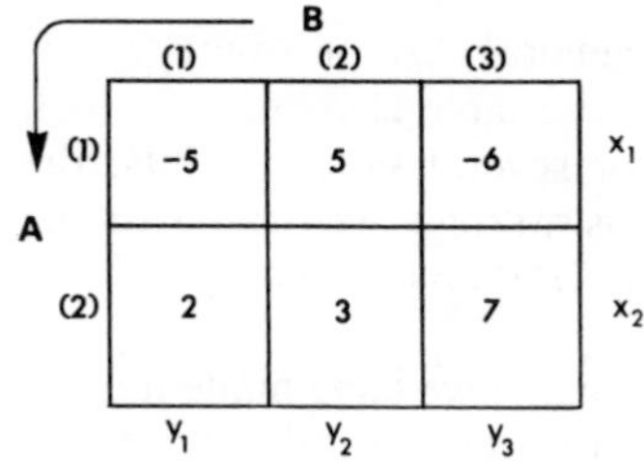

Figure 29·3

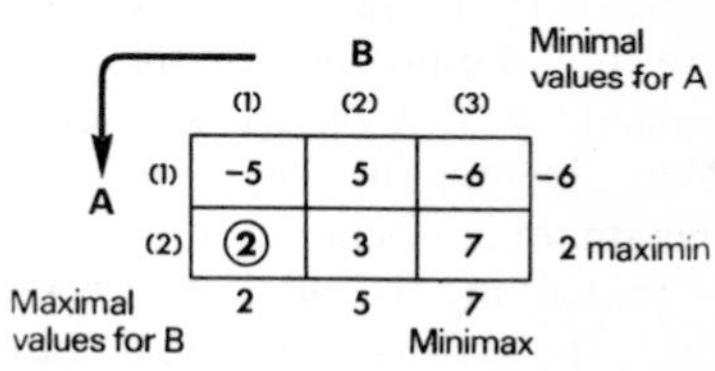

Figure 29·4

column (2), 7 for column (3); I next choose the column for which I find the lowest losses, which is called in mathematics the 'minimax' (figure 29·4); thus, by choosing column (1) I am assured that my losses will not go below 2.

In this particular case, if *A* chooses the maximin and *B* chooses the minimax, whether the players take part in one turn or in any number of turns, a strategic balance arises, the winnings per turn will always be 2 for *A* and −2 for *B*. When the maximin of *A* is equal to the minimax of *B*, which is the case with the table in figure 29·4, then the rectangular game is said to have a 'saddle point', this point corresponding to cell (2) (1) in this example. A rectangular game of this nature can possess several saddle points, but the value found in these saddle points is the same, and it is the value of the game.

The behaviour for a player *A* which consists in choosing the line corresponding to the maximin (for *B* in choosing a column corresponding to the minimax), has often been described as the careful man's criterion. A player, in this way, can insure himself against the worst in a duel; he might obtain better results with another behaviour, but this would entail risks.

Now it will be shown that in the case of a repetitive duel, the rectangular table of which does not hold a saddle point, as that of figure 29·1, the maximin behaviour (or minimax for the other) corresponds to the optimal strategies obtained, from the

Von Neumann theorem. Thus in the general case of a rectangular game with m lines and n columns and the table elements of which are a_{ij}, whether or not there is one or several saddle points, the behaviour of a player who chooses his strategy according to the Von Neumann theorem is called 'minimax behaviour' or 'Neumannian behaviour'.

In defining the rules of a rectangular game we have made it clear that: the results of successive turns were declared only at the end of a game of n turns. If the results were declared after each turn it would introduce information because the players could progressively estimate the frequencies of choice of their opponent. Nevertheless, in the practical cases, few enough it must be said, where the theory of games is applied to practical, civil or military problems, the information of the results is given after each turn, or is known after a slight time-lag, and these games are not completely without information. Also, when a player has chosen a strategy, i.e. a certain proportion of rows (or columns), either, for instance, p_1 times line (1), p_2 times line (2), p_m times line (m), so as to guard against a too-rapid determination of his strategy by his opponent, he will entrust to a mechanical means the drawing of an artificial sample of the law of probability corresponding to his strategy. Drawing at random by means of suitable devices (wheel of fortune, icosahedron, table of random numbers) will do the trick in practice.

During the Second World War, the dispositions of bombing or defence formations were diversified by random selection – otherwise the enemy would have had more success as a result of information acquired. The headquarters preparing the operations had at their disposal a certain number of variants, and often, in order to minimise the information the enemy might have gathered, the variant to be used was drawn at random on the day in question. A wise precaution, but one that was best concealed from the crews, as they might have been somewhat shocked, albeit quite wrongly, to be sent into danger on the throw of a dice!

Here now is an example of strategies of attack and defence, being a simplified statement of a problem put forward by Professor

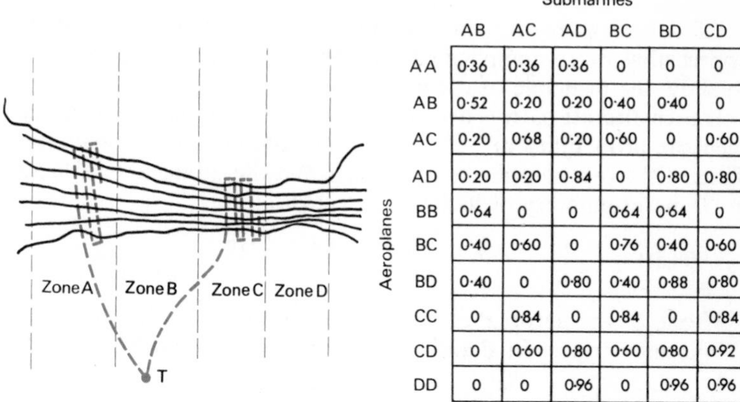

Aeroplanes \ Submarines	AB	AC	AD	BC	BD	CD
AA	0·36	0·36	0·36	0	0	0
AB	0·52	0·20	0·20	0·40	0·40	0
AC	0·20	0·68	0·20	0·60	0	0·60
AD	0·20	0·20	0·84	0	0·80	0·80
BB	0·64	0	0	0·64	0·64	0
BC	0·40	0·60	0	0·76	0·40	0·60
BD	0·40	0	0·80	0·40	0·88	0·80
CC	0	0·84	0	0·84	0	0·84
CD	0	0·60	0·80	0·60	0·80	0·92
DD	0	0	0·96	0	0·96	0·96

Figure 29·5

Figure 29·6

P.M.Morse ('Mathematical Problems in Operations Research', *Bulletin of the Mathematical Society*, pp 602–21, 1948).

An underwater craft, with a small operating range and occupied by a crew, must cross a narrow channel; it cannot stay submerged for more than 60 miles; the captain of the submarine knows that the enemy has two aircraft able to look for him and that the straits have been divided into four zones under observation: *A*, *B*, *C*, *D*. An aircraft surveys one zone and one only; the submarine must navigate submerged under two zones, and surface for two others, consecutive or otherwise. When the submarine surfaces in a zone where there is no aeroplane, the probability of its being detected and sunk is nil. If one of the two aircraft happens to be in the zone, the probability of the submarine being detected and sunk is:

$$p_A = 0{\cdot}2 \text{ in zone } A$$
$$p_B = 0{\cdot}4 \text{ in zone } B$$
$$p_C = 0{\cdot}6 \text{ in zone } C$$
$$p_D = 0{\cdot}8 \text{ in zone } D \qquad \text{[Equation 29.10]}$$

Of course in reality the statement of this problem would be appreciably more complicated. We only use this simple example to show the principle of the method used.

If each aircraft patrols over a zone where the submarine surfaces, then the probability of detection is the compounded probability. Thus, if the two aeroplanes patrol in *B* and the submarine surfaces in *B*, the probability of its being detected is:

$$p_{BB} = p_B + p_B - p_B p_B = 0{\cdot}4 + 0{\cdot}4 - 0{\cdot}16 = 0{\cdot}64 \quad \text{[Equation 29.11]}$$

If one of the aeroplanes is in *B* and the other in *C*, and if the submarine surfaces in *B* and in *C*, the probability will be:

$$p_{BC} = p_B + p_C - p_B p_C = 0{\cdot}4 + 0{\cdot}6 - 0{\cdot}24 = 0{\cdot}76 \quad \text{[Equation 29.12]}$$

The submarine has six choices: (*A*, *B*), (*A*, *C*), (*A*, *D*), (*B*, *C*), (*B*, *D*), and (*C*, *D*) whereas the two aeroplanes have 10 choices (*A*, *A*), (*A*, *B*), (*A*, *C*), (*A*, *D*), (*B*, *B*), (*B*, *C*), (*B*, *D*), (*C*, *C*), (*C*, *D*), (*D*, *D*). With the aid of formulas similar to equation 29.11 and equation 29.12, the table of the rectangular game of figure 29·6 can easily be obtained.

There are no saddle points as can easily be verified. A calculation which will not be offered to the reader, but which could be worked out without much difficulty after a brief study of the methods of calculation, gives the following results (see, for instance, reference [5]).

Optimal strategy of the submarine:

$$(Y_1^*, Y_2^*, Y_3^*, Y_4^*, Y_5^*, Y_6^*) = \left(\frac{6}{13}, \frac{4}{13}, \frac{3}{13}, 0, 0, 0\right) \quad \text{[Equation 29.13]}$$

Optimal strategy of the aircraft:

$$(X_1^*, X_2^*, X_3^*, X_4^*, X_5^*, X_6^*, X_7^*, X_8^*, X_9^*, X_{10}^*) = (0, 0, 0, 0, 0, \frac{7}{13}, \frac{5}{13}, 0, \frac{1}{13}, 0) \quad \text{[Equation 29.14]}$$

The value of the game is 0·369.

Thus, as long as the aircraft patrols according to the strategy: 7 times out of 13 in *BC*, 5 times out of 13 in *BD*, once out of 13 in *CD*, they will have a probability of detection and destruction which will be at least equal to 0·369. As for the submarine, by choosing *AB* 6 times out of 13, *AC* 4 times out of 13, *AD* 3 times out of 13, its risks will not increase beyond 0·369.

To this very simplified example we must add the following notes which would be indispensable in the case of real problems of this kind.

(1) If the detection and destruction of the submarine by the first aeroplane is represented by a random variable, Z_1, which can take the value 1 (submarine detected and destroyed) or the value 0 (submarine undetected) the definition of a random variable Z_2 for the second aeroplane being made in the same way, we accept the hypothesis that Z_1 and Z_2 are independent random variables.

(2) We suppose that the problem in question is sufficiently repetitive for the probability 0·369 to be representative.

(3) In practice, the submarine would probably know nothing of the manner in which the aircraft is controlled. For the aircraft the uncertainty would be arbitrarily structured, but not so for the submarine. It would not be a duel in a rectangular game, but a game against nature for the patrollers. Of course, it is necessary, for a game of strategy to be expressed as a rectangular game, that the two opponents have a complete knowledge of the structure of the proposed game.

There is another method of determining the optimal strategies of a game $m \times 2$ (or $2 \times n$):

Consider the 5×2 game of figure 29·7. Call r_1 the elements of column (1) and r_2 the elements of column (2). Let us use a system of orthogonal axes r_1Or_2 (figure 29·8) and draw on this reference plane the points corresponding to the five rows: that is (12·8), (10·7), (7·2), (3·5), (11·9).

Now draw the convex frame which holds all the points. Take a point S, inside this convex polygon, which will represent a certain

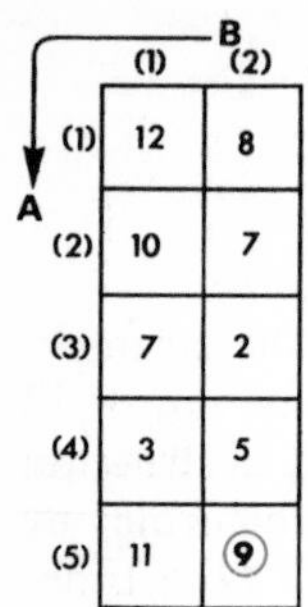

Figure 29·7

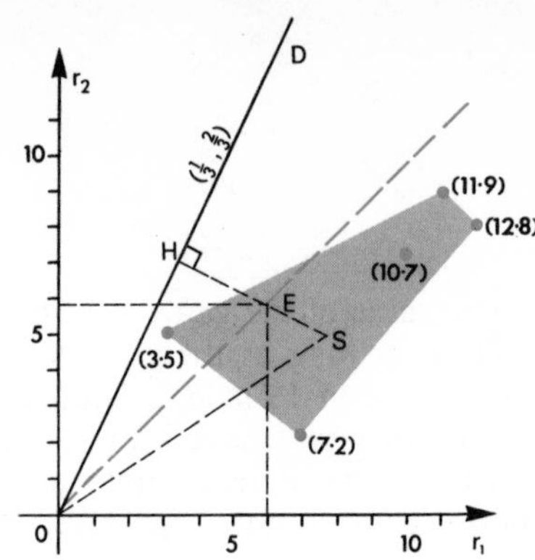

Figure 29·8

weighting of rows, i.e. a certain strategy of A. Now let us suppose that B chooses a strategy $(Y_1, Y_2) = (\alpha, \beta)$. Now draw a straight line D which passes through the origin and with a slope equal to α/β. From S drop a perpendicular line on the straight line D; this perpendicular crosses the bisector of the angle r_1Or_2 at point E. We shall see that the projections of E on Or_1 or on Or_2 gives the payment that must be made by B to A, if A chooses the strategy determined by point S, and B chooses the strategy determined by the straight line D.

From elementary vector calculus we have:

$\vec{U} = \vec{i}\alpha + \vec{j}\beta \leftarrow$ ($\vec{i}$ and $\vec{j}$ being the unit vectors along Or_1 and Or_2)
($\vec{U}$ being a vector along D) [Equation 29.15]

Let (W_1, W_2) be the line formed by the rows of the game if A chooses his strategy determined by point S.

$\overrightarrow{OS} = \vec{i}W_1 + \vec{j}W_2$ [Equation 29.16]

We also have:

$\overrightarrow{OE} = \vec{i}W + \vec{j}W = (\vec{i} + \vec{j})W$ if we call W the ordinate and the abscissa of E [Equation 29.17]

Compare the following scalar products:

$\overrightarrow{OS}.\vec{U} = \overrightarrow{OE}.\vec{U} = \text{OH}$ [Equation 29.18]

that is to say:

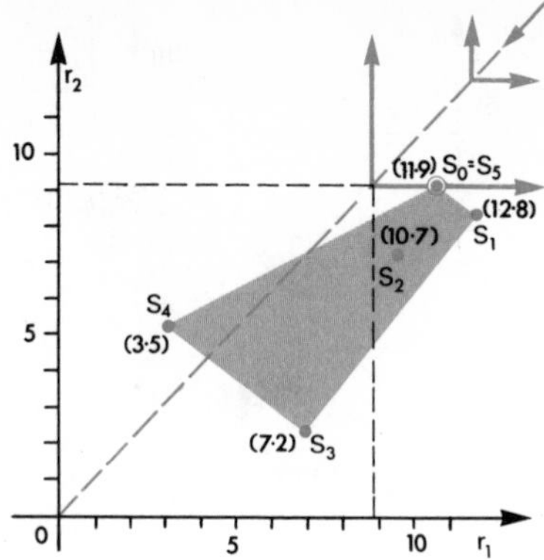

Figure 29·9

$$(\vec{i}W_1 + \vec{j}W_2)\,(\vec{i}\alpha + \vec{j}\beta) = (\vec{i} + \vec{j})W.(\vec{i}\alpha + \vec{j}\beta) \qquad \text{[Equation 20.19]}$$

or:

$$\alpha W_1 + \beta W_2 = (\alpha + \beta)W = W \qquad \text{(Equation 29.20]}$$

Thus the abscissa (or the ordinate) of E, or W, represents the payment made by B to A if A chooses the strategy determined by point S and B the strategy determined by the straight line D.

Now let us consider point S_0, which we obtain by sliding parallel to itself from $+\infty$ towards $-\infty$, a reference plane whose sides are respectively parallel to Or_1 and Or_2, the top of this reference plane being maintained on the internal bisector (figure 29·9). The first point of contact of this mobile orthogonal reference plane with the convex outline will give the maximin S_0 strategy of A and the coordinates of the top of the reference plane will give the value of the game. Indeed, any strategy of A placed on the bisector of $r_1\widehat{O}r_2$ gives a rule which is independent of the strategy of B (slope of D). The mobile reference plane can reach the outline in a vertex S_0 of this outline, in which case there is a saddle point (figure 29·9) and S_0 gives both the minimax strategy of B and the value of the game. Or again, the mobile reference plane can reach the outline on a point belonging to this outline; in which case there is no saddle point (for instance, the game of figure 29·10 which is related to figure 29·11). In the latter case the side encountered is separated by point S_0 into two segments proportional to the weights of the maximin strategy of A.

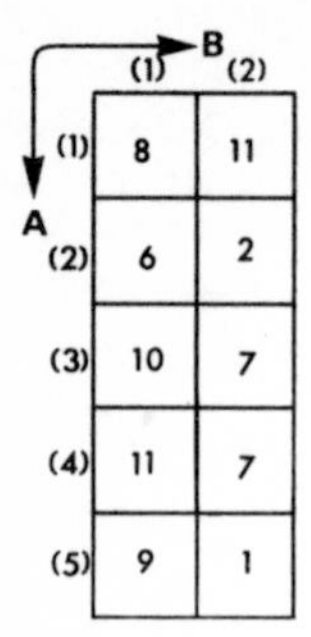

A \ B	(1)	(2)
(1)	8	11
(2)	6	2
(3)	10	7
(4)	11	7
(5)	9	1

Figure 29·10

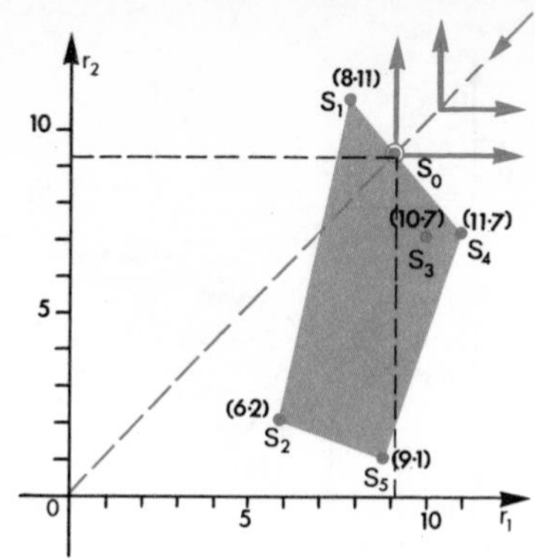

Figure 29·11

It is easy to find that the maximin strategy of A is $(x_1^*, x_2^*, x_3^*, x_4^*, x_5^*) = \left(\frac{4}{7}, 0, 0, \frac{3}{7}, 0\right)$, that the minimax strategy of B is $(y_1^*, y_2^*) = \left(\frac{4}{7}, \frac{3}{7}\right)$; no particular importance need be given in the present example, to the fact that the weights are the same in the two optimal strategies; this is due to the fact that the table made up by rows (1) and (4) of the table of the game is symmetrical.

In dealing with a $2 \times n$ game instead of an $m \times 2$ game, we shall use the same method, but here the convex frame will be obtained from the columns of the table instead of the lines. The mobile reference plane which has its axes orientated in the inverse direction to those of the fixed reference line, will then be taken and it will be made to move from $-\infty$ to $+\infty$. Figure 29·12 gives an example of the solution of a 2×7 game.

Nevertheless, as I have pointed out earlier, the general method to be used for rectangular games having more than two lines, or more than two columns, is the solution by means of a linear program or its dual, dealt with by the simplex method or one of its variants (see references [5], [75] and [77]).

30 Choice of a criterion under uncertainty

To avoid extensive mathematical calculations, we shall again use a game of strategy against nature, in the simple rectangular form

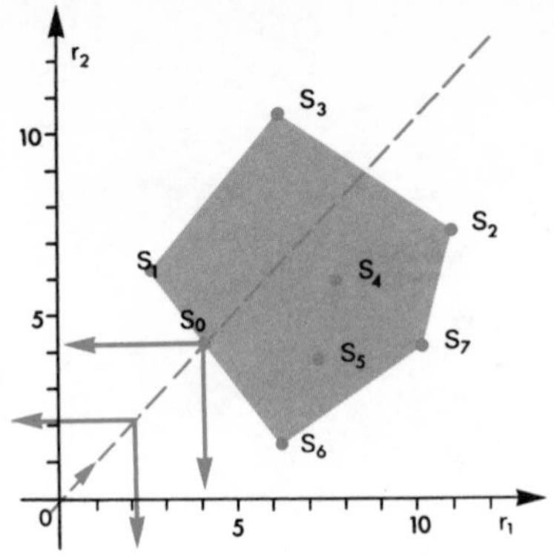

Figure 29·12

	C_1	C_2	C_3	C_4	Mean return gaining
V_1	4	2	0	1	7/4
V_2	2	3	4	0	9/4
V_3	5	0	2	3	10/4 ←

Figure 30·1

studied in the previous paragraph. Thus the structure of the uncertain universe will appear quite clearly even to the reader unfamiliar with mathematics. The attitude in the case of structured uncertainty is a subject which has been much written about and will probably continue to be so for a long time. As far as non-structured uncertainty is concerned, it is not easy to see how to introduce any sort of criterion and we shall not deal with this aspect.

Let us examine certain criteria suggested for a game without any information (a player against a demon – remember that a demon, according to the dictionary, can be good or bad).

Criterion of the mean, or the Laplace criterion. Laplace used to say: 'If I know nothing of nature but the states it can take, I assume these states to be equiprobable'. Thus, using this criterion, the attitude of the player towards the game suggested in section 28 will consist in estimating the average values of each row in the pay-off table. He will then obtain:

$$\text{Line 1: } \frac{4+2+0+1}{4} = \frac{7}{4}$$

$$\text{Line 2: } \frac{2+3+4+0}{4} = \frac{9}{4}$$

$$\text{Line 3: } \frac{5+0+2+3}{4} = \frac{10}{4}$$

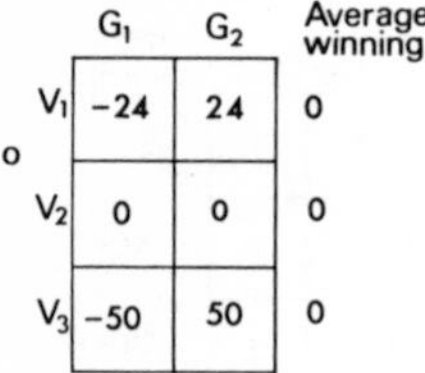

Figure 30·2

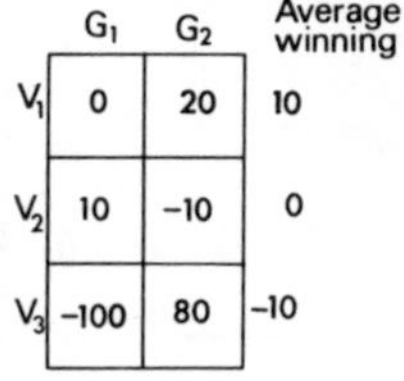

Figure 30·3

According to this criterion, he will choose to play row 3 for each turn, which gives an average of 10/4 (figure 30·1).

The fundamental criticism which could be made on the choice of such a criterion is about the hypothesis of equiprobability: why should nature prefer this law to another? Furthermore, such an attitude does not take into account the possible risk if nature chooses to put the player in very unfavourable situations.

For instance, in suggesting to the player a game with two columns (figure 30·2), according to the Laplace criterion, the three lines would be equivalent and yet the risks are quite different. The game of figure 30·3 emphasises once more the lack of balance the player can be faced with.

Minimax or Wald criterion in a game against nature. This is the criterion of the maximin or minimax (depending whether the player has to maximise or minimise). Against nature, the player behaves as in a duel, assuming that nature is an intelligent opponent.

By taking the minimax (or maximin) the player insures himself a result at least (or most) equal in mathematical expectation to the value of the game.

Let us look at an example where the criterion may quite reasonably be applied.

A farmer owns a field suitable for growing two cereals, C_1 and C_2. According to the summer weather, dry, average or wet, the yield will differ greatly and, of course, so will the profits. The table of

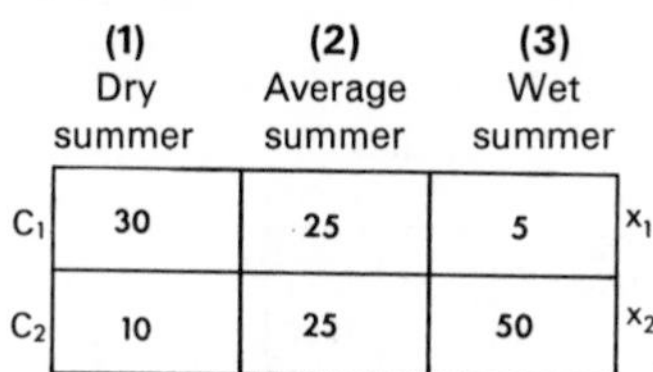

	(1) Dry summer	(2) Average summer	(3) Wet summer	
C_1	30	25	5	x_1
C_2	10	25	50	x_2

Figure 30·4

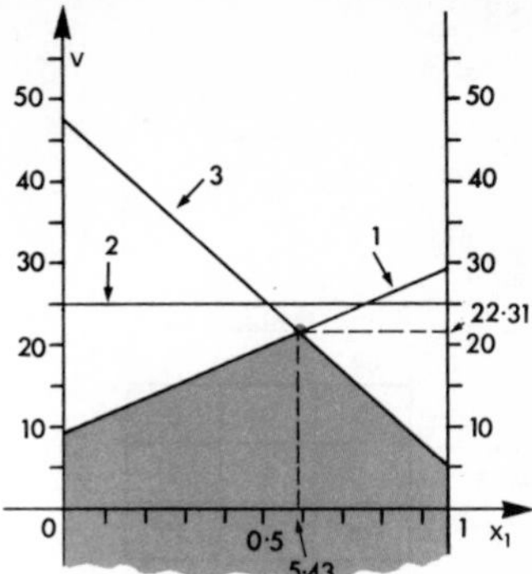

Figure 30·5

figure 30·4 gives the corresponding profits in a certain monetary unit. In such conditions, which proportion of C_1 and C_2 should be sown?

A quick calculation, working as in section 29, illustrated by figure 30·5, shows that if the farmer sows 8/13 with C_1 and 5/13 with C_2, his profit will be at least equal to 22·31, whatever the weather of the coming summer. In that case, we can talk of profit and not mathematical expectation of the profit because in carrying out in the same year a proportional sowing instead of sowing C_1 8 years out of 13 and C_2 5 years out of 13, the farmer will find himself in a position where the mathematical expectation is perfectly acceptable.

The criterion of the maximin (or minimax) in the case of a game against nature is often called 'Wald criterion', after the great statistician Abraham Wald who focused attention on the introduction of certain concepts of the theory of the duel into the problems of statistical decisions.

This criterion of minimax may be unacceptable in many cases. Let us consider, for instance, the game of figure 30·6 and let us suppose that the player has absolutely got to win, and thus, ultimately, will accept a risk. He cannot choose row (1) for which there is a saddle point with a zero pay-off. He will prefer to choose another row. This attitude can be taken quite justifiably, whether the game has a great many turns or not, or even if it has only one turn.

Another example (figure 30·7) shows the excessive pessimism of

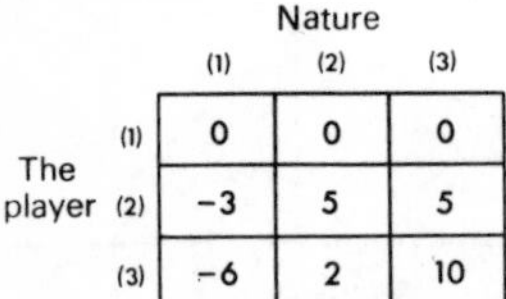

		Nature (1)	(2)	(3)
The player	(1)	0	0	0
	(2)	−3	5	5
	(3)	−6	2	10

Figure 30·6

		Nature (1)	(2)
The player	(1)	1	5
	(2)	−1	1000

Figure 30·7

the Wald criterion. If we put the question to a number of people, we shall find that a large majority will choose row (2), although row (1) has a saddle point. To risk winning 1000, while risking a loss of only 1, seems much more tempting than to win 1 or 5, as long as the loss of 1 does not lead to bankruptcy.

Optimism and Pessimism. The optimism coefficient of Hurwicz. To lessen the pessimistic effect of the Wald criterion, Hurwicz suggested taking into account for the player maximising (or minimising) a scale of utility which would replace the scale of values of the game. The means suggested by Hurwicz to transform a rectangular game on values into a game on utility, consists in the introduction of a coefficient of optimism $a(0 \leqslant a \leqslant 1)$ which multiplies the highest number in each line, whereas its complement $1 - \alpha$ multiplies the lowest number in each line, the values of intermediate numbers being ignored.

Consider the game against nature of figure 30·8. A quick calculation gives:

$$(X_1^*, X_2^*) = \left(\frac{4}{11}, \frac{7}{11}\right), V = \frac{9}{11}$$

Now, let us give ourselves a coefficient of optimism $\alpha = \frac{1}{4}$. Hence $1 - \alpha = \frac{3}{4}$.

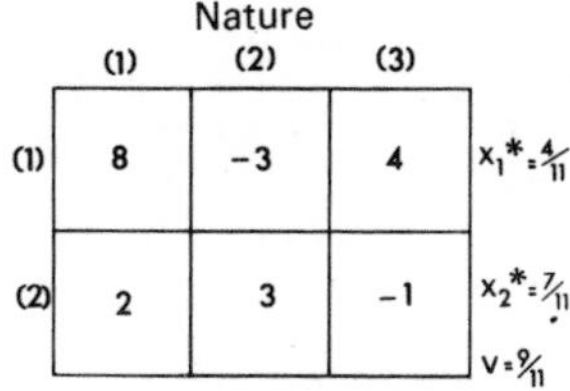

Figure 30·8

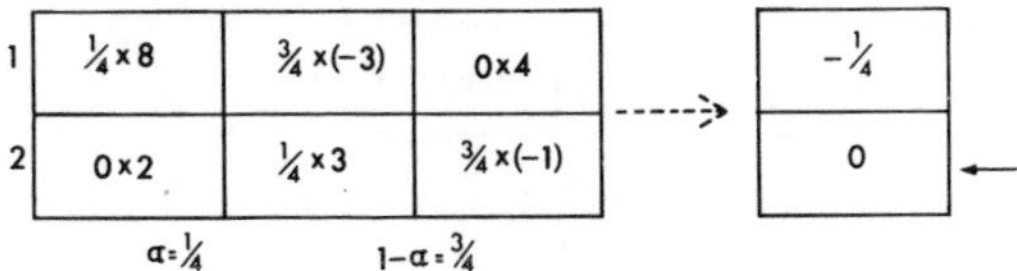

Figure 30·9

This 2×3 game will be transformed into a game 2×1 by the addition of rows, after weighting.

It appears then with this new criterion that the optimal strategy is (0, 1). Now taking $\alpha = \frac{3}{4}$, $1 - \alpha = \frac{1}{4}$, figure 30·10 gives us for an optimal strategy (1, 0). The Hurwicz criterion is open to criticism. First, the estimation of the coefficient of optimism is very tricky in real problems. On the other hand, the effect of the intermediate values is neglected, and this might well be criticised in certain cases. Let us look at another example where a more serious criticism can be brought against the coefficient of optimism. Take once more the example of figure 30·4. A quick calculation (figure 30·11) shows that, whatever the value of X, C_2 will always be preferred to C_1. It is not paradoxical: in the Hurwicz criterion we want to ignore the possible strategies of nature by interesting ourselves in extreme cases only. The opposite criticism could be made of the Laplace criterion, for which we want to ignore the

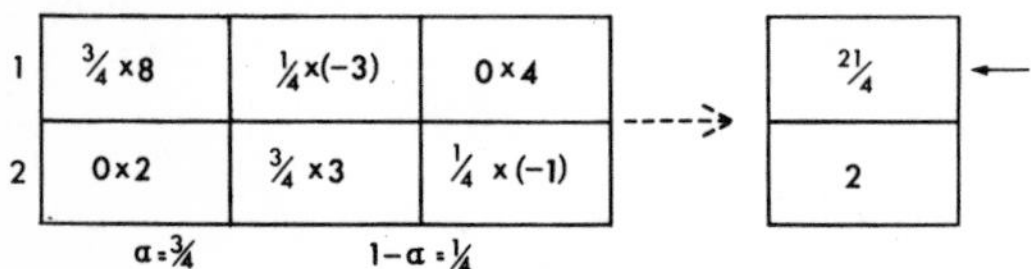

Figure 30·10

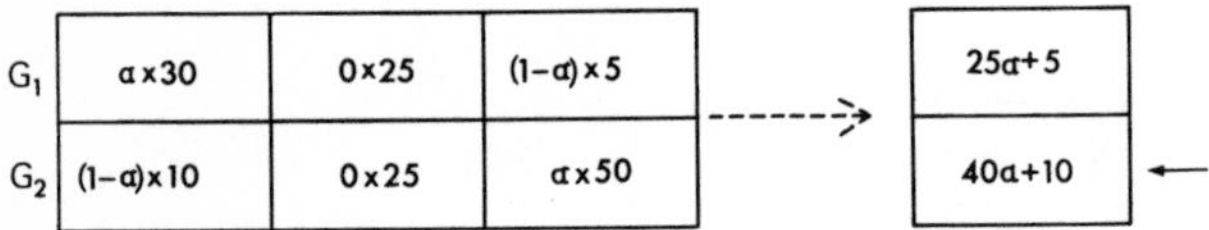

Figure 30·11

possible strategies of nature by supposing that it wishes to avoid extreme cases.

Criterion of minimal regret (Savage). Consider once more the problem of figure 30·4 and let us suppose that the farmer argues in the following way. If I sow C_1 and the summer is dry, my regrets in relation to the most favourable result will be nil. If I sow C_2 and the summer is dry, my regrets in relation to the most favourable result will be $10 - 30 = -20$. If I sow C_1 or C_2 and the summer is average, my regrets will be nil. If I sow C_1 and the summer is wet, my regrets in relation to the most favourable result will be $5 - 50 = -45$. If I sow C_2 and the summer is wet, my regrets will be nil.

Let us then form a rectangular game 2×3, where the values are the regrets calculated as above (figure 30·13). For this new game, we calculate the strategy which gives the farmer a mathematical expectation of regrets which he is sure not to exceed. The calculations made from figure 30·14 show that, if the farmer chooses the strategy $(X_1^*, X_2^*) = \left(\frac{4}{13}, \frac{9}{13}\right)$ the mathematical

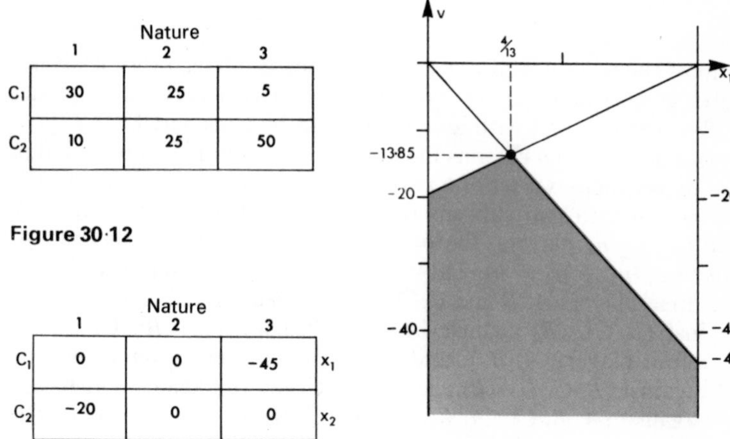

	Nature 1	2	3
C_1	30	25	5
C_2	10	25	50

Figure 30·12

	Nature 1	2	3	
C_1	0	0	−45	x_1
C_2	−20	0	0	x_2

Figure 30·13

Figure 30·14

expectation of his regrets will not exceed $\frac{180}{13} = 13{\cdot}85$.

By reasoning in this manner the farmer used an economic criterion which is quite fashionable at the moment, the minimum regrets criterion – or criterion of lack of winnings. It was suggested by Savage. From a rectangular game, a new game is formed by subtracting from the terms of each column of nature the highest number in each of these columns. The table thus obtained expresses the regrets. The optimal strategy is then calculated and the value of this new game.

Other criteria have been suggested for games against nature. I advise readers interested in this fascinating question to look up the bibliography of this chapter.

31 More complicated strategic games

A rectangular game of strategy as it has been defined in section 29 is a zero-sum game. By this we mean that whatever the decisions are, the sum won by one is equal to the sum lost by the other. The sum of the winnings of one and of the losses of the other is always zero. Rectangular games with more than two persons or games with n persons and with a zero-sum can be considered.

In a game with n persons the notion of 'coalition' is fundamental. Let us say there is a set of n players. We call a 'coalition' a splitting of this set into two sub-sets of players (neither set being empty), one having n_1 players, the other n_2 players who will play in opposition, $(n_1 + n_2 = n)$. Thus, by way of example, let us say there are three players A, B and C. We can consider three coalitions (A) against (B, C), (B) against (A, C), (C) against (A, B). Or again, with four players, A, B, C and D, we can consider seven coalitions (A) against (B, C, D), (B) against (A, C, D), (C) against (A, B, D), (D) against (A, B, C), (A, B) against (C, D), (A, C) against (B, D), (A, D) against (B, C). It is easy to prove that in a set of n players, $2^{(n-1)}$ distinct coalitions can be formed.

I shall provide some simplified explanations from an elementary example made up by a zero-sum game with three persons. Let us suppose that player A has the choice of two decisions A_1 and A_2, player B has two decisions B_1, B_2, player C has two decisions C_1 and C_2. Now consider a table of payments (table 7).

Let us examine first the case in which the players do not worry about coalitions. If, separated from one another, with no possibility of communicating before taking their decision, the players choose respectively A: A_1, B: B_2, C: C_1 then A will pay 2, B will receive 5 and C will pay 3, the total giving a zero-sum. Now let us call (X_1, X_2) (Y_1, Y_2) (Z_1, Z_2) respective mixed strategies for A, B and C in the case in which a large number of turns are taken. If a_{ijk} are A's winnings when A chooses A_i, B chooses B_j and C chooses C_k, then the mathematical expectation of A's winnings for each turn will be, for strategies (X_1, X_2) (Y_1, Y_2) (Z_1, Z_2):

$$\begin{aligned}\bar{g}_A = & a_{111}\,X_1\,Y_1\,Z_1 + a_{112}\,X_1\,Y_1\,Z_2 \\ & + a_{121}\,X_1\,Y_2\,Z_1 + a_{122}\,X_1\,Y_2\,Z_2 \\ & + a_{211}\,X_2\,Y_1\,Z_1 + a_{212}\,X_2\,Y_1\,Z_2 \\ & + a_{221}\,X_2\,Y_2\,Z_1 + a_{222}\,X_2\,Y_2\,Z_2\end{aligned}$$

[Equation 31.1]

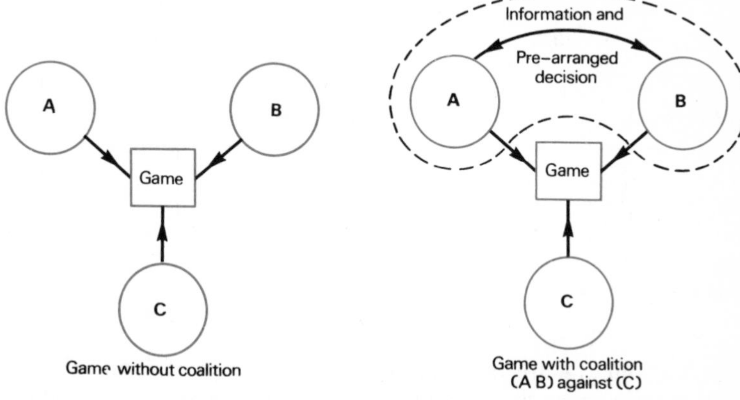

Figure 31·1

Figure 31·2

Table 7

Decision			Winnings		
A	*B*	*C*	*A*	*B*	*C*
A_1	B_1	C_1	6	−3	−3
A_1	B_1	C_2	0	2	−2
A_1	B_2	C_1	−2	5	−3
A_1	B_2	C_2	−3	0	3
A_2	B_1	C_1	−1	2	−1
A_2	B_1	C_2	−4	−1	5
A_2	B_2	C_1	3	−1	−2
A_2	B_2	C_2	2	−2	0

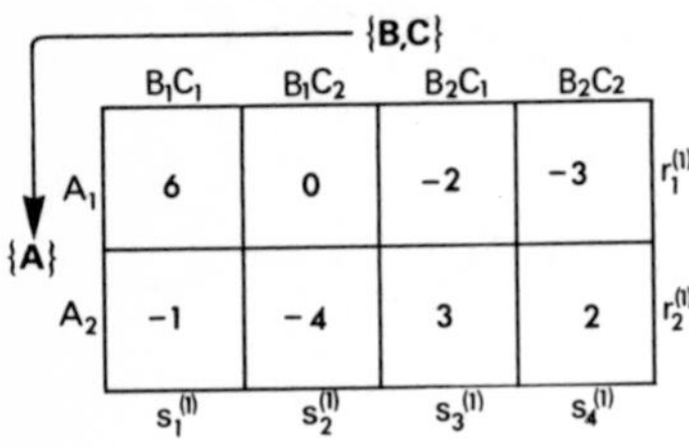

Figure 31·3

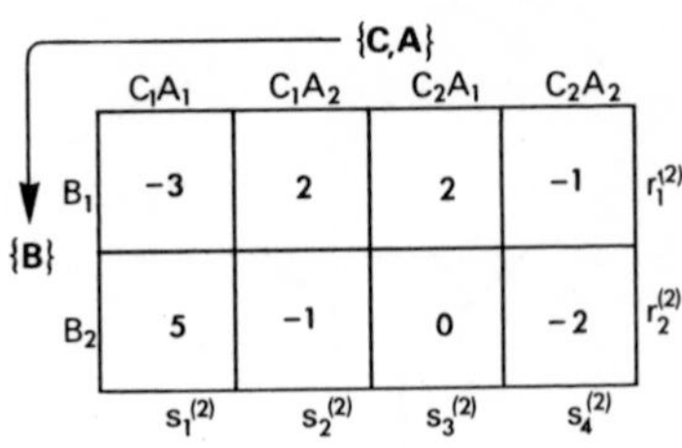

Figure 31·4

If b_{ijk} and c_{ijk} are the corresponding winnings of B and C, we shall then have similar formulas for $\bar{g}_B$ and $\bar{g}_C$ and, for any value of $i, j, k = 1, 2$.

$$a_{ijk} + b_{ijk} + c_{ijk} = 0 \qquad \text{[Equation 31.2]}$$

Hence:

$$\bar{g}_A + \bar{g}_B + \bar{g}_C = 0 \qquad \text{[Equation 31.3]}$$

For instance, if the chosen strategies are $(X_1, X_2) = \left(\frac{3}{5}, \frac{2}{5}\right)$ $(Y_1, Y_2) = \left(\frac{1}{6}, \frac{5}{6}\right)$, $(Z_1, Z_2) = \left(\frac{1}{10}, \frac{9}{10}\right)$ the mathematical expectation of respective winnings for each turn will be:

$$\bar{g}_A = -\frac{281}{300} = -0{\cdot}937 \qquad \text{[Equation 31.4]}$$

$$\bar{g}_B = -\frac{84}{300} = -0{\cdot}280 \qquad \text{[Equation 31.5]}$$

$$\bar{g}_C = \frac{365}{300} = 1{\cdot}217 \qquad \text{[Equation 31.6]}$$

But each of the players may consider that it might be in his interest – or in his adversary's interest – to enter into a coalition. For each of the three possible coalitions let us examine the 2-person zero-sum games which correspond to them. Figures 31·3, 31·4 and 31·5

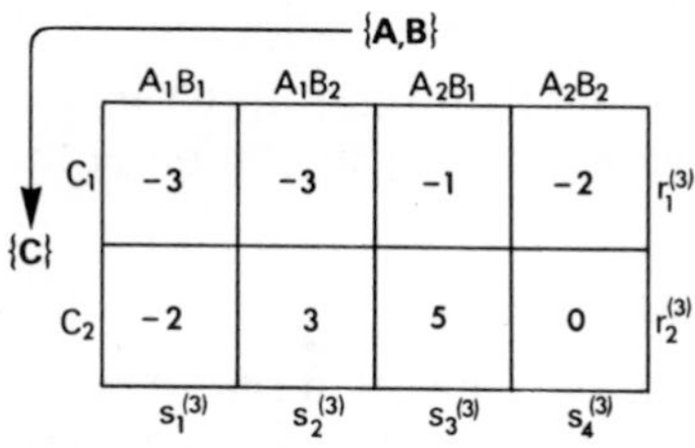

Figure 31·5

represent the games (A) against (B, C), (B) against (C, A) and (C) against (A, B). Now calculate the optimal strategies corresponding to the maximin or to the minimax for each of these games. We get simply:

(A) against (B, C)

$$r_1{}^{(1)} = \frac{2}{3},\ r_2{}^{(1)} = \frac{1}{3};\ S_1{}^{(1)} = 0,\ S_2{}^{(1)} = \frac{5}{9},\ S_3{}^{(1)} = 0,\ S_4{}^{(1)} = \frac{4}{9};$$

$$V^{(1)} = -\frac{4}{3} = -1{\cdot}333 \qquad \text{[Equation 31.7]}$$

(B) against (C, A):

$$r_1{}^{(2)} = \frac{7}{9},\ r_2{}^{(2)} = \frac{2}{9};\ S_1{}^{(2)} = \frac{1}{9},\ S_2{}^{(2)} = 0,\ S_3{}^{(2)} = 0,\ S_4{}^{(2)} = \frac{8}{9};$$

$$V^{(2)} = -\frac{11}{9} = -1{\cdot}222 \qquad \text{[Equation 31.8]}$$

(C) against (A, B):

$$r_1{}^{(3)} = 0,\ r_2{}^{(3)} = 1;\ S_1{}^{(3)} = 1,\ S_2{}^{(3)} = S_3{}^{(3)} = S_4{}^{(3)} = 0,$$

$$V^{(3)} = -2 \qquad \text{[Equation 31.9]}$$

Thus, if (A) adopts a strategy $\left(\frac{2}{3}, \frac{1}{3}\right)$ against (B, C) the mathematical expectation of his losses will not be greater than 1·333. If (B) adopts a strategy $\left(\frac{7}{9}, \frac{2}{9}\right)$ against (C, A) the mathematical expectation of his losses will not be greater than 1·222. If (*C*) adopts a strategy (0, 1) against (*A*, *B*) the mathematical expectation of his losses will not be greater than 2.

Does a strategy for *A* exist better than $\left(\frac{2}{3}, \frac{1}{3}\right)$ if *A* does not assume a coalition (*B*, *C*) to exist? The same question can be posed for all the other players. To answer it, more complex mathematical questions would be necessary. We shall only deal with them summarily; we are indebted to Von Neumann and Morgenstern[19] for a method enabling us to make a state of balance appear in a game with *n* persons and a zero-sum. Let us study this method in a simple case where $n = 3$.

We call 'characteristics' of a game with *n* persons and a zero-sum, the values of the games which correspond to each player facing a coalition of all the others. In our example we have:

$$V^{(1)} = -1{\cdot}333,\ V^{(2)} = -1{\cdot}222,\ V^{(3)} = -2 \qquad \text{[Equation 31.10]}$$

These are the characteristics of the game being considered. We shall now introduce the important notion of 'imputation'.

We have seen that in the worst conditions (*B* and *C* grouped against him) *A* could not lose more than 1·333. He will therefore interest himself only in the strategies which can guarantee him a loss lower than 1·333. For their part, *B* and *C* taken separately will argue likewise; therefore a set of strategies $((X_1, X_2)(Y_1, Y_2)(Z_1, Z_2))$ will be considered as acceptable by each of the players if the corresponding winnings are all higher than the values of the game of each of the respective games in which one player is in opposition to all the others: i.e. $\bar{g}_A \geqslant V^{(1)}$, $\bar{g}_B \geqslant V^{(2)}$, $\bar{g}_C \geqslant V^{(3)}$, or again:

$$\bar{g}_A, \bar{g}_B, \bar{g}_C) \geqslant (V^{(1)}, V^{(2)}, V^{(3)}) \qquad \text{[Equation 31.11]}$$

considering the sets formed by the winnings. In our example, any set such as $(\bar{g}_A, \bar{g}_B, \bar{g}_C) \geqslant (-1{\cdot}333, -1{\cdot}222, -2)$ will constitute an imputation.

Von Neumann and Morgenstern have determined as follows the

solution of a game with n persons and a zero-sum: *A set of imputations exists in such a way that in this set no imputation dominates any other*. For any imputation not belonging to the set, at least one imputation of this set dominates it (we have explained in section 12 the meaning of the word domination).

As far as the zero-sum games with three persons are concerned, it has been proved that a single finite set of three imputations forming the solution exists; or their solution is constituted by a set holding an infinity of imputations and this set is not unique. There is an infinity of it. It has also been demonstrated that any game with four persons has a solution.

Non-zero sum game. If, in a game with n persons, the total of winnings is different from the total of losses, the game is said to be a non-zero sum game. In economic reality the structures are such that it is rare, among a set of competitors in the same market, for the profit of some to be equivalent to the loss of the others. Generally the State constitutes an $n + 1$th player. It is often in opposition to the coalition of players and in these games of non-zero sum the State is a maximising player who questions the rules of the game when he does not win sufficiently.

We reduce the search for a solution of an n person non-zero sum game to one for a game with $n + 1$ persons and a zero sum, nature being a $(n + 1)$th player. But, as this $(n + 1)$th player is unable to join sub-sets formed by other players to make up a coalition, it is advisable to modify the meaning given to the words 'imputation' and 'solution' so that only the preferences by domination of n real players over the $n + 1$ players are brought in.

Continuous games. We can imagine that two players A and B have the choice, one, of a value of x in an interval (a_1, a_2) and two of a value of y in an interval (b_1, b_2). These choices being made, A pays B the sum given by $F(x, y)$ – for instance $F(x, y) = \frac{x - y}{x + y}$ in which x can take all the values from 0 to 2 and y all the values from

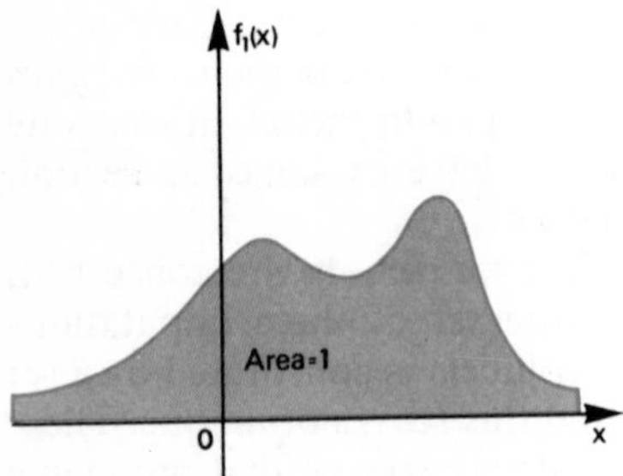

Figure 31·6

-1 to $+1$. Thus, if A chooses $x = 1{\cdot}5$ while B chooses $y = 0{\cdot}4$, then B will pay A the sum of $\frac{1{\cdot}5 - 0{\cdot}4}{1{\cdot}5 + 0{\cdot}4} = 0{\cdot}579$.

If the players have a large number of turns at their disposal, a strategy of A can present itself under the form of a function of x for A which will be such that, in calling $f_1(x)$:

$$f_1(-\infty) = 0,$$
$$f_1(+\infty) = 0,$$

with a surface of unit area included between the curve of $f_1(x)$ and the axis OX (figure 31·6). In the same way a function $f_2(y)$ having the same properties will constitute a strategy of B.

The search for the functions $f_1(x)$ and $f_2(y)$ in a continuous game with two persons and a zero sum, so that they form a maximin strategy for A and a minimax strategy for B, requires rather complex calculations with which we cannot deal here. The continuous game with n persons presents great mathematical difficulties and is the subject of important research.

The problems of economic competition and the problems of military operations are in fact infinitely more complex games of strategy with hundreds of variables of state and decision, some discrete and others continuous in a permanently developing system.

The theory of games with n persons and a zero sum represents, for the economist and the military strategist, more an attitude of mind than the working out of an optimal strategy according to a criterion. It is from this theory, dating back no more than thirty years, that the study of balance in action can be envisaged. When the means of calculation by computers and by new machines which will take their place for highly combinatorial problems, are sufficient, it will become possible to deal with models much nearer reality and we shall then discover what astonishing modifications these new possibilities will have brought into men's lives.

In fact life in society is a game with n persons for each one of us. Happiness is perhaps nothing more than a state of balance in a game with n persons, the structure of which is continually being modified.

6 The sequential processes of decision

32 Introduction

In this chapter we shall examine the processes of sequential optimisation known by the name of Dynamic Programming. These methods have become more and more important, not only in economic studies and business management, but also in problems arising from the movement of manned and unmanned spacecraft. We are thus brought back, via another route, to the 'calculus of variations', the first examples of which were given by Huyghens, and subsequent examples by Rayleigh, Hamilton and Lagrange. More recently Bellman in the USA and Pontryagin in the USSR have introduced a fundamental principle for this kind of problem: 'The principle of optimality' which is now used in most of the algorithms for sequential optimisation.

The sequential processes of decision lead to processes of adaptation and/or learning, which give a particularly faithful reflection of human behaviour in an evolutionary milieu. The evolution of the situations in which a man of action in our own times may find himself can be compared to the trajectory of a machine or of a physical system in a suitable space: though the equations may be different, various principles remain the same. We thus become involved in the work of the cyberneticians, whose interest is in systems where information and control figure. Although the variables considered in these methods can take their values in domains belonging to finite or infinite sets, the examples chosen here will still be such that the states will be in finite number.

33 Deterministic and sequential methods of decision

I am now going to describe a game in which neither chance nor uncertainty occurs. The reader is asked to choose a letter six times in succession from the set (A, B, C, D, E). Having chosen a letter on date (0) he receives a certain sum of money as indicated in column (0) of figure 33·1. Thus, if he chooses B, he receives 2. On date (1) he must choose a new letter but he has been told *in advance*

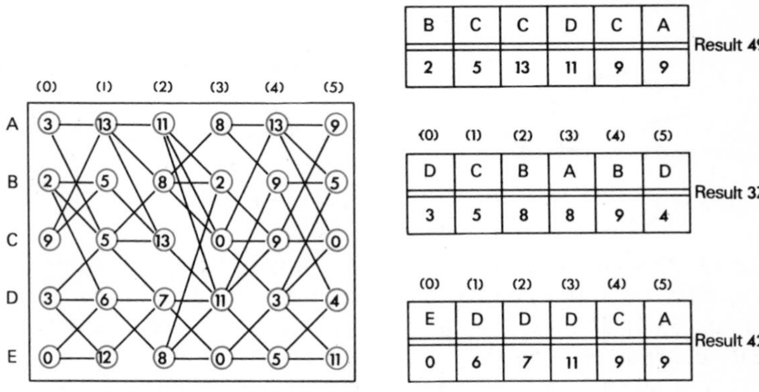

(0)	(1)	(2)	(3)	(4)	(5)	
B	C	C	D	C	A	Result 49
2	5	13	11	9	9	

(0)	(1)	(2)	(3)	(4)	(5)	
D	C	B	A	B	D	Result 37
3	5	8	8	9	4	

(0)	(1)	(2)	(3)	(4)	(5)	
E	D	D	D	C	A	Result 42
0	6	7	11	9	9	

Figure 33·1

Figure 33·2

which letters he can now make his choice from. Figure 33·1 shows him what are the possible choices, and he now receives a certain sum. Thus, since on date (0) the reader was in *B*, he has a choice between *B*, *C* and *D* on date (1); and if he chooses *C* he collects 5. On date (2) he makes another choice and so on. Finally he receives *in toto* the sum of the numbers placed on the path he has chosen.

This game is a deterministic and sequential process of decision. A sequence of decisions given beforehand, satisfying the rules of the game is called a 'policy'.

In figure 33·2 we have shown a few such policies and their respective results.

Such processes can be found in many deterministic problems of decision. Thus the research on the possible routes for a road and the final choice of a route occur in this way (figure 33·3). The choice of certain investments which will follow one another year after year, after a suitable interval of anticipation, has this same structure; the choice of a trajectory for a space capsule made to reach Mars from Earth is made from a sequential process of this

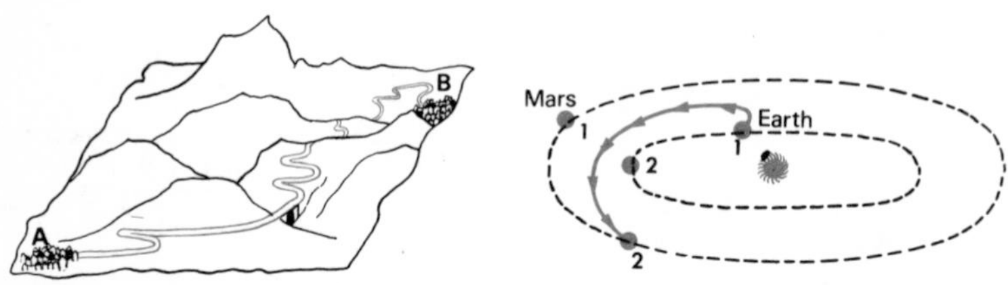

Figure 33·3

Figure 33·4

kind but, of course, according to a continuous variation, although decisions on radio control might be taken at determined dates (figure 33·4). Finally, any problem in which the state at a certain date depends only on the state at the preceding date and on the decision taken, constitutes a deterministic and sequential process of decision; provided, of course, that the decision-maker knows beforehand all the choices open to him and the values which may correspond to them. A more complex deterministic process can be considered if the state, at a certain date, depends on states and decisions at several preceding dates rather than the immediately preceding one only. Such processes are often called 'ordinal deterministic processes of decision'. The deterministic game of figure 33·5 gives an example of such a process. The policy (*A*, . . *A*, . . *D*) gives a result equal to 24. The policy (*C*, *D*, C, . . *B*) gives 30. Such processes are encountered in certain analyses of economic problems, for instance, if the cumulative effects of advertising are considered. But the ordinal process then assumes a different aspect from the game of figure 33·5 although this structure could be put into the same category as sequential phenomena.

34 The Bellman-Pontryagin theorem of optimality

In studying sequential decision processes, we are rarely satisfied with the mere descriptive aspects of policies or possible trajectories. A criterion is introduced and the analysis develops into a normative rather than a descriptive one. A theorem due to Bellman[81] and

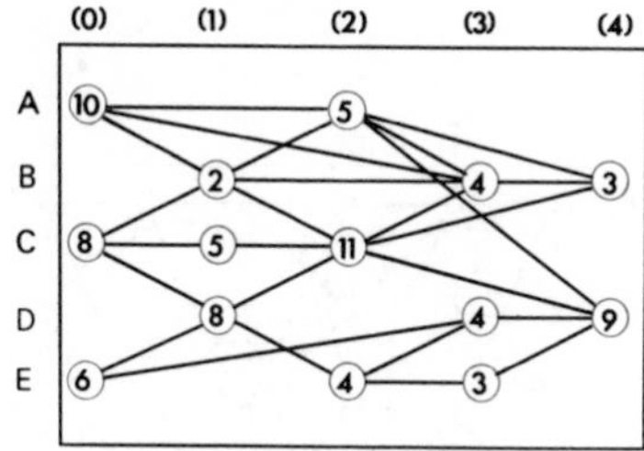

Figure 33·5

Pontryagin[88] plays a vital part in the search for the optimal policy or policies of a deterministic and sequential process of decision. We shall present this theorem in a slightly modified form to make it more intelligible. We shall refer to a sequence of contiguous or continuous decisions belonging to a policy or a trajectory as a sub-policy or sub-trajectory. Then this very simple theorem can be stated as follows: *An optimal policy can be formed only from optimal sub-policies.*

To demonstrate this theorem, so simple as to be considered a truism by some, let us turn to the case which deals with a trajectory on a three-dimensional surface in space (figure 34·1). Let us suppose that the trajectory A, M, P, N, B is optimal between A and B. Let us take a sub-trajectory M, P, N – the sub-trajectory belonging to A, M, P, N, B – which must be optimal between M and N. Indeed if we suppose there is a better trajectory, for instance M, Q, N, then it is through this sub-trajectory that the optimal trajectory between A and B would pass, and this is contrary to the hypothesis.

We shall apply this theorem to the game of figure 33·1. On date (1), for each state, i.e. for each letter, the path of maximal value will be estimated. Thus in A we shall compare (A, A) which gives $3 + 13 = 16$, with (C, A) which gives $9 + 13 = 22$. We shall then put the maximum up to 22 under the position A on date (1). In B, we shall compare (B, B) with (C, B) and we shall write 14; in C we shall compare (A, C), (B, C) and (D, C) and we shall write 8; in D we shall write 9; in E we shall write 15. On date (2), for each state, we shall estimate the path of maximal value – it

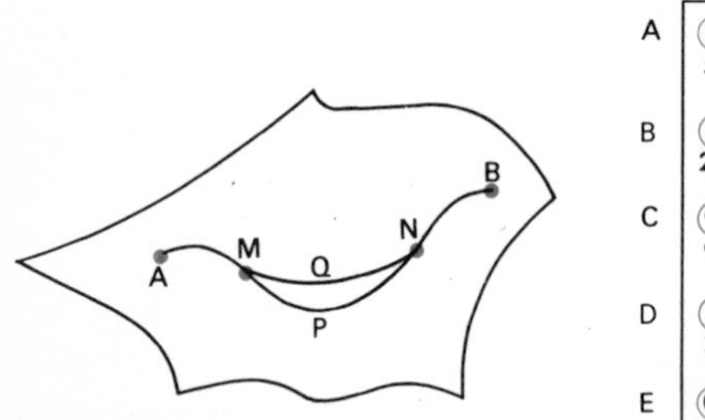

Figure 34·1

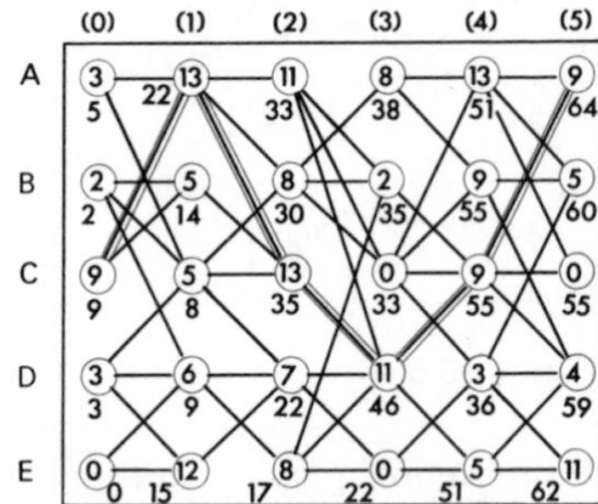

Figure 34·2

will then be enough to add to the maximal values estimated in date (1) the values written in the circles on date (2), this under the terms of the theorem of optimality (an optimal policy can be formed only by maximal sub-policies). There is no point, therefore, in going back to date (0). We shall write in this way in A: 33, in B: 30, in C: 35, in D: 22, in E: 17, and we shall carry on until date (5) where we shall find in A: 64, B: 60, C: 55, D: 59, E: 62. The result from these elementary calculations is that the optimal policy gives 64. To obtain the policy itself, it will be enough to go back from date (5) to date (4), then (3), (2), (1) and (0) and to examine which decisions have given a total result equal to 64 (figure 34·2). For instance, since on date (5) we are to be in A with 64, where had we to be on date (4)? $64 - 9 = 55$. Therefore we had to be in C. On (4) we have $55 - 9 = 46$. Therefore on (3) we had to be in D. On (3) $46 - 11 = 35$, therefore on (2) we had to be in C, and so on. Finally the path or trajectory corresponding to the optimal policy (figure 34·3) is represented by thick lines on figure 34·2. We note that, in other cases, there can be more than one optimal policy. We note also that the optimisation has been carried from the past into the future, but could, in the present example, just as well be taken from the future to the past – the same optimal policy would be found.

0	1	2	3	4	5
C	A	C	D	C	A
9	13	13	11	9	9

Result: 64

Figure 34·3

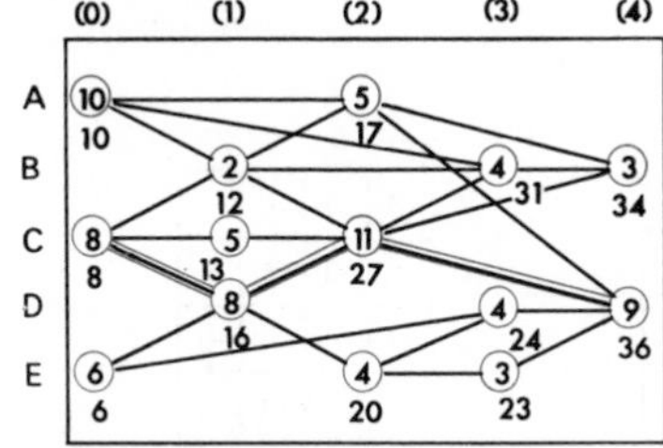

Figure 34·4

The process used is extended without any difficulty into an ordinal process (figure 33·5) of optimisation as presented in figure 34·4. The reader may wish to practise on the examples given in figure 33·1 and figure 33·5 to find policies giving the minimal value or values.

35 Random and sequential decision processes

Once again I shall use the form of a game to present an example which permits a sufficiently general introduction of the idea of random and sequential decisions processes.

We have four wheels of fortune representing the known effects of chance (figure 35·1). The rules of the game are as follows. At the beginning of the first turn we have one of the positions *A*, *B*, *C* or *D*. This position is given to the player. He then decides, according to the relationships given in figures 35·4 and 35·7, whether or not to change to another wheel, paying the appropriate amount. For instance, let us suppose that if at the beginning of the first turn he is in *C*, he can choose to change to *A* and pay 4, or change to *D* and pay 2. Once this choice is made, chance intervenes, as the player spins the selected wheel. This wheel will give him a new position, with a probability indicated on the wheel or by means

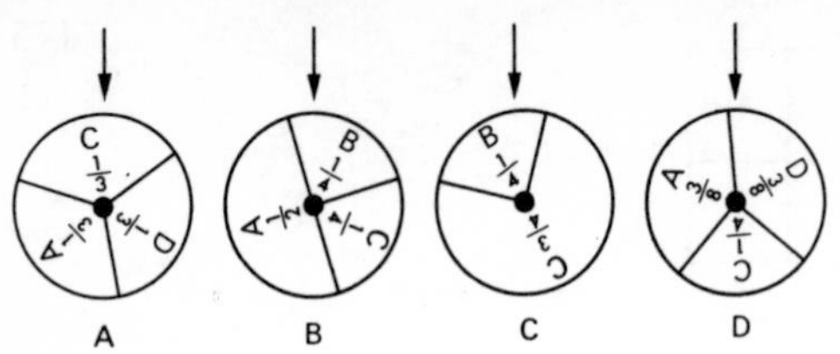

Figure 35·1

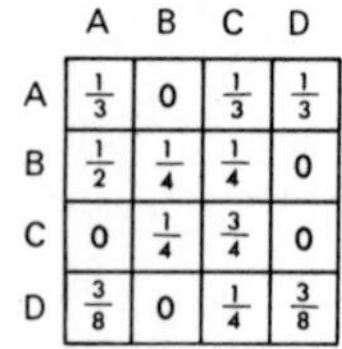

	A	B	C	D
A	$\frac{1}{3}$	0	$\frac{1}{3}$	$\frac{1}{3}$
B	$\frac{1}{2}$	$\frac{1}{4}$	$\frac{1}{4}$	0
C	0	$\frac{1}{4}$	$\frac{3}{4}$	0
D	$\frac{3}{8}$	0	$\frac{1}{4}$	$\frac{3}{8}$

Figure 35·2 probabilities of transition.

	A	B	C	D
A	5	·	10	2
B	9	8	4	·
C	·	5	3	·
D	2	·	3	5

Figure 35·3 values of transitions due to chance.

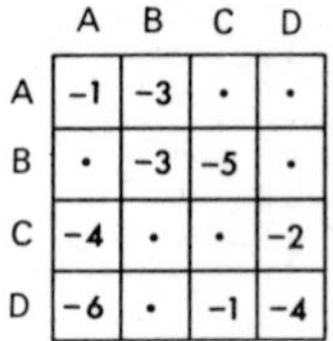

	A	B	C	D
A	−1	−3	·	·
B	·	−3	−5	·
C	−4	·	·	−2
D	−6	·	−1	−4

Figure 35·4 values of transition due to decisions.

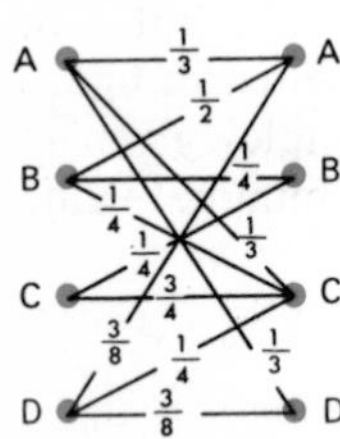

Figure 35·5 Alternative presentation of figure 35·2.

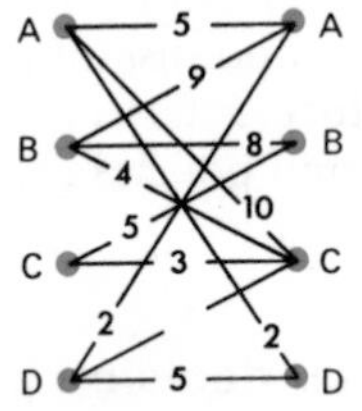

Figure 35·6 alternative presentation of figure 35·3.

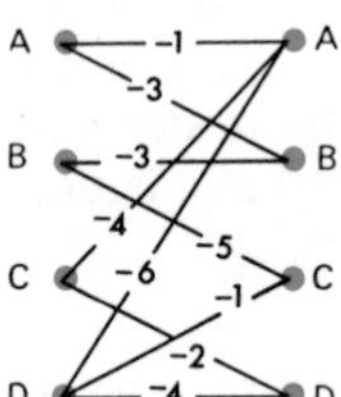

Figure 35·7 alternative presentation of figure 35·4.

of the other representations given in figures 35·2 and 35·5. He then receives a sum indicated by figures 35·3 and 35·6. Thus, for instance, if the decision of the player put him in *A*, chance can keep him at *A* with a probability of $\frac{1}{3}$ and a gain of 5, to *C* with a probability of $\frac{1}{3}$ and a gain of 10, or to *D* with a probability of $\frac{1}{3}$ and a gain of 2.

He then starts a second turn in the same conditions, then a third turn. Three turns taken in this manner make up a game;

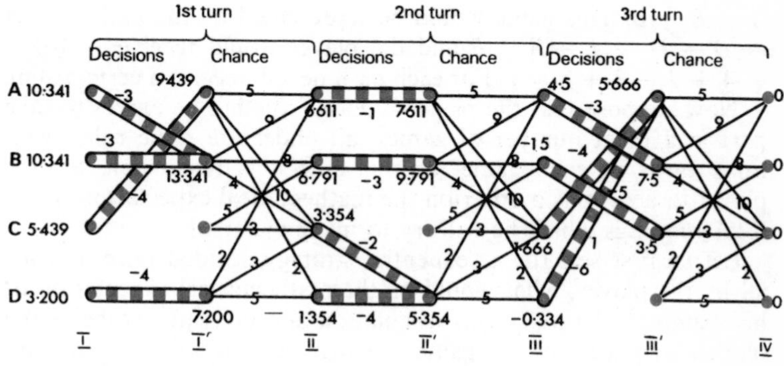

Figure 35·8

Position at the time of decision	Decisions 1st turn	Decisions 2nd turn	Decisions 3rd turn
A	B	A	B
B	B	B	C
C	A	D	A
D	D	D	A

Figure 35·9

at the end of the game or as the turns are being taken, the player pays out and receives the sums indicated.

In the face of chance, the player will take a 'sequential strategy'. It will be presented in the form of decision sequences, taking into account the states in which chance and, initially, an external will may have put the player. Figure 35·8 represents a possible sequential strategy (thick dotted lines). This strategy has been shewn in a different form in figure 35·9. Suppose that the game has gone like this: 1st turn: $C \rightarrow A \rightarrow D$, 2nd turn $D \rightarrow D \rightarrow A$, 3rd turn

$A \to B \to B$. This game would be represented by the path $C \to A \to D \to D \to A \to B \to B$ and the player would receive $-4+2-4+2-3+8=1$. For each path he will receive a certain sum.

Now suppose that the player is asked whether he agrees to take part in a great number of games, all under the same rules, with three turns in each game. In this case it is reasonable for the player to accept as a criterion the mathematical expectation of the total winnings which he will try to make maximal.

Let us first see, for a sequential strategy decided once and for all by the player, what would be the mathematical expectation of his winnings. To make this calculation and take advantage of the sequential nature of the game – which can considerably simplify the calculations – we shall start with the third turn and go back to the second and then to the first; otherwise we would have to consider all the possible paths and calculate their probability and their winnings. To see how we work out such calculations, we shall use an example of strategy. Suppose that the player has decided once and for all to take the sequential strategy indicated in figure 35·8 or 35·9. Let us call I, I′, II, II′, III, III′, IV, certain dates shown in figure 35·8. If the player is in A on III′, the mathematical expectation of his winnings will be: $(5)\left(\frac{1}{3}\right)+(10)\left(\frac{1}{3}\right)+(2)\left(\frac{1}{3}\right)$ $=5{\cdot}666$; if he is in B, this expectation will be: $(9)\left(\frac{1}{2}\right)+(8)\left(\frac{1}{4}\right)$ $+(4)\left(\frac{1}{4}\right)=7{\cdot}5$; if he is in C it will be: $(5)\left(\frac{1}{4}\right)+(3)\left(\frac{3}{4}\right)=$ $3{\cdot}5$; if he is in D it will be: $(2)\left(\frac{3}{8}\right)+(3)\left(\frac{1}{4}\right)+(5)\left(\frac{3}{8}\right)=3{\cdot}375$.

When the player is on III and in A, according to his decision, he wins: $7{\cdot}5-3=4{\cdot}5$; in B he wins $3{\cdot}5-5=-1{\cdot}5$; in C he wins $5{\cdot}666-4=1{\cdot}666$; in D he wins $5{\cdot}666-6=-0{\cdot}333$. Now, if the player is in A on II′ what is the mathematical expectation of his profit *if on the third turn he has chosen the strategy under consideration*? This expectation is $(5+4{\cdot}5)\left(\frac{1}{3}\right)+(10+$

1·666) $\left(\frac{1}{3}\right)$ + (2 − 0·333) $\left(\frac{1}{3}\right)$ = 7·611. In the same way if he is in *B*, it will be (9 + 4·5) $\left(\frac{1}{2}\right)$ + (8 − 1·5) $\left(\frac{1}{4}\right)$ + (4 + 1·666) $\left(\frac{1}{4}\right)$ = 9·791; we calculate in the same way the values corresponding to *C* and *D*. Now, according to the decision chosen in advance for the second turn, the player will receive: in *A*: 7·611 − 1 = 6·611, in *B*: 9·791 − 3 = 6·791, in *C*: 5·354 − 2 = 3·354, in *D*: 5·354 − 4 = 1·354. He will do the same for dates I′ and I so as to find finally: 10·341 if the player is in *A* on date I; 10·341 if he is in *B*; 5·439 if he is in *C*; 3·200 if he is in *D*. These numbers represent the mathematical expectation of the winnings for each starting position of the chosen sequential strategy.

Now how can we obtain the optimal strategy or strategies, the criterion being the maximisation of the mathematical expectation of the total winnings over *n* games (*n* being sufficiently large to give this mathematical expectation some significance)? We shall for this purpose use Bellman and Pontryagin's theorem of optimality, but first we must make the following observation: When at a certain date a mathematical expectation has been estimated, the future is considered *as a value* as determined for what follows, and this expectation, evaluated and known, is all that is taken into account. The optimisation will necessarily have to be made from the future towards the present. In figure 35·10 we show the calculations in detail. We have seen that in III′ the mathematical expectations were, respectively 5·666, 7·5, 3·5, 3·375. If the player is in *A* on date III, what is his best decision? If he goes to *A*, he will receive 5·666 − 1 = 4·666. If he goes to *B* he will receive 7·5 − 3 = 4·5. He will naturally choose to go to *A*. If the player is in *B* he can choose between 7·5 − 3 = 4·5 and 3·5 − 5 = −1·5. He will therefore go to *B*. If the player is in *C* he can choose between 5·666 − 4 = 1·666 and 3·375 − 2 = 1·375. He will then choose *A*. If the player is in *D* he has the choice between 5·666 − 6 = −0·334, 3·5 − 1 = 2·5 and 3·375 − 4 = −0·625, and

Figure 35·10

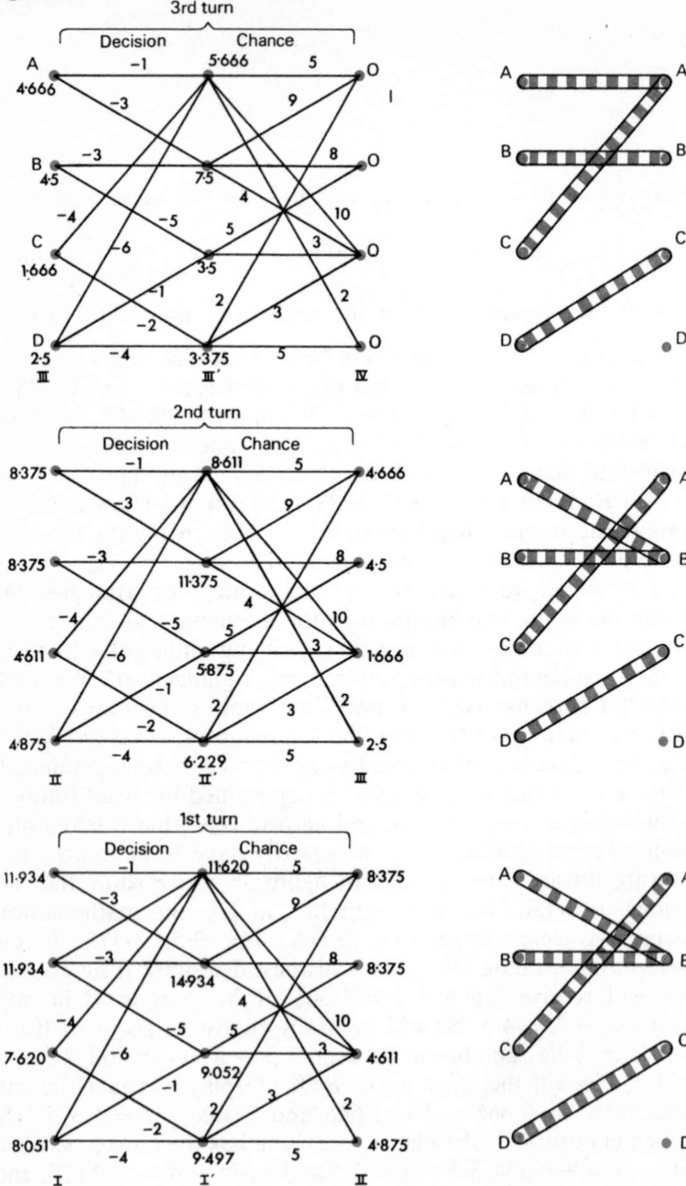

3rd turn
Decision
Chance
A
4·666
–1
5·666
5
O
–3
9
I
B
–3
4·5
7·5
8
O
4
10
–4
–5
5
C
3
1·666
–6
3·5
O
–1
2
2
D
–2
3
2·5
–4
3·375
5
O
III
III′
IV
2nd turn
Decision
Chance
8·375
–1
8·611
5
4·666
–3
9
8·375
–3
11·375
8
4·5
4
10
–4
–5
5
4·611
–6
5·875
3
1·666
–1
2
2
–2
3
4·875
–4
6·229
5
2·5
II
II′
III
1st turn
Decision
Chance
11·934
–1
11·620
5
8·375
–3
9
11·934
–3
14·934
8
8·375
4
10
–4
–5
5
7·620
–6
9·052
3
4·611
–1
2
2
–2
3
8·051
–4
9·497
5
4·875
I
I′
II
A
A
B
B
C
C
D
D
A
A
B
B
C
C
D
D
A
A
B
B
C
C
D
D

Position at the decision time	1st turn	2nd turn	3rd turn
A	B	B	A
B	B	B	B
C	A	A	A
D	C	C	C

Figure 35·11

he will therefore choose to go to *C*. These decisions are shown by the thick dotted lines.

Let us examine now the second turn. Calculate the mathematical expectation in II′. In *A*: $(5 + 4{\cdot}666)\left(\frac{1}{3}\right) + (10 + 1{\cdot}666)\left(\frac{1}{3}\right) + (2 + 2{\cdot}5)\left(\frac{1}{3}\right) = 8{\cdot}611$; in *B*: $(9 + 4{\cdot}666)\left(\frac{1}{2}\right) + (8 + 4{\cdot}5)\left(\frac{1}{4}\right) + (4 + 1{\cdot}666)\left(\frac{1}{4}\right) = 11{\cdot}375$; in *C*: $(5 + 4{\cdot}5)\left(\frac{1}{4}\right) + (3 + 1{\cdot}666)\left(\frac{3}{4}\right) = 5{\cdot}875$; in *D*: $(2 + 4{\cdot}666)\left(\frac{3}{8}\right) + (3 + 1{\cdot}666)\left(\frac{1}{4}\right) + (5 + 2{\cdot}5)\left(\frac{3}{8}\right) = 6{\cdot}478$.

If the player is in *A* on II, his best decision is *B*, for which he will receive 8·374; in *B* it would be *B* with 8·375; in *C* it would be *A* with 4·611; in *D* it would be *C* with 4·875. We shall operate in the same way for the first turn and finally we shall have the optimal sequential strategy shown in figure 35·10. Starting point in *A*: 11·934. Starting point in *B*: 11·934. Starting point in *C*: 7·620. Starting point in $D = 8{\cdot}052$. In certain cases the optimal strategy (or strategies) does not appear as a sequence of decisions repeating themselves identically from a certain future date towards the present but causes a cyclic effect to appear.

Games of this kind can be found in problems of stocks (costs of restocking, uncertainties of demand, receipts from sales, research

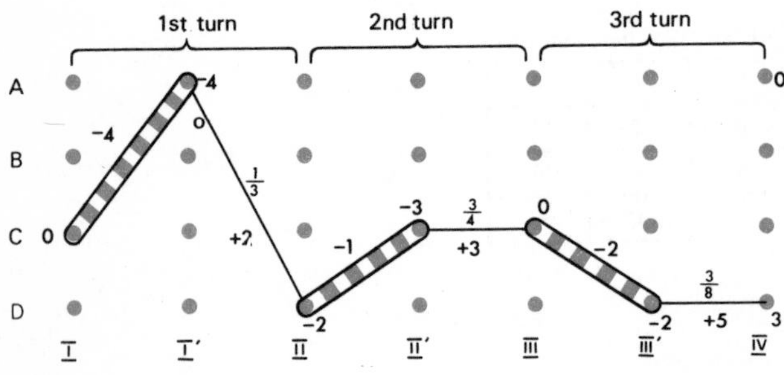

Figure 35·12

into maximal mathematical expectation of profit) in problems of investment, of plant management, which are in fact games against nature, with statistical information. Some of these problems present a non-stationary aspect. They are often seasonal, and the tables given in figures 35·2, 35·3 and 35·4 can change with the dates. But the method remains exactly the same.

If we are faced with a problem in which the number of repeated games is not large – if the game is a single one, even – what criterion can we then suggest? The problem is appreciably more complex and we can only deal with it briefly here, while referring the reader to [5].

What is the law of probability of the profit corresponding to each sequential strategy, for a given starting-point? Suppose that we know this set of laws and the criterion is to choose the sequential strategy for which the probability of winning at least a certain sum is maximal (in another problem it would be the sequential strategy for which the probability of losing at least a certain sum would be minimal). Granted that it requires the set of all the strategies to be known; this set may hold an enormous number of factors. Even a problem as simple as the one constituted by the game stated in this paragraph has a very high number of possible sequential strategies – their enumeration alone can present a considerable problem. In real problems of human action, the possible sequential strategies generally form a set with an astronomical number of factors, and the help of powerful computers is needed for their enumeration and for the corresponding calculations. For certain problems conversion to continuous variables sometimes enables them to be solved electronically, but cases of a combinatorial character, though they are easy enough to state, are sometimes still beyond the possibilities of present-day machines. Nevertheless, new machines – specifically designed to deal with combinatorial problems whose construction we are only just beginning to grasp – will certainly allow us to tackle this kind of difficulty in the near future.

I have reproduced in figure 35·12 the history of a game dealt with in this paragraph. For this path the total winnings are 3.

36 Sequential methods of decision under uncertainty

Let us examine first the case of a sequential duel between two opponents *A* and *B*, by taking an easy example. Suppose that *A* and *B* can choose a colour: violet (*V*) or red (*R*). On date I the player *A* can be in *R* or in *V* and this position is fixed at the beginning of the game (figure 36·1). On this date *A* chooses to go to *R* or *V* with certain winnings (figure 36·1). On date II, *B*, not knowing what *A* has chosen, chooses *R* or *V* with certain losses. On date III, *A* chooses *R* or *V* not knowing the choice of *B* on date II. He collects certain winnings. At the end of the game, the total winnings are evaluated. It is easy to reduce this game to a rectangular one as shown by figure 36·2 if *A* begins with *R* and by figure 36·3 if *A* begins with *V*. As far as the choice of *A* is concerned, the notation *R*,*R* means: *A* chooses *R* on date I and *R* on date III; *R*,*V* means *A* chooses *R* on date I and *V* on date III, etc. A quick calculation shows that for the game in figure 36·2 the maximin strategy of *A* is to choose *R*,*R* 7 times, and *R*,*V* 9 times, out of 16. The minimax strategy of *B* is to choose *R* 7 times and *V* 9 times out of 16, the value of the game being 10·06. The value of the game in figure 36·3 is 12·5.

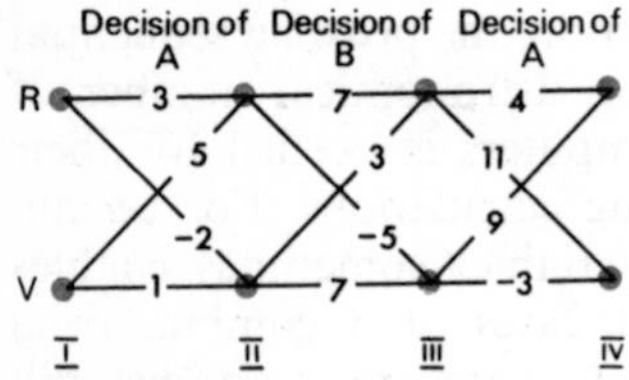

Figure 36·1

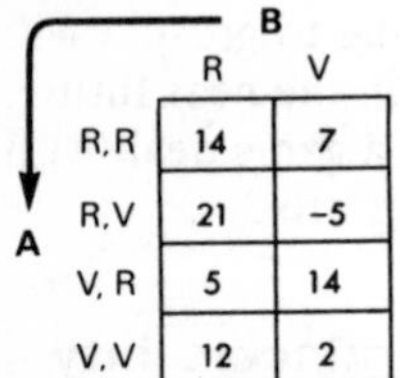

A \ B	R	V
R, R	14	7
R, V	21	−5
V, R	5	14
V, V	12	2

Initial position of A: R

Figure 36·2

A \ B	R	V
R, R	16	9
R, V	23	−3
V, R	8	17
V, V	15	5

Initial position of A: V

Figure 36·3

B \ A	R/R, R/V	R/R, V/V	V/R, R/V	V/R V/V
R; R/R, R/V	14	14	7	7
R; R/R, V/V	14	14	−5	−5
R; V/R, R/V	21	21	7	7
R; V/R, V/V	21	21	−5	−5
V; R/R, R/V	5	14	5	14
V; R/R, V/V	5	2	5	2
V; V/R, R/V	12	14	(12)	14
V; V/R, V/V	12	2	12	2

Initial position of A: R

Figure 36·4

B \ A	R/R, R/V	R/R, V/V	V/R, R/V	V/R V/V
R; R/R, R/V	16	16	9	9
R; R/R, V/V	16	16	−3	−3
R; V/R, R/V	23	23	9	9
R; V/R, V/V	23	23	−3	−3
V; R/R, R/V	8	17	8	17
V; R/R, V/V	8	5	8	5
V; V/R, R/V	15	17	(15)	17
V; V/R, V/V	15	5	15	5

Initial position of A: V

Figure 36·5

The sequential game we have just considered is totally without information Let us now modify the rules of the game: in II *B* knows the choice of *A*, in III *A* knows the choice of *B* in II. This time the sequential game is one with complete information. The decision of *A* or of *B* will be conditional; for *B* to choose *Y* in II if *A* has chosen *Z* in I, or to choose *u* in II if *A* has chosen *A* in I, will be written Y/Z, u/t; for *A* to choose *X* in I, then to choose *Y* in III if *B* has chosen *Z* in II, or to choose *u* in III if *B* has chosen *t* in II, will be written *X*; Y/Z, u/t; all the considered variables *X*, *Y*, *Z*, *u*, *t* can take the states *R* or *V*. This is complex and could become even more so if the number of states and/or of turns was higher, but it is in the very nature of these sequential games with complete information to possess a very great combinatorial complexity. Nevertheless, it can be shown that a rectangular game with complete information always possesses one or several saddle points. Thus in the example that we are now studying, the best strategy of *A* if he moves to *R* is *V*; V/R, R/V. In this case, he is certain to receive at least 12 and the best strategy of *B* for this game is V/R, R/V, in which case *B* is certain not to give more than 12. For the other game (*A* moving to *V*) the optimal strategies are the same but the value of the game is 15.

Chess and draughts are games with complete information. The definition of decision sequences of each of these games is still outside the scope of combinatorial analysis except for the last moves of a game, but progress in this domain of mathematics is considerable and, furthermore, computers and adaptive combinatorial machines have ever-increasing possibilities of dealing with the problem. Scientists who are interested in this field think that in a few years' time it will be possible to enumerate and find the conditional decisions and optimal strategies for a very large number of successive moves. It will then be possible to build an automatic chess or draughts player, or to transform the art of playing into a science.

We can envisage games with incomplete information. Thus in the example in figure 36·1, if we suppose that *A* has no information

	R/R, R/V	R/R, V/V	V/R, R/V	V/R V/V
R,R	14	14	7	7
R,V	21	21	−5	−5
V,R	5	14	5	14
V,V	12	2	12	2

Initial position of A:R

Figure 36·6

	R/R, R/V	R/R, V/V	V/R, R/V	V/R V/V
R,R	16	16	9	9
R,V	23	23	−3	−3
V,R	8	17	8	17
V,V	15	5	15	5

Initial position of B:V

Figure 36·7

but that *B* knows in II the choice of *A* in I, we have a new rectangular game without a saddle point (in a game with incomplete information, we either meet or do not meet a saddle point) which, according to the case is given by figure 36·6 or figure 36·7.

Important theorems have been demonstrated (see references [74] and [75] for example) about the influence of information on the value of the game; in particular, we can show that the information favourable to player *A* (maximin criterion) might increase the value of the game, whereas information favourable to *B* (minimax criterion) might decrease it.

We can also consider more complex sequential games, where *A* and/or *B* choose values (or even sets of values) at different given intervals, at given dates or, to complicate the situation still further, continuously in time. If we could describe the mathematical model of a fencing match or a judo encounter, we should have a sequential game with information (total or partial) continuous in time and space. Games of strategy or of military tactics (war games, etc.) have, however, been constructed with an educational purpose, for military staffs (see section 45).

Case dealing with a combat against Nature. A sequential game between a player and nature (figure 36·8) can now be easily imagined. Let us suppose that the states in which the phenomenon under consideration can be found, on each date where either player or nature intervene, are known; if there is a finite number of these states we shall be able to put this game into rectangular form. We shall then have to deal with the important problem of selecting a criterion (see section 30).

Other more complex sequential games can be imagined. For instance, two players and chance (figure 36·9), three players (figure 36·10); two players, a phase of risk and a phase of un-

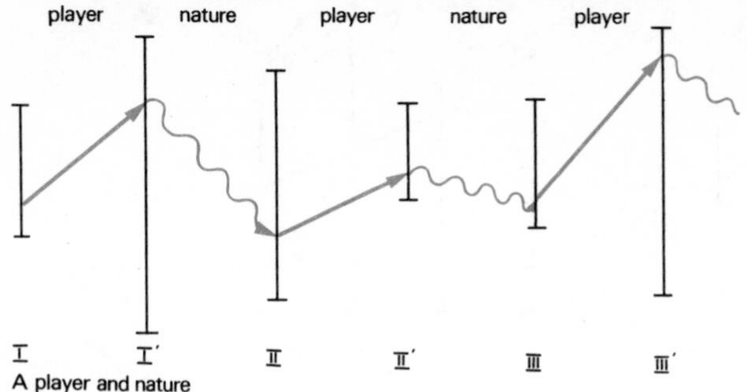

Figure 36·8

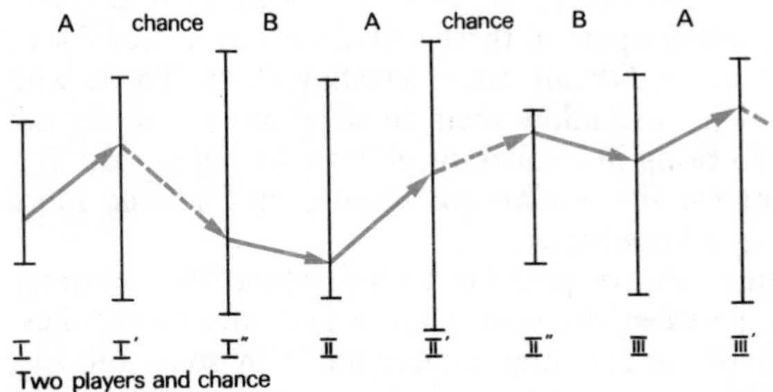

Figure 36·9

certainty, etc. In all these models the available information – which can often be presented in the form of a very complex structure – must be taken into account and it may completely change the aspect of the sequential game.

We know that in this way we can get nearer to real cases of human action where decision-makers (allies, opponents, neutrals, even waverers), where hazards and uncertainties (structured or not) intervene in a continuous and/or discrete way.

At present we do not know how to build acceptable models of these situations, in spite of the powerful range and ability of computers. The problems are astronomically combinatorial; we are now satisfied with being able to build a few models of very simple cases. But tomorrow, perhaps in a year or two, these problems will be easier to deal with by praxeological calculation.

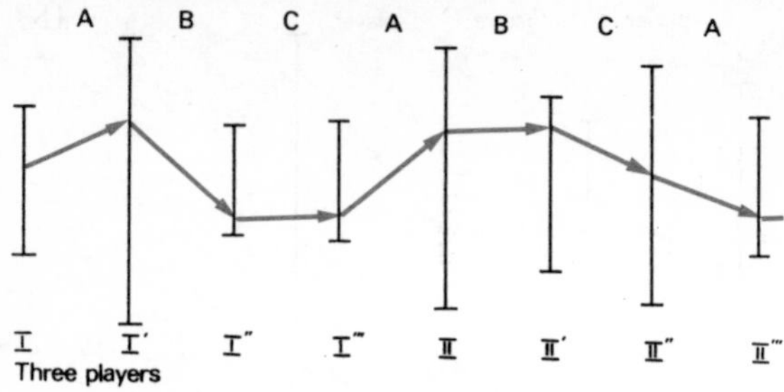

Figure 36·10

Nevertheless, many more factors will have to be added to the models and there will still be plenty of scope for intuitive decision – indeed, in my humble opinion, there will always be a need for it, and in more and more difficult but interesting cases. Those who think that praxeology will allow them to sleep more soundly are sadly mistaken. To bring in a touch of philosophy, let us add that what is important for the human condition is not solving more easily but knowing a little better.

Finally, it is not always possible to see where the arbitrary separation made between decision, chance and uncertainty lies: such temporal divisions are often unacceptable in some models, because the benefit of sequential description in the representations built is then lost. This last difficulty is generally the most frequent and most awkward to overcome.

By their very nature, certain phenomena require models, no longer sequential but ordinal; the state of nature at a certain date depending not only on the state on the immediately preceding date but on the states on all or certain previous dates. Thus the effect of advertising is a cumulative effect, with a weakening of the past toward the future, just as it is, more generally speaking, in education and all the forms in which information makes its imprint on the mind. I shall return to this question a little later.

37 Statistical exploration of nature

Shortly before the beginning of the selling season, the managing director of a firm with several selling points, is engaged in putting two variations of the same product *P*, say P_1 and P_2 on the market. He does not know the tastes of his clientele and can stock only one of these varieties because of existing contracts with one or other of the manufacturers. He would very much like to know whether the majority of his customers prefer P_1 or P_2. In practice he should ask himself this question, in the following form: is it 100 per cent of P_1 and 0 per cent of P_2, 90 per cent of P_1 and 10 per cent of P_2, 80 per cent of P_1 and 20 per cent of P_2 etc?. This would give him eleven states of nature.

We could also imagine a more subtle analysis, with a far greater number of states of nature. To avoid becoming enmeshed in complicated calculations, we shall suppose that the clientele is made up of 120 customers per selling point, and two possible states of nature:

E_1: 80 preferring P_1, 40 preferring P_2
E_2: 40 preferring P_1, 80 preferring P_2

But the managing director does not know which *is* the state of nature. Let us suppose that the following very simple commercial conditions obtain:

Every time a product P_1 is sold, the profit is 5
Every time a product P_1 is unsold, the loss is 3
Every time a product P_2 is sold, the profit is 4
Every time a product P_2 is unsold, the loss is 1

Let us see what the situations are in which the industrialist can find himself:

He decides to stock 80 P_1 and the state of nature is E_1. He will gain $80 \times 5 = 400$. He will lose $0 \times 3 = 0$. Profit: $400 - 0 = 400$.

He decides to stock 80 P_1 and the state of nature is E_2. He will gain $40 \times 5 = 200$, he will lose $40 \times 3 = 120$. Profit: $200 - 120 = 80$.

He decides to stock 80 P_2 and the state of nature is E_1. He will gain $40 \times 4 = 160$. He will lose $40 \times 1 = 40$. Profit: $160 - 40 = 120$.

He decides to stock 80 P_2 and the state of nature is E_2. He will gain $80 \times 4 = 320$. He will lose $0 \times 2 = 0$. Profit: $320 - 0 = 320$.

Finally, in these conditions the industrialist puts himself in the situation of the game against nature given in figure 37·1. In reality, as has already been said, the number of separate hypotheses should be very much larger for problems of this kind, but then the game against nature would be much more complicated and we would be going beyond the limits that I have set for this book. The important thing is the manner of reasoning that is to be employed. I apologise for the somewhat over-simple appearance of this problem.

The industrialist, perplexed by the decision that has to be taken, calls in the services of a market research company. This organisation asks him for 10 monetary units for sampling one person in the population making up the clientele. Let us then suppose that the businessman chooses the following strategy S_1: if the sample gives a result of one person preferring P_1, he stocks P_1, if the sample gives one person preferring P_2, he stocks P_2. Facing the states E_1 and E_2, what are the profits which the businessman can expect, according to this strategy? If the state is E_1, there is a probability $p_1 = \frac{2}{3}$ that the sample will give a result of one person preferring P_1. The profit is then $400 - 10 = 390$; but there is a probability $p_2 = \frac{1}{3}$ that the sample will give one person preferring P_2, the profit is then $120 - 10 = 110$. In the case where the state of nature is E_1, this strategy leads to an average profit of

$$(390)\left(\frac{2}{3}\right) + (110)\left(\frac{1}{3}\right) = \frac{890}{3} = 296{\cdot}66 \qquad \text{[Equation 37.1]}$$

We suppose that, in the nature of the problem being considered, the mathematical expectation is significant, i.e. the selling points are in sufficient number, and that at each point, the law of demand is the same. In reality it would not be so, generally speaking, and we would then have to argue from more complex aspects, and that is what we want to avoid.

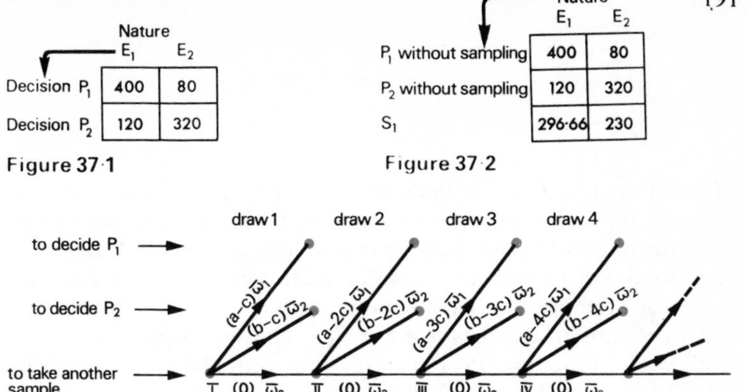

	Nature E_1	E_2
Decision P_1	400	80
Decision P_2	120	320

Figure 37·1

	Nature E_1	E_2
P_1 without sampling	400	80
P_2 without sampling	120	320
S_1	296·66	230

Figure 37·2

Figure 37·3

If the state is E_2, there is a probability $p_1 = \frac{1}{3}$, that the sample gives a result of one person preferring p_1, the profit is then: $80 - 10 = 70$, but there is a probability $p_2 = \frac{2}{3}$ that the sample will give a person preferring p_2, the profit will then be $320 - 10 = 310$. Thus, in the case of the state of nature being E_2, this strategy leads to an average profit of:

$$(70)\left(\frac{1}{3}\right) + (310)\left(\frac{2}{3}\right) = \frac{690}{3} = 230 \qquad \text{[Equation 37.2]}$$

Let us compare the results of this strategy with those obtained without market research. Figure 37·2, in which the various different results are entered, shows the advantage of such an investigation. Is it possible to carry out other types of investigation, again improving the average results? We can imagine an infinity of other types of samplings but we shall examine one, 'the sequential sampling' which is particularly interesting for this kind of problem.

Suppose that the sample and the decision taken enable us to describe the following strategy.

Sampling two persons in the population under consideration costs $2 \times 10 = 20$. If it gives (P_1, P_1) P_1 is stocked, if it gives (P_2, P_2) P_2 is stocked, if it gives (P_1, P_2) or (P_2, P_1) a new sample costing 20 is taken and we carry on in this manner until we obtain

(P_1, P_1) or (P_2, P_2). To determine the results of this sequential strategy we shall make a calculation which is a little more complex but which does not really go beyond an elementary level, where the idea used will be that of the differential coefficient of a function.

Let us suppose that each sample costs C and that the profit is a if P_1 is chosen, whereas it is b if P_2 is chosen. Suppose the probability of obtaining (P_1, P_1) is ω_1, the probability of obtaining (P_2, P_2) is ω_2 and the probability of obtaining (P_1, P_2) or (P_2, P_1) is ω_3; of course we have $\omega_1 \geqslant 0$, $\omega_2 \geqslant 0$, $\omega_3 \geqslant 0$ and $\omega_1 + \omega_2 + \omega_3 = 1$. On date I the decision can be: P_1 with a profit $(a-c)$ and a probability ω_1, P_2 with a profit $(b-c)$ and a probability ω_2, or to take a new sample with a probability ω_3. (The costs of sampling are deducted from the profits when a decision is reached, which is the reason why in figure 37·3 the horizontal arrows have zero values). On date II the decision can be: P_1 with a profit $(a-2c)$ and a probability ω_1, P_2 with a profit $(b-2c)$ and a probability ω_2 or we pass to date II with a probability ω_3; and so on with $(a-3c)$ and ω_1, $(b-3c)$ and ω_2, etc. The mathematical expectation $\bar{P}$ of the profit taking into account all possibilities is then:

$$\bar{P}: (a - c)\omega_1 + (b - c)\omega_2 + (a - 2c)\omega_3\omega_1 + (b - 2c)\omega_3\omega_1 + (a - 3c)\omega_3^2\omega_1 + (b - 3c)\omega_3^2\omega_2 + \ldots$$

$$= a\omega_1(1 + \omega_3 + \omega_3^2 + \ldots) + b\omega_2(1 + \omega_3 + \omega_3^2 + \ldots)$$

[Equation 37.3]

$$- c(\omega_1 + \omega_2)(1 + 2\omega_3 + 3\omega_3^2 + \ldots\ldots)$$

but since $0 \leqslant \omega_3 < 1$; $1 + \omega_3 + \omega_3^2 + \ldots =$

$$\frac{1}{1 - \omega_3} = \frac{1}{\omega_1 + \omega_2}$$ [Equation 37.4]

on the other hand:

$$1 + 2\omega_3 + 3\omega_3^2 + \ldots = \frac{d}{d\omega_3}(\omega_3 + \omega_3^2 + \omega_3^3 + \ldots)$$

$$= \frac{d}{d\omega_3}[\omega_3(1 + \omega_3 + \omega_3^2 + \ldots)]$$

$$= \frac{d}{d\omega_3}\left(\frac{\omega^3}{1-\omega_3}\right) = \frac{1}{(1-\omega_3)^2} = \frac{1}{(\omega_1+\omega_2)^2}$$ [Equation 37.5]

Substituting the results obtained in equations 37.4 and 37.5 into 37.3 we get:

$$\bar{P} = \frac{a\omega_1 + b\omega_2 - c}{\omega_1 + \omega_2}$$ [Equation 37.6]

Going back to our example, if the state is E_1, we have

Probability $(P_1, P_1) = \frac{2}{3} \times \frac{2}{3} = \frac{4}{9}$ (value of ω_1 in this case)

Probability (P_2, P_2) $\frac{1}{3} \times \frac{1}{3} = \frac{1}{9}$ (value of ω_2 in this case)

Probability (P_1, P_2) or $(P_2, P_1) =$
$\frac{2}{3} \times \frac{1}{3} + \frac{1}{3} \times \frac{2}{3} = \frac{4}{9}$ (value of ω_3 in this case)

[Equation 37.7]

If the state is E_2, we have:

Probability $(P_1, P_1) = \frac{1}{3} \times \frac{1}{3} = \frac{1}{9}$ (value of ω_1 in this case)

Probability $(P_2, P_2) = \frac{2}{3} \times \frac{2}{3} = \frac{4}{9}$ (value of ω_2 in this case)

Probability (P_1, P_2) or (P_2, P_1)
$= \frac{1}{3} \times \frac{2}{3} + \frac{2}{3} \times \frac{1}{3} = \frac{4}{9}$ (value of ω_3 in this case)

[Equation 37.8]

Let us now use the general formula (equation 37.6) which we have just calculated:

If the state is E_1, we have:

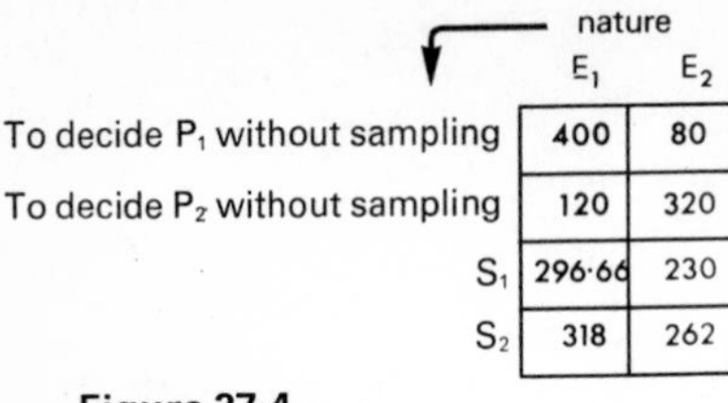

	E_1	E_2
To decide P_1 without sampling	400	80
To decide P_2 without sampling	120	320
S_1	296·66	230
S_2	318	262

Figure 37·4

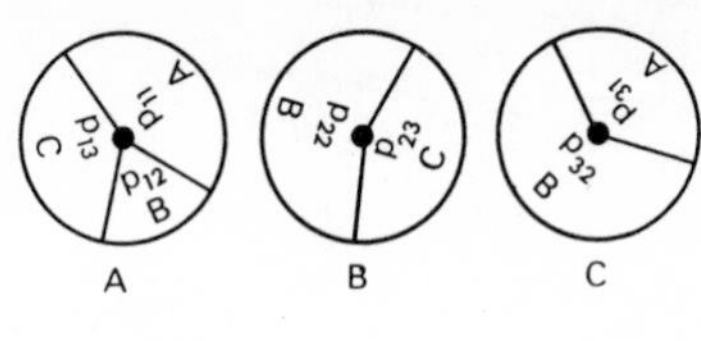

Figure 38·1

Mathematical expectation of profit:

$$\frac{(400)\left(\frac{4}{9}\right) + (80)\left(\frac{1}{9}\right) - 10}{\frac{4}{9} + \frac{1}{9}} = 318 \qquad \text{[Equation 37.9]}$$

If the state is E_2 we have:

Mathematical expectation of profit:

$$\frac{(120)\left(\frac{1}{9}\right) + (320)\left(\frac{4}{9}\right) - 10}{\frac{5}{9}} = 262 \qquad \text{[Equation 37.10]}$$

Compare the results of this sequential strategy which we shall call S_2, with the results given in figure 37·2. Figure 37·4 shows the progress of this strategy compared with the previous ones. In particular we see that the sequential strategy S_2 dominates S_1 and therefore is always preferable to it.

The process of decision used constitutes a way of exploring nature. We can, of course, imagine many others. This way of operating from sequential strategies is in use particularly in the theory and application of statistical quality control (SQC). These concepts are tending to be used more and more in sequential decision processes related to various spheres of human actions and particularly in those involving market research.

By means of this very simple example, I have tried to show the advantages of gathering information progressively.

Naturally, depending on the criterion chosen in a combat against nature, we can imagine various rules to stop the expenditure on

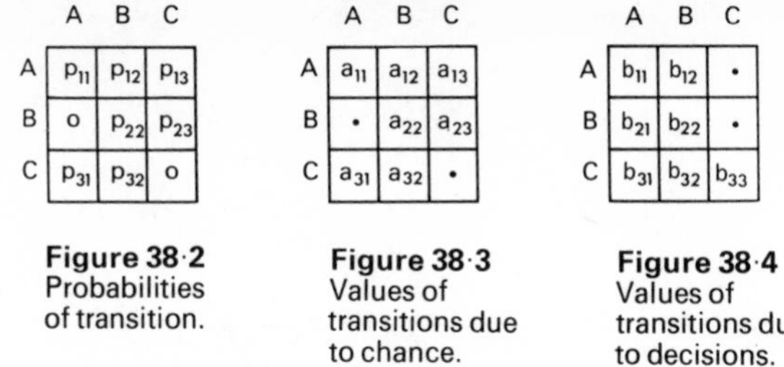

Figure 38·2 Probabilities of transition.

Figure 38·3 Values of transitions due to chance.

Figure 38·4 Values of transitions due to decisions.

exploration. For instance, let us suppose that the chosen criterion is that of the maximin (or of the minimax), one good rule consists in stopping when a new outlay for obtaining information no longer increases or decreases the value of the game.

In the case of non-repetitive, or not particularly repetitive, problems, taking the form of a game against nature with statistical exploration, the notion of mathematical expectation can no longer be justified in the choice of a criterion. We can adopt more complex rules, permitting the sampling to be stopped when the probability of crossing a certain threshold, or stopping short of it, is reached. Nevertheless, a general theory of sequential sampling remains to be evolved, although certain works, particularly [63] give its most useful known elements.

38 Statistical learning

A distinction must be made in statistical exploration. In the first case, the information is evaluated before decision, and gathering this information can be sequential or not. In the second case, the information clarifies itself progressively as the sequential decisions are made. Once again, let us use an example. We have three wheels of fortune. The player is told the structure of the sequential game which is proposed (figure 38·5). He also knows the tables shown in figures 38·3 and 38·4, but he does not know the transition probabilities (figure 38·2), i.e. the value of the angles of the sectors of the wheels of fortune. These constitute a 'black box' of which he can only know at each date $t' = 1', 2', 3', \ldots, (k-1)', k', (k+1)', \ldots$ what decision was taken by nature. For the player it will be a question of choosing a good strategy under uncertainty, which will become random, thanks to the information obtained progressively in successive periods.

Among the possible 'statistical learning strategies', of which we

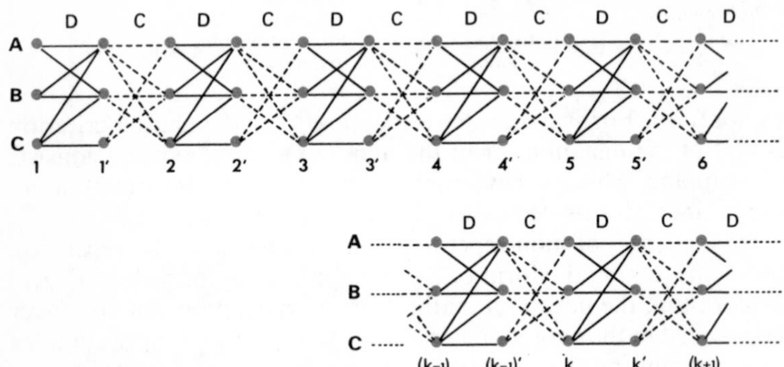

Figure 38·5

can imagine an infinitely large number, we shall consider those which form a 'Laplace–Bayes process'. Such a process will now be described by an example.

Let us suppose that a game includes a sufficient number of moves for the learning process to occur and that the mathematical expectation of the player's winnings can be significant. We give the player, at the end of the game, the quotient of his winnings per number of moves made, and he will be given the option of stopping whenever he wishes.

The player, not knowing at the start of the game the transition probabilities p_{ij}, will follow the Laplace–Bayes hypothesis and assume them to be equal for all transitions stemming from the same initial state. Thus:

$$p_{11} = p_{12} = p_{13} = \frac{1}{3} \qquad \text{[Equation 38.1]}$$

$$p_{22} = p_{23} = \frac{1}{2} \qquad \text{[Equation 38.2]}$$

$$p_{31} = p_{32} = \frac{1}{2} \qquad \text{[Equation 38.3]}$$

Now suppose that on Date I the player is in A. He looks for the

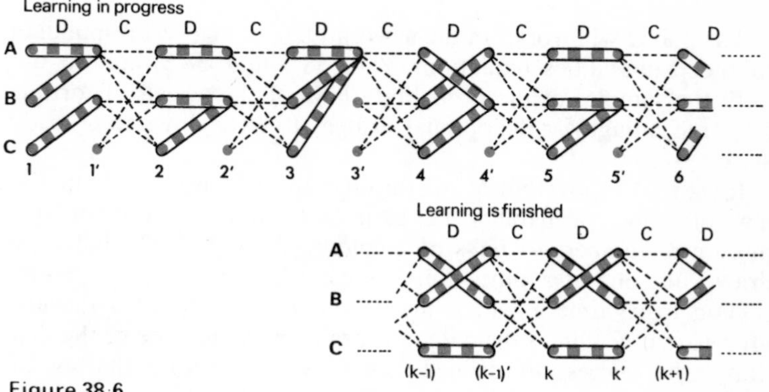

Figure 38·6

optimal sequential strategy (i.e. the strategy which minimises the total winnings over a large number of moves) and decides according to this strategy represented in $1 - 1^1$ in figure 38·6. Then chance intervenes in $1^1 - 2$. Suppose that it sends the player from A to C. From then on the player will transform the probabilities (equation 38.1) by taking

$$p_{11} = \frac{1}{3+1} = \frac{1}{4}, \; p_{12} = \frac{1}{3+1} = \frac{1}{4}, \; p_{13} = \frac{1+1}{3+1} = \frac{2}{4}$$

[Equation 38.4]

The probabilities (equation 38.2 and equation 38.3) remain unchanged. The player will then look for the optimal strategy corresponding to the set of probabilities (equation 38.4, equation 38.2 and equation 38.3). Suppose that the optimal strategy, corresponding to these probabilities, gives a set of decisions represented in $2 - 2^1$ in figure 38·6. The player will thus decide to go to B. Chance then intervenes, sending the player to B, and he assumes a new set of probabilities.

$$p_{22} = \frac{1+1}{2+1} = \frac{2}{3}, \; p_{23} = \frac{1}{2+1} = \frac{1}{3}$$

[Equation 38.5]

The player will work out the new optimal strategy corresponding to the probabilities (equations 38.4, 38.5 and 38.3) and so on, until the samples of the probability laws of the wheels of fortune are large enough for the optimal strategy to settle down to a steady state.

It is easy to show that by operating in this way we can obtain the laws of chance probability. Let us in fact suppose an urn contains unknown numbers of balls of r colours $C_1, C_2, \ldots, C_r$. Balls are drawn out one at a time, non-exhaustively, several times in succession (each time a ball is drawn out it is replaced in the urn afterwards). Calling i the date of a draw and 0 the date of the first draw, the succession defined below will constitute the set of Laplace–Bayes probabilities for the appearance of the colours C_1, C_2, C_r. i.e.:

$$p_1(0) = \frac{1}{r},\ p_2(0) = \frac{1}{r},\ \ldots,\ p_r(0) = \frac{1}{r},\ \ldots \qquad \text{[Equation 38.6]}$$

$$p_1(i) = \frac{m_1 + 1}{i + r},\ p_2(i) = \frac{m_2 + 1}{i + r},\ \ldots,\ p_r(i) = \frac{m_r + 1}{i + r}$$

[Equation 38.7]

if on date i, the following occurrences have been noted: m_1 appearances of C_1, m_2 appearances of $C_2, \ldots, m_r$ appearances of C_r. If the urn contains n_1 balls C_1, n_2 balls $C_2, \ldots, n_r$ balls C_r, $n_1 + n_2 + \ldots + n_r = n$, then the probabilities will converge so that for i sufficiently great:

$$\frac{m_1}{i} \to \frac{n_1}{n},\ \frac{m_2}{i} \to \frac{n_2}{n},\ \ldots,\ \frac{m_r}{i} \to \frac{n_r}{n} \qquad \text{[Equation 38.8]}$$

We shall not develop here certain complicated theoretical aspects concerning the rapidity of convergence of the learning process, but the reader has been able to observe the principle. An objection to this process concerns the use of equal probabilities as a starting hypothesis (Laplace Hypothesis) but, lacking any prior knowledge of the probabilities, we should find any other hypothesis just as open to criticism. In recent works, other processes for increasing the rapidity of convergence have been suggested.

The processes of statistical learning are called upon to play an important role in praxeology.

39 Sequential adaptation: cybernetics

Let us first compare the concepts of exploration, learning and adaptation of which arbitrary definitions are given in this book.

Exploration Acquiring a quantity of information before the decision (or the sequential decisions) which takes this information into account.

Learning Acquiring a quantity of information which increases progressively as the decisions which take it into account are made.

Adaptation Acquiring at each date a quantity of information over a certain period of anticipation and adjusting the decisions to this information. Adaptation is especially concerned with evolutionary phenomena and particularly, in random cases, non-stationary phenomena, i.e. those for which the laws of probability evolve as a function of time.

Still working from an example, let me explain what is meant here by 'sequential adaptation'. Figure 39·1 represents a process of decision with chance extending over a sufficiently large number of time periods to make our arguments acceptable and usable. Suppose also that the player or decision-maker can only anticipate the future as far ahead as 3 Decision-Chance cycles. Thus, in Time Period I the values and probabilities up to date 4. He then looks for sequences of optimal decision for $3 - 3'$, $2 - 2'$, $1 - 1'$, by using the theorem of optimality. Suppose that on date 1 he is in the state shown in figure 39·2, he takes the decisions corresponding to the optimal sequential strategy and chance puts him in another state shown in figure 39·2. The decision-maker is then on date 2 and

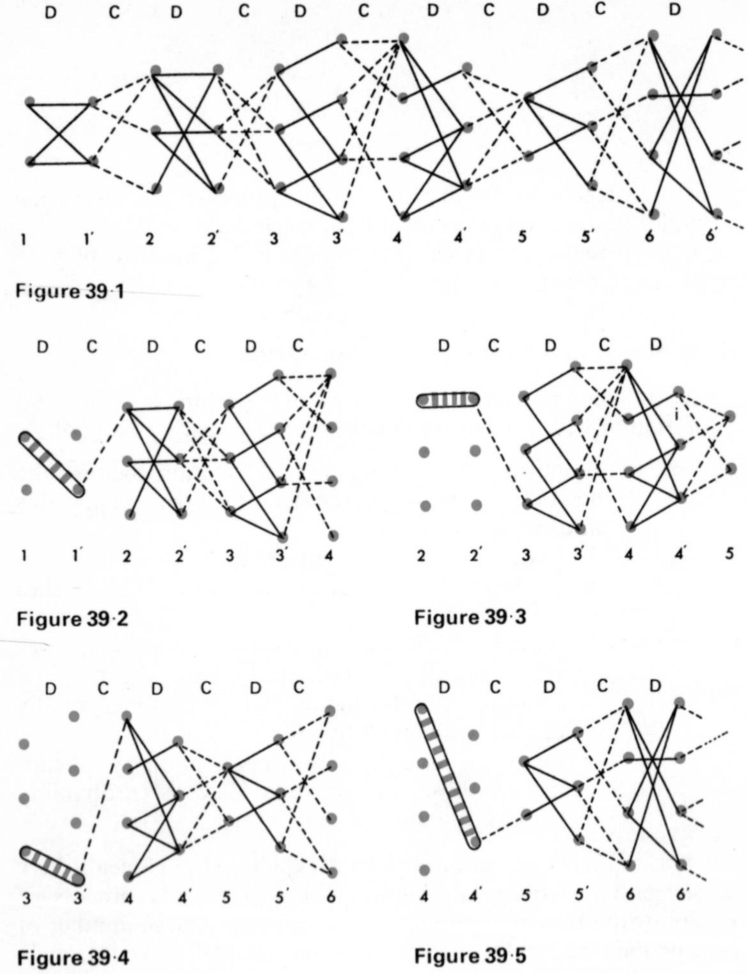

Figure 39·1

Figure 39·2

Figure 39·3

Figure 39·4

Figure 39·5

now knows the future up to date 5. Instead of continuing to choose his decisions according to the optimal sequential strategy obtained on date 1, the decision-maker 'adapts himself' according to his new period of anticipation, from date 2 to date 5. Thus in 2, using the theorem of optimality, he determines the optimal sequential strategy corresponding to this period and decides according to

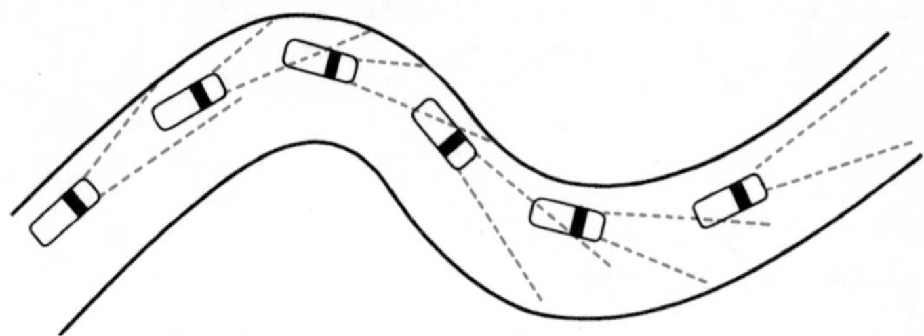

Figure 39·6

this strategy. Then chance leads him into some state on date 3. At this date he has at his disposal a period of anticipation from date 3 to date 6. He looks for the optimal sequential strategy, he decides, chance intervenes, etc., etc. (see figures 39·3, 39·4 and 39·5). Thus, at each date of decision, he adapts himself to new information which he possesses about the future.

The adaptive behaviour just described is no different from the behaviour of the driver of a motor car, but as far as the motorist is concerned, the events happen in a quasi-continuous way. His vision of the road is limited (period of anticipation). He chooses the best decision every time (according to his general criterion of driving), taking into account everything he learns in the period of anticipation. Then as his car moves forward, his period of anticipation allows him to make a new decision, taking into account the new situation. As the vehicle goes along, the driver adapts himself to the new conditions of what is generally a very evolutionary environment. The driver's experience allows him to estimate, in probabilities which are rough but sufficient, the future positions of other moving objects (pedestrians, cars, etc.).

Processes with sequential adaptation lead us directly to the concepts of cybernetics, which might be described as a kind of kinematics of action.

The behaviour of a company director, an administrator, a general, a hunter (whether of female conquests or of less dangerous game), of the pilot of an aeroplane, of a scientific research worker,

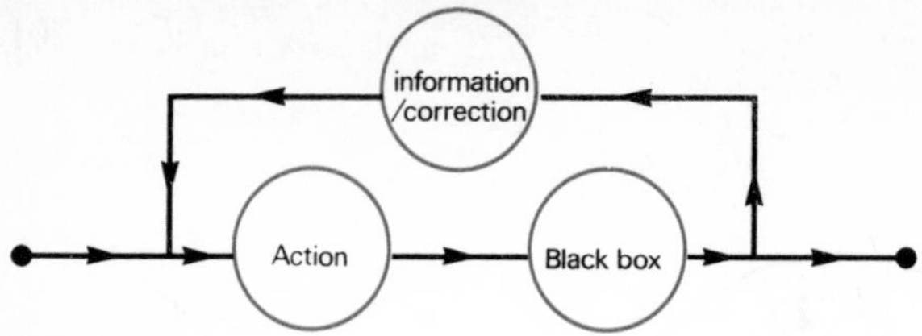

Figure 39·7

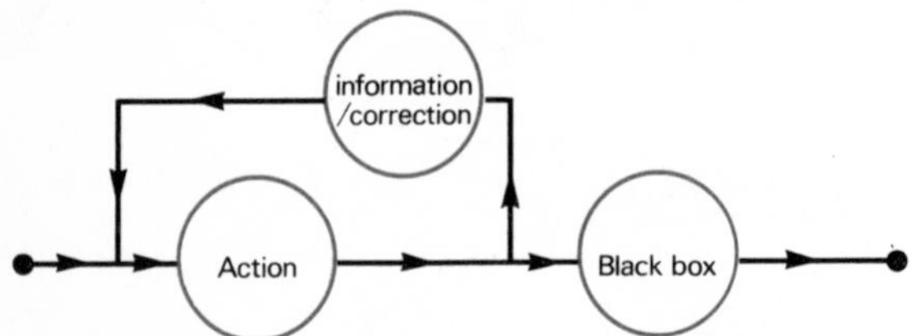

Figure 39·8

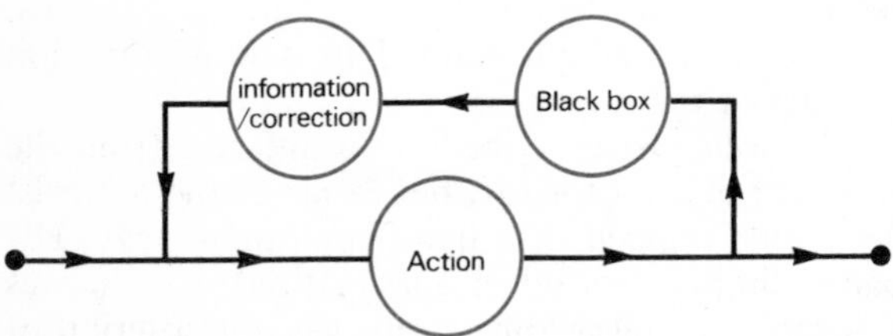

Figure 39·9

constitute behaviour which can be reduced to more or less complex models. In these models we can see the sequences decision/chance/uncertainty taking place, chance resulting from measures due to experience, uncertainty more or less well structured, and resulting from the mobility and the variations of the environment in which favourable or hostile influences show themselves.

In figures 39·7 to 39·9 are represented some topological dispositions of the elements action, information/correction, black box (uncertainty, chance), which are used by the engineers who build equipment for reproducing cybernetic phenomena. We find the same elements and dispositions again in economic problems

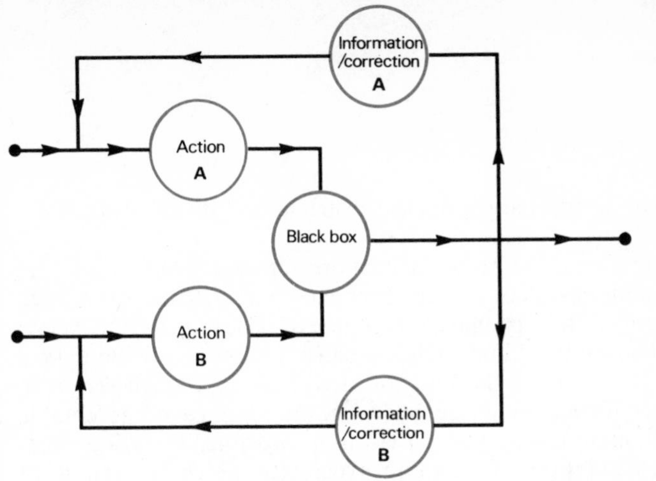

Figure 39·10

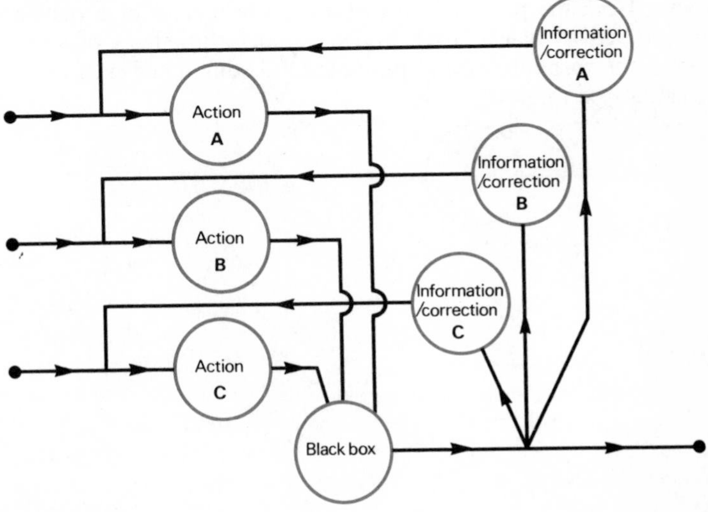

Figure 39·11

relating to a company: stocks, distribution, investments, sales promotion, etc.

From this we go on to envisage more complex structures, where two decision-makers or players intervene (figure 39·10), or an even larger number of decision makers (figure 39·11). For the time being, in our present state of knowledge, we do not know of any theoretical methods applicable to the study of such complex, though very real, situations. As we shall see later, in the absence of acceptable analytical methods in real cases, it is possible, by using men-machine simulations, to acquire experience which is capable of effectively guiding intuition.

It should also be noted, in examining the graphs of figures 39·10 and 39·11, that the actions of the opponent or opponents can also, from the point of view of a decision-maker or a player, be considered as black boxes. Indeed, under the effects of some stimulus, the response of an opponent (and sometimes even of an ally) cannot be foreseen.

7 Learning by experience and simulation

40 Introduction

It is possible, from experiments conducted with the collaboration of skilled, qualified men, to determine laws corresponding to reality, but unfortunately such rewarding cases are rather infrequent. Generally, these experiments on simulation have an educative purpose or are suitable for practice in rapid decision-taking. Hundreds of simulation models have been made in civil and military spheres. These are real practical exercises in research on strategy or tactics, and their worth has been well proved. I shall try to show in a few pages something of the nature of these procedures which have been the object of so many extensive and varied studies. The bibliography gives only a modest sample of them.

41 Value of experience based on actual facts: artificial experimentation

Artificial experimentation. Men's lives are, and must necessarily be, an adventure. If there be no risk, no decision, no judgment, how are we to define the soul? In a society where everyone seeks to protect himself with insurance systems, just how much adventure is left? For many people, for most people, how much action is left?

From the lines of thought that I have tried to develop in this work, it emerges that criteria of logical preference should not be imposed on man, but that a higher form of freedom, associated with criteria of free preference, should be left to him. What is of continuing importance is his knowledge of the nature, logical or free, of the preferences he feels.

The systems of preference of an individual are shaped by the education he receives and by the experiences he undergoes. For the well-endowed inhabitants of rich, developed countries pedagogic problems, and more generally those relating to the acquisition of intellectual powers, are beginning to take precedence over social or economic problems. Education springs from the transmission of knowledge, but also from everyday experience. What is the value of this everyday experience – does it not give too narrow and too fleeting a vision of real facts, with the mechanisms of causality intervening in the preparation of action? Just as the student practises on simplified problems so as to deal later with real ones, just as the pilot practises with link-trainers or 'flight simulators', just as the astronaut gets used to space travel in 'cosmic simulators', just as we get a child to drive a car made to his size in order to improve his future standard of driving, so by simulations of management, of combat, of psychological behaviour, the man of action prepares to exercise his responsibilities.

With the first prehistoric manifestations of human intelligence appeared the 'simulacrum', dances reconstituting fights with wild animals or everyday activities, dances and rites to invoke the favour of the gods of nature. The theatre, a psychological and social model, came with the first appearance of civilisation: in China, in Greece, in Mexico, for example. The educative and experimental value of the theatre for acquiring feelings and attitudes is unquestionable, and it is even more true when one participates in the play, not as a member of the audience, but as an actor. Some psychiatrists, adherents of Moreno, even make use of psycho-drama, in which the patient is one of the actors, to delve more deeply into the secrets of the subconscious. Team games are also a model and training for actual experiences. Soccer, rugby, or baseball, for instance, have a great formative value in the development of calculated decisions and speed of execution.

It is with this in mind that simulations of management are being increasingly used for the establishment of staff in commerce and industry. In this way it is possible to acquire experience from artificial facts reconstituting economic aspects with which such staff must be made thoroughly familiar. These simulators, which are also called 'business games', correspond, in the economic sphere, to armchair manoeuvres, to games of military strategy (war games).

These 'management simulations' or 'combat simulators' have

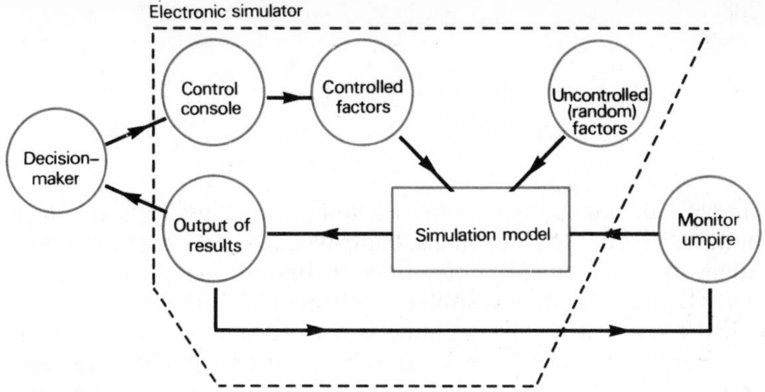

Figure 42·1

become an indispensable complement to the formation and training of executive staff. Where actual experience of the facts is lacking, they constitute excellent practice in the taking of decisions.

42 Simulations of management

The first type of business simulation to be considered relates to a process of sequential management, the diagram of which is given in figure 42·1. A computer is programmed so that a decision-maker may intervene in certain variables of a mathematical model. By means of a control console, punched cards or other type of input, the decision-maker modifies as he pleases the factors which he controls. These factors occur in the model at the same time as certain other uncontrolled ones, which are generally random and are generated in the computer by means of samples taken according to one of the methods described in section 25. The results of the decisions taken can appear at certain prearranged times or at random intervals, or yet again at the request of the decision-maker. A monitor or umpire (if there is one) can intervene to stop the simulator temporarily and advise the decision-maker. In some simulations the computer itself points out any mistakes made, and in a given code, suggests modifications to improve the quality of the management decisions, the computer working in real time.

Let us suppose that the simulation model concerns the management of stocks. Between the uncontrolled variables, predetermined or random (costs of stocks, selling price, loss on surplus, transport charges, demand, re-stocking schedules, stocking capacity, location, etc.) and the variables controlled by the decision-maker (quantity to be stocked, quantities to be re-ordered, to be transported), more or less complex mathematical relations are established from which a programme is worked out for the computer. The umpire can intervene to introduce – if this can be foreseen – certain effects whose causal relationships are not well known (effect of shortage on demand, for instance). The computer having had total or partial information on the problem to be dealt with, takes more or less arbitrarily a certain sequential strategy. It will readjust if necessary as results emerge from the computer. The simulations will, of course, be accompanied by a proper set of accounts worked out by the computer, which could also be interrogated by the decision-maker about certain results relating to the financial management. Other simulation models can be imagined, relating to personnel, or works management, to the employment of technical resources, etc.

One of the drawbacks of this simulation is the immobilisation of an electronic calculator over an indefinite period, merely to train one person for management. When one considers the hourly running costs for a computer of average or high power (about £250 an hour in Britain) they seem quite out of proportion to the advantages to be gained from educating one person. Therefore, electronic simulators have been specially developed for this purpose (for example the computer built by Ramo-Wooldridge, in Los Angeles, a few years ago) and they have much lower running costs.

To make the costs per person trained more acceptable they can also be made to work in teams, as we shall see in the paragraph given to business games.

It is likely that, in the near future, methods of simulating management for training in calculated decision, will assume even greater importance. The need for staff trained to deal with the complex situations of the economic world is continually on the increase (one need only cast a glance at the advertisement columns

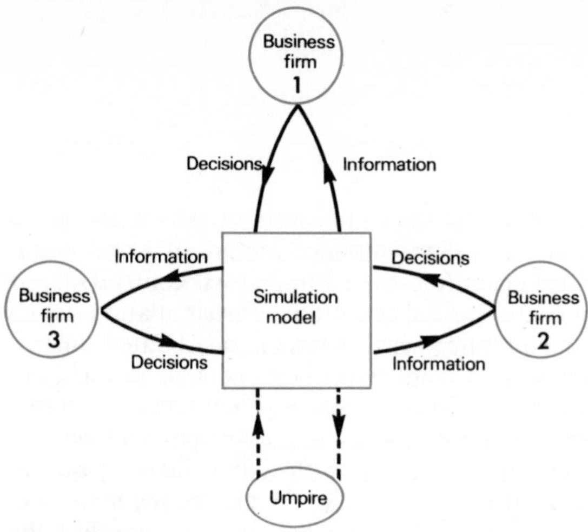

Figure 43·1

of newspapers and periodicals in order to be convinced of this). It will be necessary for them to have really 'practical work in business economy' available and such simulations will be able to fill this role well.

Simulations of management or of administrative procedures have also been produced, by considering models of large scale services, for instance in the USA the model of an Air Force and its logistic services. Simulation laboratories are in fact in existence at the Rand Corporation and at the System Development Corporation in Santa Monica and Los Angeles. In these laboratories scores of people reproduce the activities, data-processing and data-handling of organisations comprising in reality thousands of active members. Very large computers are associated with these simulations.

43 Business games

In this section I shall deal at some length with business games.

We construct a mathematical model (simulation) of an oligopoly, i.e. a set of business firms (generally three or four in these models). These businesses are in competition in one or several markets.

This model, an example and certain details of which are given further on, is of course a rather simplified picture of a real oligopoly. In the model we again find the main factors, controllable or not, which occur in similar actual situations. The simulation model is programmed on a computer which works in accelerated time.

Three or four teams, with from six to eight persons in each, are isolated from each other in different offices. Each team represents a fictitious business. In these teams, various responsibilities are allocated to members in accordance with a free internal set-up. One of the members of the team will take the part of the managing director, another the part of the financial director, another the sales director or director of production, etc. The teams can be geographically near the centre of calculation or be remote and linked to it by suitable means of communication (teleprinter, telephone, messengers, etc.). The conditions under which the teams may communicate with each other are given in the rules of the game.

The simulation works in an appreciably accelerated time-scale: three months of management will be contracted into about two hours. A business simulation of this kind is generally carried out within a limit of three years, that is to say twelve terms, which gives in accelerated time twenty-four hours, distributed over three days of eight hours.

At the beginning of the simulation each team representing a business is notified of the conditions of the market, of the economic parameters which are usually known in reality and of the particular conditions attached to the functioning of the simulated corporation. The past history of each business is given as information to the corresponding team, as well as some information on the past history of the other businesses. To avoid the temptation of acting from the mathematical model instead of carrying out correctly their role of competitor, the teams are not told the mathematical structure of the model.

One or several umpires may intervene, either over the team, or over certain parameters of the model which are available to them.

A staff (ushers, messengers, programmers) is at the disposal of the umpires and the teams.

For the first two hours the teams work out their strategies, and more especially the decisions to be taken for the first three months of management. These decisions are set out in groups on pages specially prepared for this purpose. These pages are handed over or transmitted after suitable coding, to the calculation centre. The mathematical model, processed in a few minutes by the computer, enables the results of all the decisions taken for this simulated period of three months to be obtained. In reality, the events and their consequences do not necessarily take place at set times like the ends of the quarterly terms, but for practical reasons this has to be made so in the simulation. In any case, the acceleration of time makes an accumulation of decisions and information at the end of the quarterly exercise essential. Immediately after data-processing, the sheets of recorded decisions have been processed electronically, information reports are issued and transmitted to the teams. The information will be used for working out decisions relating to the following quarterly term, and so on. After twelve exercises of three months, the simulation is stopped by the umpires and all the teams together review the behaviour induced by the business decisions which were made. This discussion is generally very instructive and fruitful. Finally, the story of these three years of management will be used as a history for a new simulation, with other people occupying the role of decision-making teams.

Example of a business game. Here is a summary of a simulation model to give the reader the opportunity of appreciating the contents of the mathematical models used.

Object of competition	Buyers of consumer goods or a homogeneous set of consumer goods to be called a 'product'. One defines a customer location representing a centre of potential demand or sales for the product.

Market

At the beginning of the simulation the market in previous years is stipulated as well as its characteristics (seasonal or otherwise) and its trends. The market includes four economic internal zones and an export sector. The number of sales centres making up the market in a period of three months is random but not greatly distributed about its average quarterly value.

Factors affecting the market and distribution of the market

Selling price.
Advertising.
Effectiveness of sales force.
Improvement of the product (technological advances).

These factors affect the demand with some hysteresis (delay and persistence).

Expenses to be taken into account

Initial investments.
Future investments (building of factories or of production lines).
Production costs (fixed and variable).
Advertising expenses.
Sales force.
Stock (the product can be considered as depreciable or perishable).
Expenses of technological research.
Market research.
Transportation.
Buying raw materials.
Buying manufactured products.

Production

Each business builds and operates production units (lines).

	A production unit can be sold. The capacity of a production unit is determined by the initial investment. Production capacity is kept up to date (it depreciates with time). Each business can run at most six production units and can site them in one or several economic zones. Production capacity is modified by technological progress.
Information	Certain information is free and delivered automatically on the information sheet – other items have to be paid for (market research).

To give the reader an idea of the mathematical model, I shall provide a partial, detailed description of it, dealing with the way the influence of commercial activities on the market is dealt with; for further details, see [94].

The market of each zone and of the export sector is influenced by the commercial efforts of the sets of businesses in this area. We consider the average demand (see further on):

$$G_s^T = \frac{1}{j_n} \sum_j g_{js}^T$$

T is the period
s is the zone or the sector

[Equation 43.1]

j_n being the number of companies in competition in the sector. The influence of this average demand on the market n_s^T can be given by different rules which generate sales centres N_s^T. In this model, the umpire has the right to choose between two types of rule: linear or quadratic. Other types of rule could obviously be introduced.

The market of each business is divided into orders with a fixed date G, to be delivered at period $T + 3$, and in sales of stocks G^1 to be delivered immediately at period T – we have then:

$$G_{js}^{T} = k_s N_{js}^{T} \quad \text{and} \qquad \text{[Equation 43.2]}$$

$$G_{js}^{T+3} = (1 - k_s) N_{js}^{T} \qquad \text{[Equation 43.3]}$$

The coefficient k_s varies according to the sectors but is valid for all the companies operating in the same sector. It is one of the characteristics of market behaviour.

The factors which influence the market and its distribution, or commercial activities considered in this model are:

Advertising.

Selling price.

Sales service (business expenses – after sales service).

Technological improvements (improvement in quality, in presentation of the product).

For each of the markets, the business determines a commercial strategy which can be shown by investment decisions or by decisions about investment or pricing. From these decisions taken by the team at each period, values are determined. A decision can take effect after a delay, this effect going on for a certain time (the classic example being advertising). We are therefore led to determine for each type of decision parameters of delay and persistence which are adjustable within certain limits.

We take, for the time-adjusted values, demand response curves which allow the influence of each factor on the market to be determined numerically. These curves may or may not be identical for the various factors and areas. They make up a part of the simulation model. Except for the selling price, they are 'S-shaped' or 'sigmoid' curves (figures 43·3, 43·4 and 43·5) which are made linear for machine calculation. By means of these curves, one can assign a 'local advantage' to certain companies in some sectors of the market. This advantage manifests itself by dominating the demand curves. The influence of the selling price on the customers is determined by a hyperbolic function (figure 43·2). After classifi-

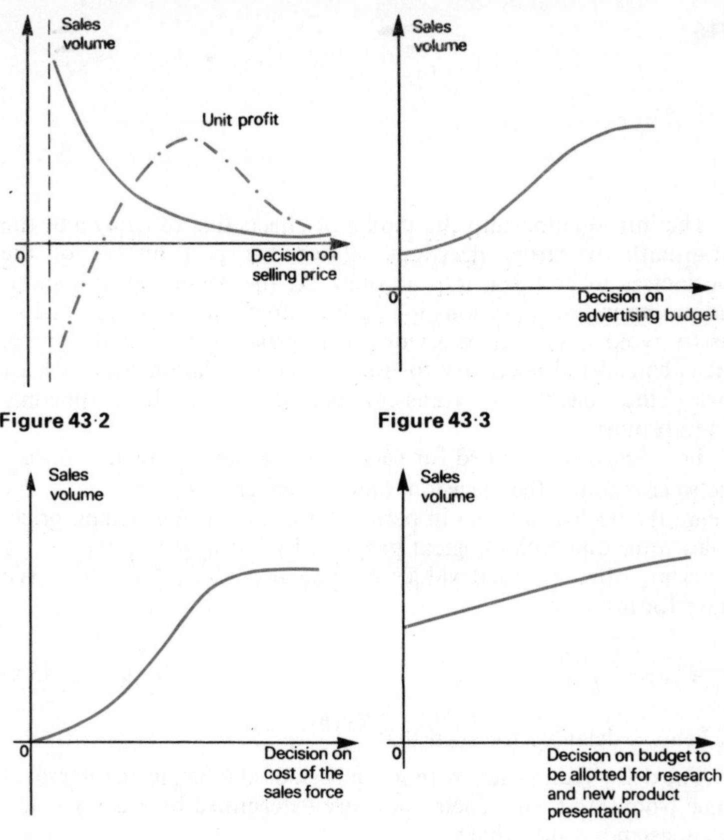

Figure 43·2

Figure 43·3

Figure 43·4

Figure 43·5

cation of the selling prices, the corresponding demand coefficients are adjusted by factors which take into account the order of classification thus obtained.

Afterwards, sector by sector, weighting coefficients intervene, which constitute the 'commercial profile' of the model and determine for each business a relative demand. This commercial profile characterises the behaviour of the market and enables, for instance, a zone to be made sensitive to publicity, or another one to the sales force, etc. Once standardised, the relative demands represent the companies' shares of the market.

The introduction into the model of effects due to delay and the aftermath of earlier decisions, allows the past history of the businesses to be taken into account. At the beginning of a simulation the initial conditions for each company must be specified so as to avoid untypical transient phenomena which would appear. (It is considered necessary to 'run in' the simulation over at least twice the 'delay' or 'transient period' to reach a dynamic equilibrium).

This delay, determined for each of the governing factors occurs between taking the decision and its effects. A_{js}^T, B_{js}^T, C_{js}^T, D_{js}^T being the decisions taken in period T for advertising, selling price, sales force and technological progress by business j in zone s, we determine the weighted values at time A_{js}^{1T}, B_{js}^{1T}, C_{js}^{1T}, D_{js}^{1T}. We have for instance:

$$A_{js}^{1T} = \frac{\Sigma a(h)}{h} A_{js}^{(h)} \qquad \text{[Equation 43.4]}$$

α being a delay vector such that $\frac{\Sigma a(h)}{h} = 1$.

The delay vectors deal with seven periods at most, in an interval of time from 0 to (−6). Their limits are determined by a delay d and a persistence p such that:

$$d + p \leqslant 7, 0 \leqslant d \leqslant 6, 0 \leqslant p \leqslant 7 \qquad \text{[Equation 43.5]}$$

The number of weighting coefficients is equal to the persistence p. In the example of figure 43·6 we have:

$$\begin{aligned} &d = 1, p = 4, \\ &\alpha^{(T-1)} = 0{\cdot}40, \alpha^{(T-2)} = 0{\cdot}30, \\ &\alpha^{(T-3)} = 0{\cdot}20, \alpha^{(T-4)} = 0{\cdot}10 \end{aligned} \qquad \text{[Equation 43.6]}$$

For each one of the governing factors we take a demand curve which allows the influence of each factor on the market to be determined. Let us look in more detail at the use of the demand curves.

The weighted investments determine the demand from curves

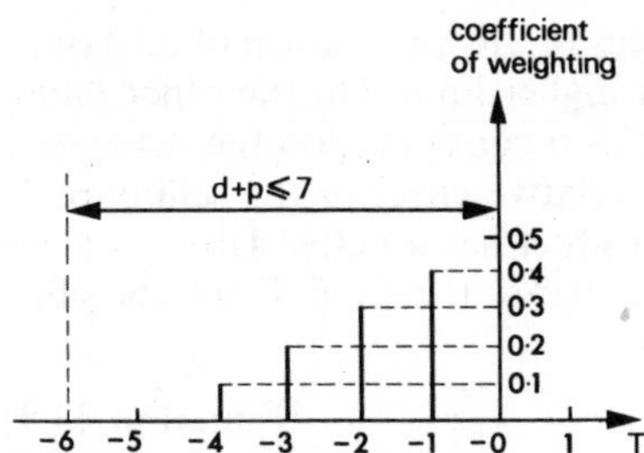

Figure 43·6

which may resemble the curves given in figures 43·3 to 43·5. We have:

$$a^{1T}_{js} = f_{js}(A^{1T}_{js}) \text{ with } 0 \leqslant a^{1T}_{js} \leqslant 1 \qquad \text{[Equation 43.7]}$$

One can have five different curves for each governing factor. Since the curves represent in fact the reactions and the receptivity of the customers to a given factor, we can introduce the idea of local advantage by dominant demand curves. Thus the same investment in advertising will have, for instance, for two different businesses, more influence over this or that set of customers in this or that area, than over another type of customer in another sales area.

The calculation of the demand coefficient of the selling price differs slightly from those for the other coefficients. The demand curve for the selling price is in fact composed of arcs of hyperbolas. We shall then have:

$$b^{T}_{js} = f_{js}\left(\frac{\psi}{B^{1T}_{js}}\right) \qquad \text{[Equation 43.8]}$$

where B^{1T}_{js} is the weighting of the selling prices and ψ a parameter.

A lower limit to the selling prices will avoid too great a 'dumping' effect, whereas the pegging of prices or any other form of economic restriction will be expressed by a higher limit. On the other hand, it has appeared necessary to take into consideration the behaviour of the market in interpreting the relative effect of the selling price (no doubt a high consumption product has a better sale at a price of 0·99 than at 1·00). The selling prices at period T are classified in decreasing order for each area:

$$B_1 \geqslant B_2 \geqslant B_3 \geqslant B_4 \qquad \text{[Equation 43.9]}$$

for instance, j_n being the number of businesses in competition (here $j_n = 4$) and j' being the serial number of a society in the classification adopted, a weighting factor will be determined:

$$k_{j}' = k_{j}'_{-1} + 1 + \frac{B_{j}' - 1 - B_{j}'}{B_1 - B_{j_n}} \text{ with } k_1 = 1 \qquad \text{[Equation 43.10]}$$

The number 1 conveys the fact that a variation of price exists, the linear weighting conveys the importance of this variation.

The real demand coefficient b' will be a linear combination of the demand b obtained with the selling prices weighted by time and the classification coefficient k:

$$b' = \frac{b}{2}\frac{(k_{j}' + 1)}{k_{j_n}} \qquad \text{[Equation 43.11]}$$

For instance, suppose that four firms in competition in the same market have announced in different periods the prices given in the following table:

Period	Firms 1	2	3	4
$T-4$	600	700	450	600
$T-3$	600	650	400	550
$T-2$	500	600	700	600
$T-1$	550	550	650	550

[Equation 43.12]

Multiplying each of the columns of this table by the delay vector as given in figure 43·6 will give:

Firm 1: $(0{\cdot}1)(600) + (0{\cdot}2)(600) + (0{\cdot}3)(500) + (0{\cdot}4)(550) = 550$
Firm 2: $(0{\cdot}1)(700) + (0{\cdot}2)(650) + (0{\cdot}3)(600) + (0{\cdot}4)(550) = 600$
Firm 3: $(0{\cdot}1)(450) + (0{\cdot}2)(400) + (0{\cdot}3)(700) + (0{\cdot}4)(650) = 595$
Firm 4: $(0{\cdot}1)(600) + (0{\cdot}2)(550) + (0{\cdot}3)(600) + (0{\cdot}4)(550) = 570$

[Equation 43.13]

If we suppose also that the demand curve is made up of a single hyperbola within the price limits specified, and that a demand $b = 1$ corresponds to a selling price of 350 (ψ is then 350), the demand coefficients are then established as follows:

$$b_1 = 0{\cdot}636 \quad b_2 = 0{\cdot}583 \quad b_3 = 0{\cdot}588 \quad b_4 = 0{\cdot}614$$

[Equation 43.14]

In period T, the prices are respectively: 400, 500, 600, 700. The classification of these prices in decreasing order gives an inverse order for the four companies:

Firm 4: $k_1 = 1$

Firm 3: $k_2 = 1 + 1 + \dfrac{700-600}{700-400} = 2{\cdot}33$

Firm 2: $k_3 = 2{\cdot}33 + 1 + \dfrac{600-500}{700-400} = 3{\cdot}66$

Firm 1: $k_4 = 3{\cdot}66 + 1 + \dfrac{500-400}{700-400} = 5$ [Equation 43.15]

The demand coefficients are, in order of firms:

$$b'_1 = \frac{0{\cdot}636}{2}\left(\frac{5}{5} + 1\right) = 0{\cdot}636$$

$$b'_2 = \frac{0{\cdot}583}{2}\left(\frac{3{\cdot}66}{5} + 1\right) = 0{\cdot}505$$

$$b'_3 = \frac{0{\cdot}588}{2}\left(\frac{2{\cdot}33}{5} + 1\right) = 0{\cdot}430$$

$$b'_4 = \frac{0{\cdot}614}{2}\left(\frac{1}{5} + 1\right) = 0{\cdot}368$$

[Equation 43.16]

A comparison of the coefficients shows that the latest price policies have changed the order of the firms: 4, 3, 2, 1 now becomes 1, 2, 3, 4. On the other hand, the values of the coefficients b' show that the weighting system, which takes relative prices into consideration has introduced an extra penalty and that the curve of the influence of selling price on the market is, in fact, no longer hyperbolic.

Finally a 'metrics' or 'commercial profile' is introduced representing the sensitivity of the market to the governing factors. We take ten non-negative coefficients λ_i such that $\sum_i \lambda_i = 1$. Thus for each firm, for each zone, the computer will have to calculate:

$$g_{js} = \lambda_1 a'_{js} + \lambda_2 b'_{js} + \lambda_3 c'_{js} + \lambda_4 d'_{js} + \lambda_5 \sqrt{(a'_{js}.b'_{js})} + \lambda_6 \sqrt{(a'_{js}.c'_{js})} + \lambda_7 \sqrt{(a'_{js}.d'_{js})} + \lambda_8 \sqrt{(b'_{js}.c'_{js})} + \lambda_9 \sqrt{(b'_{js}.d'_{js})} + \lambda_{10} \sqrt{(c'_{js}.d'_{js})} \quad \text{[Equation 43.17]}$$

Weighting with the geometric means of some pairs of coefficients allows some composite aspects to be taken into account: a fall in price, for instance, may be connected with advertising, or again good advertising makes the work of the sales representative easier.

The adjustment of the values λ_i is a delicate and somewhat subjective task, achieved after suitable trial and error; it is carried out in advance and inserted into the computer program. The activities of the firms are afterwards standardised in such a way that:

$$\sum_j g'_{js} = 1 \quad \text{[Equation 43.18]}$$

These weighted and standardised activities represent the shares of the market gained by each firm. It is then a matter of urgency to redistribute the market of sector s:

$$N^T_{js} = N^T_s . g'_{js} \quad \text{[Equation 43.19]}$$

This share of the market can in turn be corrected by 'carrying forward' unsatisfied customers, whose orders are brought from T to $T + 1$ according to the rules included in the model.

I must apologise for these rather lengthy explanations, but I think it is desirable for the reader to realise the internal complexity of these simulation models. This complexity is unknown to the player, as he is only aware of the external economic and industrial aspects available, as is the case in the real world. If we had to give a detailed description of the complete mathematical model as programmed on the electronic computer, we would need about fifty pages covered with hundreds of formulas. It can be appreciated that the theoretical and practical preparation, and then the perfecting of such models, require many months of work from a group of research workers.

Figure 43·7 shows a few decisions and results which can appear for a team in the course of a simulation session. The interpretation of such results plays a very important instructive role.

Let us also add that these simulations of management, while thoroughly effective in shaping our awareness of the principal problems of business, may also be accompanied by studies of group-dynamics in the teams, by placing observers, psychologists specialised in group dynamics, in each of them. In the course of the simulation, the observations made on the behaviour of the members of the team towards each other, their attitudes, tensions, relationships, communications can be studied in a manner which is profitable, not only for the persons concerned but also for the psychologists themselves.

Finally let me quote an interesting figure: in the model of simulation taken as an example, at each period, each team must take eighty decisions; it is not difficult to imagine what a wide variety of problems may arise in reaching them.

It is a real model of a market and its suppliers which is simulated. There are models which are much more complex and adjustable. A final question: what criteria are adopted by the teams? In fact we find that they behave as they would in reality! They adopt various criteria, each team organises itself and fixes its objectives

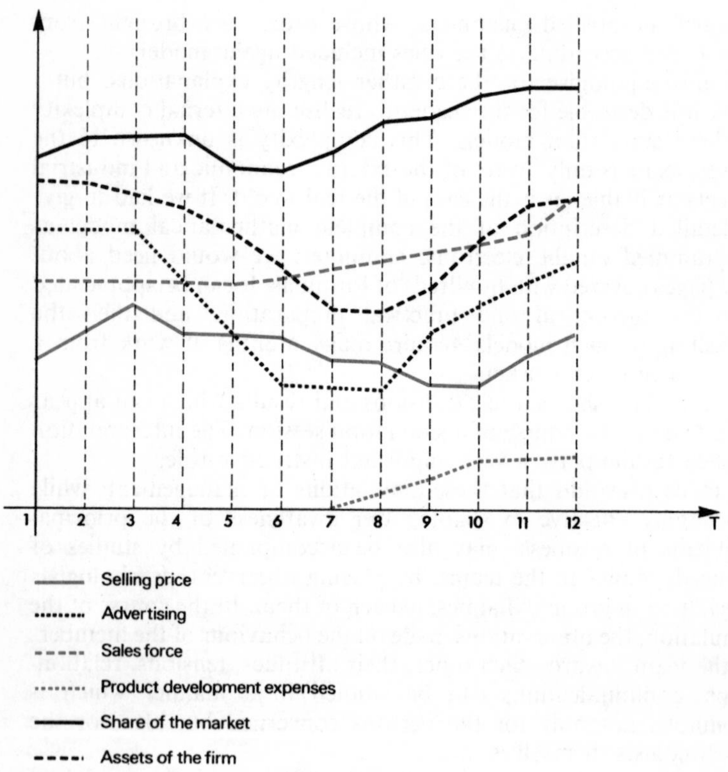
1
2
3
4
5
6
7
8
9
10
11
12
T
Selling price
Advertising
Sales force
Product development expenses
Share of the market
Assets of the firm

Figure 43·7

to be reached, its preferences, and, rather less frequently, a global economic function. It is very often through partial optimisations and a sequential learning, with a reappraisal of the criteria, that the team makes progress in its understanding of the outside world, and its own.

Operational research is an indispensable device for dealing with certain problems which appear in the course of the simulation, but for want of time in reaching the decisions it cannot be considered as doing anything more than bringing certain arguments and pre-established formulas to bear.

44 Towards a praxeology laboratory

In a physics laboratory, experiments are performed to discover new relations of causality in the general laws acceptable in our present state of knowledge; and the same motives operate in a chemistry or biology laboratory.

Will the economist, the sociologist, the operational analyst be able tomorrow to use real laboratories in which, through simulation with very powerful computers, behaviours or laws would be discovered? For the time being this is still purely hypothetical. The difficulties are immense. First, the combinatorial complexity is so great that today's computers with stored programs would still be painfully inadequate, even if they dealt a thousand times more quickly with the information than they do at present. Another difficulty is the need to repeat the experiments a considerable number of times before being able to evolve any formal or probabilistic laws. If the simulations include men – which obliges the computers to work in real or slightly-accelerated time – the repetition of a large number of histories would lead to proceedings which could last for years; and finally, another difficulty, and by no means the least considerable, the human environment in which praxeology finds its level is renewing itself continuously.

The structure of the computers will have to be reconsidered and from machines with algorithms, i.e. machines in which things occur in succession, they will have to become combinatorial machines, with simultaneous feeding and operations coupled with thousands, even hundreds of thousands, of items of input data, just as in the senses and the brains of mature human beings, who perceive simultaneously millions of micro-stimuli, analyse them, decide and command.

The laboratory of praxeology will then not be just a mental concept. Individual and collective behaviours will be studied there, the optimal strategies of very complex real problems will be determined, and their risks will be measured. Intuition will benefit from it, for it will then be possible to concentrate on higher considerations, on what approximates more nearly to ethics.

In the meantime, however, simulations of management, business games, strategic war games, applied to restricted and voluntarily limited cases, will bring us less fragmentary information, less artificial knowledge of situations in time and space, and acceptable pictures of reality. Without waiting for the intervention of machines with simultaneous combinatorial treatment, which will probably soon be in existence, computers are even now becoming indispensable in industrial and administrative life. They are in a sense the machine-tools of the mind for men with responsibility.

45 Military games of tactics or strategy (war games)

War games were already in use by the Prussian army at the time of Frederick II, for staff officers' tactical drill, but the idea of building a model of battle situations on which tactics, even strategies, could be tried out, is probably as old as fratricide. Chess is also a 'war game', and is merely the best-known example of a large number of games of strategy, with complete or incomplete information. Furthermore, in many research centres, for the instruction or entertainment of the scientists, variants of the game of chess have been invented, with incomplete information. The game of 'Battleships', known to schoolboys the world over, is a game of strategy with incomplete information.

Before examining what a military game of tactics is, it is important to agree on the meaning of tactics. (From the Greek *tasso* = to arrange, whereas strategy comes from *strategia* or *stratos* = army and *ago* = to lead). A strategy is, as has been mentioned, 'a set of decisions' in the face of all the decisions of the opponent. If the word strategy is used with various meanings by the military, economists and mathematicians, so it is with the word tactics. Here let us give it its military significance, where it generally means: putting military resources into action, given their previous disposition. The line between the domain of strategy and the domain of tactics, however, is a fine one to draw.

There are very many models of war games and new ones are continually being created by the staff of national or multi-national armies. Military games of strategy, i.e. on a larger scale, including for instance a whole theatre of hypothetical operations, are less frequently found. I will explain by means of an example how a typical game is made up.

We consider a chequer-board of 900 little squares, each one representing a surface of 100 yards by 100 yards. A map of a certain region is represented on this board, with its contours, forests, roads, etc. Generally a map thus drawn up is arranged on a large table, at the disposal of manipulators who will be able to place objects on it which symbolise the real elements occurring in the battle. Sometimes such maps are drawn up in relief with the different features of the terrain, thoroughfares, forests, small villages, etc.

Suppose that the scheme of the battle to be studied is as follows: a blue force (*B*) composed of twenty tanks of type *B*, five anti-tank squads and four accompanying detachments of infantry encounter a red force (*R*) composed of fifteen tanks of type *R*, twelve anti-tank squads and four accompanying detachments of infantry. The operations are taking place in real or slightly accelerated or expanded time.

Forces *B* and *R* are initially placed in certain squares (figure 45·1). A clock gives the time intervals within which each movement is carried out on the map. For each tank, squad and detachment, the firing force is fixed in advance by rules of random distance and spread. Thus, if a tank B fires a shell from a point defined by coordinates towards another point similarly defined, there is a probability P of success which depends on the coordinates of the points. The situation is the same, with appropriate laws of probability, for the other fighting units. Conditional probabilities are also determined in this manner for some actions which depend on others. Rules are given concerning the information to be obtained from the opponent: positions, concealment, camouflage, penetrations etc. The speeds of movements related at any given moment, are stipulated. The whole set of these rules is rather complex and established from expert professional knowledge. Computers are coming to be used more and more frequently for large-scale games.

At each moment, the two opposing teams move their units and make use of their military resources, taking into account the restrictions of the ground, the rules of the game and the information granted. The teams are placed in different rooms, each with the same geographical map enabling them to follow the operations; B, of course, knows the positions of B but very little about those of R, and the same is true for R concerning himself and B. The umpires generally have a third map at their disposal. Naturally many types of appropriate equipment are used in making the game easy to run (for example, closed circuit television and automatic plotting boards).

A 'history' or 'game' includes the development of a situation over a predetermined number of periods of time. The object of the game is usually to enable the effect of varying a given parameter to be observed, all the others being fixed. This makes it necessary to repeat the proceedings a sufficient number of times for the statistics established from their results to be acceptable. One can therefore use a war game as a means of measuring the effectiveness of certain aims or certain tactics, and thus to gather quantitative information, which is seldom possible with a business game, except when the model deals with a small and well-specified part of

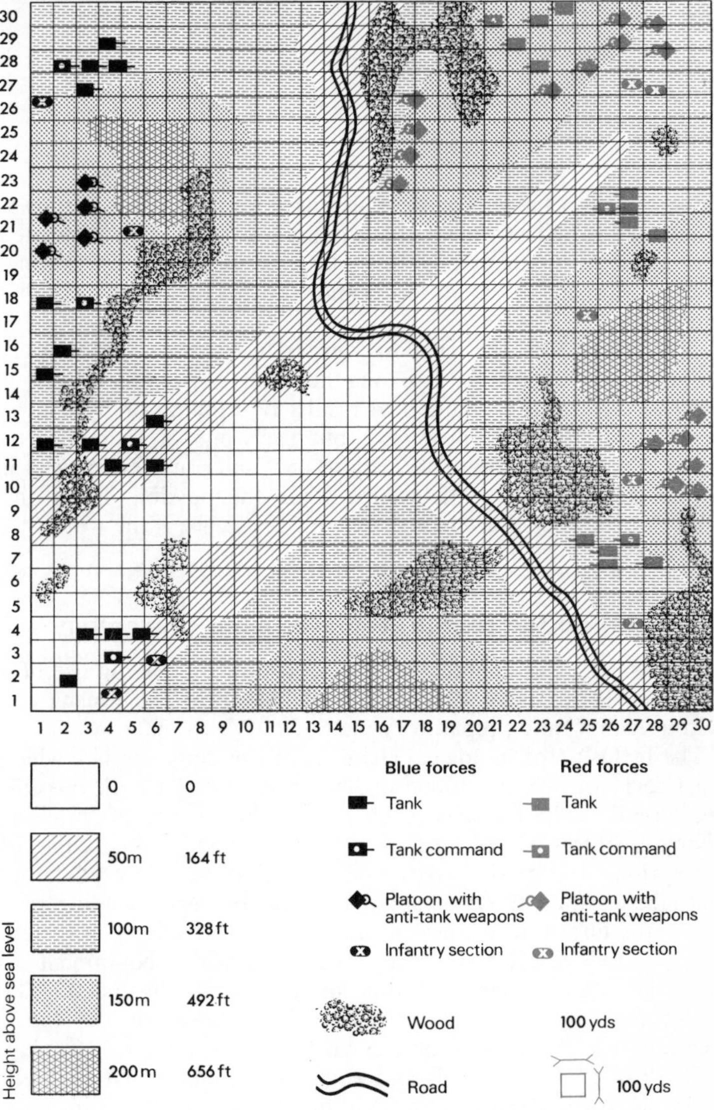

30
29
28
27
26
25
24
23
22
21
20
19
18
17
16
15
14
13
12
11
10
9
8
7
6
5
4
3
2
1
1 2 3 4 5 6 7 8 9 10 11 12 13 14 15 16 17 18 19 20 21 22 23 24 25 26 27 28 29 30
Height above sea level
0 0
50m 164 ft
100m 328 ft
150m 492 ft
200 m 656 ft
Blue forces
Tank
Tank command
Platoon with anti-tank weapons
Infantry section
Red forces
Tank
Tank command
Platoon with anti-tank weapons
Infantry section
Wood
Road
100 yds
100 yds

Figure 45·1

the system. But the war game is also used for instructive purposes. When used as an instrument of evaluation, it is very often associated with studies of mathematical formulas used in military operational research (Lanchester equations or more advanced dynamic combat equations).

The army, like the civilians, experiences great difficulty in choosing valid criteria for assessing the results of a combat. Various processes aggregating numerical results by ranking or by convex weightings have been proposed, but each one of them has its critics. To win a battle or to lead an encounter in a better way is not an easy matter to determine when the possible states and variables considered are many. But this in essence is the work of a staff officer.

46 Nature to the rescue: towards a bio-praxeology

Before closing this chapter, let me point out, by making use of a few *avant garde* ideas, how studies of biological phenomena can help in elaborating preparatory methods of decision.

The inclusion of biological elements in electronic circuits which must carry out certain functions, has been deemed both possible and useful. This idea has given rise to the science of 'bionics'. Living creatures possess in their nervous system, in their chain of perception → analysis → decision → action, far more advanced mechanisms than those invented by man for corresponding purposes (the ultrasonic 'radar' of bats, the ultrasensitivity of certain animals and insects to scents, the navigatorial equipment of migratory birds, special forms of gregarious instincts). The Bionicians envisage inserting parts of the chain, or the whole creature, into an artificial system which has a specific role to play.

One can go even further and envisage a study in nature itself, where all sorts of battles are continually taking place (life itself being only a universal battle of cells), of the way in which living creatures develop and fight. Military research workers have studied the behaviour of various insects, of certain species of germs or viruses, and of sea mammals like the dolphin. For instance, these research workers have been interested in the way two species of ants from Central America fight one another by using, instinctively, tactics and even strategies that no human intelligence, even when helped by powerful means of calculation, would know how to formalise in our present state of knowledge. It so happens that these species have been fighting one another for hundreds of thousands of years, and that the information relating to the success or failure of certain tactics must have been transmitted – we have not the faintest idea how – through the genetic messages of the chromosomes. We have a lot to learn from these battles which take place everywhere in nature, not only in order to learn how to fight if necessary, but also to find how situations of evolutionary balance are created, for peace, after all, is just such a situation.

What we call Bio-praxeology is the study, in living nature, of strategies of the species to defend, to maintain, or even to transform themselves.

8 The flexible world

47 Introduction

In this last chapter I would like to take up again the thesis that I have already defended, with J. Cathelin, in our book *Le Gaspillage de la liberté*. We maintained there that the great problems of tomorrow would disappear in the face of a still bigger one: the problem of continuous education – how to create on a universal scale this process of continual readjustment of knowledge, information, and finally of action.

This vital problem is beginning to make itself very apparent in the affluent countries, both capitalist and socialist. While hunger is a fundamental problem for one third of the world, the rich countries must face an internal self-destroying danger: the failure to adjust themselves to their own progress. This is rather like an insufficiently mature individual who, growing rich, might not be able to put his wealth to good use. We have to decide whether this affluent world will be one of people who 'strike it rich', or of people of 'merit'. We must decide whether science will be able to play its part or be a mere tool of ambitious men or groups.

Rabelais said 'Science without conscience is merely the ruin of the soul'. But conscience, without knowledge, information, and the necessary education, can be unsteadying. We can be bad while believing ourselves to be good, we can be mere hangers-on while believing ourselves to be useful, we can be mistaken about men and about ourselves. Without this continuous education which is the real guarantee of youthfulness of outlook, which enables us to exercise our judgment, which makes us citizens and not just passive onlookers, could we talk of a Science of Action as existing for any but the privileged few, who would very quickly take advantage of the power conferred upon them by a higher vision of Beings and Things?

Overriding praxeology there is ethics; and an illiterate person cannot choose his ethics as a free man – he often accepts without question, or introspection, or analysis, the effects of all private or state propaganda aimed at conditioning him.

48 Towards a flexible world, an adaptive man

For lovers of peace and quiet it is a great pity that human society is flexible and that it becomes even more so. The reassessment of all knowledge is so continuous a process that despair finally takes hold of rigid, or in other words, lazy minds.

We witness a continual mutation of risks. No sooner has one disease become curable than another develops and holds progress up to ransom. We may manage to eliminate some dangers on the factory floor, only to be caught up in the terrible slaughter on the roads. Insecticides have scarcely got rid of a species dangerous to crops than protection has to be found against these insecticides and their danger to man and to the balance of nature. No sooner is the battle against hunger halted in some parts of the world, than we see whole populations engulfed elsewhere by such evils of civilisation as atmosphere- and water-pollution, the misery of housing estates, the disastrous effects of certain tranquillisers, etc. With each partial problem solved, we see another set, sometimes even more distressing, and the worst of this situation is that it is constantly being intensified and accelerated.

The greatest evil of a civilisation lies in the refusal to re-examine itself, to adapt itself to its own creations, to shake off complacency and to steer itself along the path of adventure. Threatened from without and even more from within, a rigid civilisation cannot resist, and worse still, it no longer has any reason for existing. We must accustom our children from their earliest years to this flexible world. They must be given an education so designed that they may become adaptive and enterprising. We may have to sacrifice the mere absorption of known facts in order to instil the ability to absorb and anticipate new ones, as Korzibski and Bachelard have advocated.

The science of action will also be, above all else, the science of 'reaction' in the sense contained in the word 'feedback' as used by the cyberneticians, but it has to be a reaction which makes forward movement easier, instead of creating a static balance.

49 The higher form of action is creation

In my opinion, those who would confine men in social systems which put them in the same category as useful and contented cells, are mistaken about the profound nature of the human mentality. The state of cerebral development of 'Homo Sapiens' makes him something more than a mere cog, destined to find happiness in the prosperity of the State; in a system whose totality represents this prosperity, or so he has been persuaded (and by what methods, in certain instances!).

Every time inventors of systems that 'will last a thousand years' have claimed to have found the definition of the human condition, the desire to think, the longing to be free, has arisen, spread, and finally prevailed, for if there is anything worse for a man than the suppression of freedom of thought, it is the suppression of thought itself.

It is a great crime to deprive people of thought by transforming them into a contented, fertile and faithful herd. What a wonderful prospect it would be for so many politicians to be able to transform these people into a host of docile onlookers and, if possible, into admirers of one man or one party, in the name of material or spiritual happiness, in a purely functional balance.

Everyone therefore must play his part and contribute his share, however modest, of his mind's work. The common interest must be embodied not in the prosperity of the Leviathan, but in the accession of others to the possibilities of action, of intervention and especially of creation. Indeed is not creation the highest form of action? Is it not what remains in the end: an enduring and sublime Sumerian work of art, found in the sand, a temple set up to the glory of gods, an enchanting poem, a principle, a new theory? From the tin-opener to the pedagogic method, from the most recent bridge over the Hudson River to the latest cooking recipe, it is by creating that man renews himself and lives, in the fullest sense of the word.

Yes, but the ability to create, some will say, is a thing reserved for the elite, for the superior, for the gifted. The people, the masses, the mediocre are quite incapable of creation . . . furthermore they are not interested in it – look around you! And yet this mass of so-called mediocrity has built cathedrals, these anonymous craftsmen have produced masterpieces for which people pay fortunes at antique dealers, these men of straw have built everything. What is more serious and dangerous for our western civilisation is the loss in some sectors of society of the desire and the need to create. An easy chair and a television set, a ticket for the football match, a betting-slip, insurance cover for the house, a new car every other year, leisure for wasting the hours of freedom on . . . and at the head of these sheep a few high-priests, the only ones capable of decision and using science properly for the purposes of governing, the technocrats, or cyberneticians on one side, the gathering of mediocrity on the other.

There is more freedom for the poor South American Indian, putting together with a fair degree of skill some small object in the Mayan style, which he will then sell to the 'gringo' tourist, than for the gringo himself, whose only function in existing is to work off the hire-purchase payments on his car and his colour television set.

To create is to bring one's imagination to life, to take a real part in the great adventure of mankind. Only through a race of creators can any meaning be given to civilisation, and ultimately, are not the two words creation and civilisation synonymous?

Thus, the science of action will also be, above all else, the science of creation. Descartes, in his *Regulae*, called this science 'heuristics'. At Le Canisy, near Deauville in France, a Generalising Centre is being built which will be a heuristics centre where scientists from all over the world will gather in inter-study groups, with the object of increasing their ability to create. But this ability must be made democratic, it must be made accessible and desirable for the less able people of today who perhaps, with courage and perseverance, might become the renovators of tomorrow.

50 Examples of methods for inventing: from the morphological method to brainstorming

One of the best known astronomers of our day, Professor F. Zwicky of the California Institute of Technology, has devised a particularly efficient method of stimulating the work of imagination and systematic research, with a view to making technological innovations, creating original processes, and hitherto unknown principles. He has called it the 'morphological method'. It consists in describing the parameters and the fundamental specification of a concept, which can be as material as a machine and as abstract as an entity. This method is very popular in the USA.

I shall first show, by way of a very simple example which does not require any previous scientific training, what this method consists of. Professor Zwicky, if he ever reads these few lines, will forgive me I trust, for having chosen such a trivial example, when his method has been the inspiration for such wonderful discoveries.

Imagine that you have to write the manuscript of a scientific book, and that you need to be able to run off about ten copies for your friends to read in order to put it into shape. It becomes, in fact, more and more necessary to have manuscripts read before editing, by people who are specially competent and/or interested in what the subject is about, and the way it has been presented. Let us suppose that the classic process for producing a manuscript is as follows: typewriter, usual ink ribbon, opaque paper, carbon paper for duplicating, rubber and scissors and paste for correcting.

We are going to look for a new process because the one just described is too long and does not yield enough copies except by too great an expenditure of time and money. The following elements form its morphology:

A: device for writing
B: product set down by writing
C: medium on which the writing is made
D: duplicating
E: correcting.

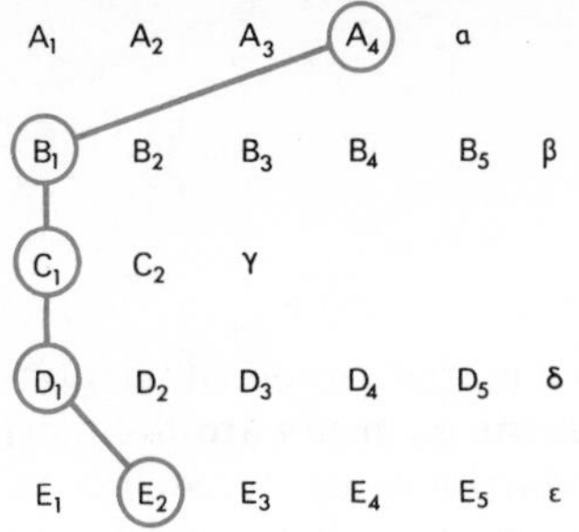

Figure 50·1

We shall now look for the elementary morphologies, by considering successively: the set **A** of the devices for writing, the set **B** of the products set down by writing, **C** the set of media, **D** the set of duplicators and **E** the set of correcting devices. As we do not know how to imagine all the elements of these sets, we shall add to each one an unknown element represented by α, β, γ, δ or ε.

Here is what we can have:

A = {penholder, fountain pen, ball-point, typewriter, α} = $\{A_1, A_2, A_3, A_4, \alpha\}$

B = {ordinary ink, fountain-pen ink, Indian ink, powdered ink, copy ink, β} = $\{B_1, B_2, B_3, B_4, B_5, \beta\}$

C = {ordinary paper, transparent paper, γ} = $\{C_1, C_2, \gamma\}$

D = {carbon paper, electrochemical photocopy, microfilm, blue-print, stencil, δ} = $\{D_1, D_2, D_3, D_4, D_5, \delta\}$

E = {scratching-out, rubbing out, sticking, cutting out and replacing, using an erasing product, ε} = $\{E_1, E_2, E_3, E_4, E_5, \varepsilon\}$

An elementary morphology will be formed by an objective $(A_i, B_j, C_k, D_l, E_m)$ whether feasible or not. Our problem will be to choose the objective or objectives, feasible or believed unfeasible, by using some preference rule. Thus, writers generally use $(A_4, B_1, C_1, D_1, E_2)$; let us exclude from our exploration for the time being the elements α, β, γ, δ and ε.

How many elementary morphologies can we count and enumerate? It is easy to show that there are $4 \times 5 \times 2 \times 5 \times 5 = 1000$ elementary morphologies forming the general morphology. As this set possesses a number of elements too high to enumerate without order, we shall place the elements of **A**, **B**, **C**, **D** and **E** according to a fully-ordered relationship (ultimately a partially-ordered relationship), for instance, the order in which the elements are the most often employed when a scientific manuscript is produced. Let us suppose that the relations of subjective order are the following (in the undermentioned sets the elements have been arranged in sequence).

$\mathbf{A}' = \{$typewriter, fountain pen, ball-point, penholder, $\alpha\} = \{A'_1, A'_2, A'_3, A'_4, \alpha\}$

$\mathbf{B}' = \{$ordinary ink, fountain-pen ink, powder ink, Indian ink, copy ink, $\beta\}\{B'_1, B'_2, B'_3, B'_4, B'_5, \beta\}$

$\mathbf{C}' = \{$ordinary paper, transparent paper, $\gamma\} = \{C'_1, C'_2, \gamma\}$

$\mathbf{D}' = \{$carbon paper, photocopy, stencil, microfilm, blue-print, $\delta\}$ $= \{D'_1, D'_2, D'_3, D'_4, D' \ \delta\}$

$\mathbf{E}' = \{$scratching-out, sticking, rubbing-out, erasing, cutting out, $\varepsilon\} = \{E'_1, E'_2, E'_3, E'_4, E'_5, \varepsilon\}$

Now we can give to the set of elementary morphologies, i.e. to the general morphology, a lattice structure, as was presented in section 12 (see figures 12·4 and 12·5).

We shall postulate that an elementary morphology (i.e. a process) is apparently of a more commonplace level than another elementary morphology if the sum of its indices is smaller; where the sums are equal, the level is the same. (This way of exploring the combinatorial structure was not given in the work of Professor Zwicky. Among the solution processes, we found that this particular one gave satisfaction in certain cases.)

On the other hand, if a morphology $(A'_i, B'_j, C'_k, D'_l, E'_m)$ has all its indices higher or equal to those of a morphology $(A'_{i'}, B'_{j'}, C'_{k'}, D'_{l'}, E'_{m'})$ it will be said that the first morphology is less commonplace than the second. The relation of commonplace thus obtained is an order relation. As an element more commonplace than all the others exists $(A'_1, B'_1, C'_1, D'_1, E'_1)$ and also an element less commonplace than all or any of the others $(\alpha, \beta, \gamma, \delta, \varepsilon)$ the structure of the general morphology is a lattice work, for which the Hasse diagram is too complex to be drawn here (it has $5 \times 6 \times 3 \times 6 \times 6 = 3240$ apices). But, to explore the lattice work, we work by using only the elements deemed to be usable, in the state of our knowledge.

Instead of exploring the whole lattice, we shall study it in parts. Suppose that the qualities we would like to find in a process of physical production of a manuscript are as follows:

To allow the printing of a sufficient number of copies (10 or 12) to be cheap, not to require a great deal of equipment, to be able to be easily corrected; these considerations will enable us to eliminate some elementary morphologies. We shall also discard those deemed 'incompatible' (technologically or for any given reason). Let us start with only **A** and **B**, leaving aside α and β. The following elementary sub-morphologies are acceptable among the $4 \times 5 = 20$ formed with **A** and **B**: (A'_1, B'_1), (A'_1, B'_4), (A'_2, B'_2), (A'_2, B'_5), (A'_3, B'_3), (A'_4, B'_1), (A'_4, B'_4), (A'_4, B'_5). Put them in the order of their indices: (A'_1, B'_1), (A'_2, B'_2), (A'_1, B'_4), (A'_4, B'_1), (A'_3, B'_3), (A'_2, B'_5), (A'_4, B'_4), (A'_4, B'_5) – we then pass to the acceptable sub-morphologies if we take into consideration **C** where γ is neglected. The eight previous ones can become sixteen, i.e.: (A'_1, B'_1, C'_1), (A'_1, B'_1, C'_2), (A'_1, B'_4, C'_2), (A'_1, B'_4, C'_2), etc. ... (A'_4, B'_5, C'_1), (A'_4, B'_5, C'_2). Then we can consider the sub-morphologies taking **D** into consideration but excepting δ, which will give, after elimination of the incompatibilities, a new set of elementary sub-morphologies, from which as a last step we can determine the elementary morphologies with five elements. These will be ordered according to the sum of its indices, studied, then retained or rejected. Thus, after a final selection out of ten processes, we have finally kept $(A_1, B_3, C_2, D_4, E_k)$, $(A_2, B_3, C_2, D_4, E_k)$ where E_k means that any elements of **E** can be used. The manuscript of the present book was done with a penholder, Indian ink and transparent paper, then ten copies were photoprinted on blue-prints; this process allows corrections to be made on the transparent paper either by scratching out, erasing or cutting off a part of the paper and replacing it by another.

This example, while rather simple, enables us to see what the morphological method consists of. If the reader refers to the work given under [108], he will be able to examine how Zwicky's method has been used in vitally important cases, in astronomy and in space research, for instance.

We can sum up the way we have used the morphological method as follows, while pointing out that it is only one variant taken from among many others which might be better adapted to other research.

1 Taking one or several elementary known morphologies and describing their constituent elements.
2 Building up the sets **A**, **B**, **C** ...
3 Giving an order for the sets **A**, **B**, **C** ... and an order in each set for each constituent element.
4 Studying the sub-morphologies created from **A** and **B**, eliminating all incompatibilities; passing on to the sub-morphologies formed from **A**, **B** and **C** eliminating all incompatibilities; passing on to the sub-morphologies created from **A**, **B**, **C** and **D**.
5 Examining the elementary morphologies obtained: selecting and accepting.

If no interesting solution has been found –

6 Starting the study again from stage 2 by adding elements α, β, γ, δ, etc.
7 Seeking how to specify the elements α, β, γ, δ, ... so that a solution can be finally accepted.

This is no more than an outline of the morphological method, which may be defined as a certain way of exploring the combinatorial universe of known things and eventually of introducing foreign elements into it. The manner of treating the general morphology so as to extract from it elementary ones representing discoveries can vary from one study to another. When enough information has been gathered on the best way to use it, it will be possible to lay the foundations of automatic heuristics, in which electronic computers will play such an essential part.

Before Zwicky, we found in various works of Pascal, Fermat, Bernoulli and Euler similar ideas on combinatorial analysis, but it was Ramon Lull (1235–1315) who, for the very first time in history, formulated in his 'Ars Magna', a systematic method of discovery based on it. If Lull formulated his theory in a way which nowadays would seem infantile, this theory contained the germ of the method which Zwicky was later able to devise and employ so ably later.

We must insist on the fact that the morphological method is a method of elaboration, of gestation of ideas and therefore can be very slow. The essential part of it is the morphological description itself, which can sometimes require months spent on it by a team of workers, but, even if this work does not lead immediately to a discovery, it at least has the great merit of training the research workers to make a more exact definition of their problems.

In section 7 we gave a very simplified list of the main methods of scientific investigation; the morphological method as well as the method of discovery matrices is a method of analysis and combinatorial synthesis.

In direct contrast to the morphological method of discovery which some find far too rigid, is the 'Brainstorming' method.

Brainstorming is to the morphological method what simulation by the Monte Carlo method is to the combinatorial analysis. Unlike step by step research by enumeration, where acceptable ideas are given structures, though not necessarily new or viable ones, while we still hope that we shall finally energe from the known field, brainstorming is a method where all the ideas which come to mind are exchanged within a group. It works, as it were, by thinking aloud, until someone or other's imagination through successive inspirations, sparks off a new idea.

The essential principles of group-working are the following:

All ideas suggested by the problem set must be expressed, and all the more freely since criticism is ruled out of this collective research. It is the preselection of one's own ideas just as much as of others'.

Members of the group are enjoined to draw inspiration from each other's opinions and to improve on them without any fear of giving offence. Cribbing from someone else can transform a simple idea, already put forward, into a new one.

The important thing is to look first for a quantity of ideas. The quality comes later when the work of imagination has progressed further.

In the case of a difficult problem, the discussion-leader tosses the idea back to the group either by recalling those already expressed, or by drawing inspiration from the following questions:

Can it be modified? (Change of colour, movement, sound, shape, for example.)
Can it be added to? (Bigger, smaller, higher, thicker, longer.)
Can anything be taken from it?
Can one element be substituted for another?
Is a combination possible?
Is the opposite feasible?

During the period of sifting and selection, those ideas are considered good which:

Can be acted upon immediately.
Do not go beyond the working limits imposed (budget, men, general policy, weather . . .).
Are compatible with other ideas already selected for other aspects of the problem.

It should be remembered that there is not one method of brainstorming but several: the Osborn method, the Gordon method, etc.

Here are some interesting results obtained as a result of using the Brainstorming method (examples already quoted in reference [103]):

Research on a new mode of classification according to a different principle from the classic lexicographical order.
New method of making the connexion of two electrical conductors (General Electric Co.).
New shapes in industrial aesthetics.
Invention of a new toy.
New ideas for reviving sales of a product.
Processes to decrease the quantity of noxious gases produced by an internal combustion engine.

Of course, such a method has rather narrow limits. Brainstorming is a research medium, valid as long as it is restricted to a problem of imagination, as opposed to problems of reflection and analysis which come within the province of operational research methods. The application of the method must be entrusted to a well-trained group-leader, and it can be a great advantage if this person also has a good knowledge of psychology, particularly in group dynamics, for Brainstorming is a random heuristic method in a system of communications, where an idea of one person stimulates the ideas of another.

Since the inception of these opposing methods, morphological on the one hand and Brainstorming on the other, a great many research workers have been engaged on the 'invention of new methods of invention'. Some of these are compromises between systematic processes and random processes.

However, we must see these methods of invention merely as exploratory aids. Induction allied to intuition, with a good dose of courage, patience and independence, will remain the most valuable method of fathoming nature's secrets. There will always be geniuses, artists and poets to bring lustre to an epoch, but each one must join in this feast of knowledge and progress as a genuine fellow member and not as a surprised outsider looking in.

51 Preparation for action and pedagogic methods: cybernetic pedagogy

The present range of possibilities of scientific decision-making must not be over-estimated. These possibilities are great for modest problems and very often modest for large-scale problems, but their greatest worth surely lies in the better understanding of the milieu and its evolution to which they lead. In the long run it all inevitably comes back to one abiding necessity: improved knowledge. A human life is of rather short duration, however, and its period of full-time education even more so, since this usually represents only fifteen to twenty per cent in the most advanced countries.

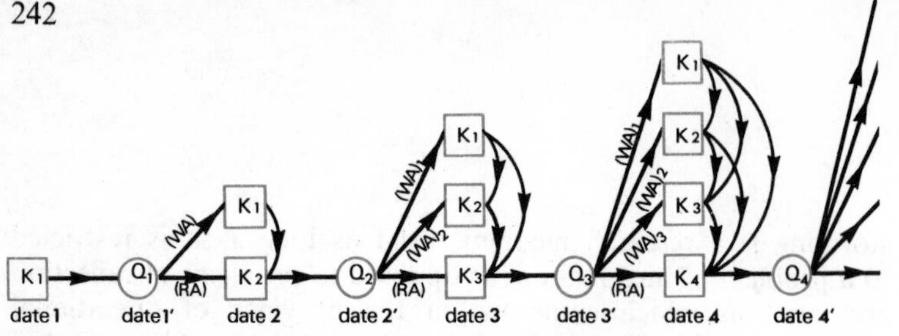

Figure 51·1 K_i knowledge acquired at date i
Q_i question asked at date i $i < i' < i+1$
(RA) right answer at date i′ passed on to K_{i+1} at date i+1
$(WA)_k$ wrong answer at date i passed on to K_k $(k \leqslant i)$ and from there to K_r $(k < r \leqslant i+1)$

I have already insisted on the moral and functional necessity of continuous education. I have also underlined the importance of simulation methods in training for decision-taking. I would now like to stress the need for pedagogic aids in acquiring this knowledge.

At present, pedagogy falls far short of being a science! A teacher presents in his own way a collection of knowledge which a certain category of pupils has to assimilate. While a few may do this well, others meet with failure that can mark a pupil for life. If some questions appear to be very difficult, when in fact they are admirably clear and simple, is this not the fault of teachers who have acquired bad teaching habits? Or who have chosen to make their explanations along lines which they themselves found difficult to follow, without trying to find, in accordance with up-to-date standards, equally strict but much simpler explanations? For instance, it is well known that physics is the trickiest subject of all to teach, and the reason is that the pupil finds difficulty in seeing the connexion between the various aspects of this subject, and is in constant doubt, throughout his studies, as to where he must develop his line of thought. There is a lack of simple and general principles: here is one that few people make use of: power can manifest itself in nature only in the form of an 'energy pair', for instance (force, speed), (voltage, current), (electric field, magnetic field), (temperature, entropy), etc. In constructing the teaching of physics around this simple principle, complicated notions such as inertia, impedance, balance, stability, etc., become appreciably clearer. Such principles exist in other subjects and the duty of the pedagogue is to make full use of them in order to mould the scientific mind.

Generally speaking, however, apart from a few geniuses and star pupils, students have minds which cannot follow the teacher's instruction or his pedagogic strategy quickly enough. These phase differences or delays have serious consequences and create conditions that are psychologically difficult to cure, and the gulf between what one wishes to teach and what one is able to teach widens most of the time. Pedagogy must become a science, perhaps even the supreme science.

Meanwhile, psychologists, teachers and electronic engineers, combining their skills and their methods, are developing new ways of teaching which are more rigorous as well as more thorough and above all, more accelerated. Audio-visual aids, programmed learning, teaching machines, machine-training in logical processes, etc. All this is still quite thinly spread, the results are still far from satisfying all our hopes, some concepts are even radically opposed to one another on certain points. The cost of these pedagogic aids is sometimes astronomic. But it does seem to be the direction in which we must advance.

If we study a diagram of programmed learning, we find it faithfully represents a process of action with adaptation. In figure 51·1 I have given the theoretical aspect of the process now in use in programmed learning; to this diagram we should add the methods of $K_i \rightarrow K_j$ shown by arrowed curves, which are drawn at times 2, 3, 4, ... These procedures constitute the part that is most difficult to work out, supplementary questions can be found in them that have not been represented in figure 51·1 so as not to make it too complicated.

Programmed learning is carried out with special books, index cards or special 'teaching-machines' or even with the aid of specially programmed computers. This teaching with machines can also be carried out in such a way as to deal with several pupils simultaneously. Finally, as I said in section 42, simulators of the learning process have been created which constitute real teaching machines.

52 Conclusion: the need for a 'science of decision-making'

The study of the chapters in this book may have persuaded the reader that a science of action is attainable. Yet such a science, a basic factor in human knowledge in the near future, will require very advanced processes of analysis and means of calculation, and the simplicity of my explanations and examples has not brought this out with sufficient emphasis. This book is no more than an invitation to reflection and research.

This science of action will ultimately make use of nearly all the knowledge of other sciences and particularly of mathematics. Education at school or university, the continuous education of adults, the need to keep everyone up-to-date and informed, it will all have to take cognizance of this entry of the exact sciences into the human sciences, and syllabuses will have to be modified accordingly. Fortunately, our students, our young executives and management staffs, have already realised that this new science will be the science of an era in which they will have to use their talents and their initiative. Older people are still dubious, indifferent, or ultra-conservative in outlook – a very restful and soothing attitude indeed! But the exponential rate of progress worries them and a few sharp setbacks will be enough to persuade them.

So many things to learn, so many hours to be sacrificed to the painful assimilation of a small complementary knowledge, of a slightly clearer vision of the activities of the world. All this in an epoch where the dream of nearly all governments would be to transform their citizens into satisfied and docile consumers, subjected to the effects of formidable media of political or commercial propaganda. And yet the effort that must be made by every one of us towards a better understanding of the human condition, the desire for progress, the continuing conquest of knowledge for the purposes of action, are the only things capable of avoiding the tensions and disorders which threaten us. Liberty and civilisation are at stake.

There can be no real liberty without a science of action, for freedom is not chance or uncertainty. In essence it is the possibility of making a rational choice in known and accepted circumstances. There can be no stability, or at best a disturbing, frightening stability, in a world where man would be subjected to technological advancement without understanding, and controlling it, and where only a handful of bosses, weighed down with technological pretensions, would have access to this science of action. It must be taught to everyone, with pedagogic circumspection, and at a level acceptable to all minds.

The fact that he has not the slightest notion of the working of domestic economy places the average citizen of a capitalist or socialist country at the mercy of commercial or political profiteers. Ignorant of the social trends in automation and scientific management, he thinks that his small corner of happiness is threatened by them. The supposition, accepted without question by too many people, that the possibilities of assimilating knowledge are dependent on natural gifts and therefore reserved for a privileged few, pushes the vast majority of people even deeper into indifference towards their advancement. The reliance on inspiration and luck rather than on thought and effort, the surrender to others of the fundamental privilege of choosing, the gadget superseding the beautiful or the functional, sport becoming an end in itself, the theatre replacing life – might not all this be described as 'the civilisation of the absurd'?

There can be no freedom for the man who is unable, or unwilling, to play his part.

Bibliographical references

1 Decision in human actions

1 R. Caude and A. Moles, *Méthodologie – vers une Science de l'Action*, Gauthier Villars, Paris 1964.

2 D. N. Chorafas, *Operations Research for Industrial Management*, Reynolds, New York, 1958.

3 C. D. Flagle, W. H. Huggins and R. H. Roy, *Operations Research and Systems Engineering*, Johns Hopkins Press, Baltimore, 1960.

4 H. H. Goode and R. E. Machol, *Systems Engineering*, McGraw-Hill, New York, 1957.

5 A. Kaufmann, *Methodes et Modèles de la Recherche Operationnelle*, 2 volumes, Dunod, Paris, 1959 and 1964.

6 A. Kaufmann and G. Desbazeille, *La Méthode du Chemin Critique* (*Système PERT*), Dunod, Paris, 1964.

7 Mason Haire, *Modern Organization Theory*, Wiley, New York, 1959.

8 Y. Muller, *Intuition à l'organisation et à la recherche operationnelle*, Eyrolles, Paris, 1964.

2 The choice of criterion

9 M. Allais, *Traité d'Economie pure*, Imprimerie Nationale, Paris.

10 C. W. Churchman, *Prediction and Optimal Decision*, Prentice Hall, New York, 1961.

11 C. W. Churchman, R. L. Ackoff and E. I. Arnoff, *Introduction to Operations Research*, Wiley, New York, 1958.

12 R. Dehem, *Traité d'Analyse Economique*, Dunod, Paris, 1958.

13 F. Y. Edgeworth, 'The Pure Theory of Taxation', *Papers relating to Political Economy*, Macmillan, London, 1925.

14 J. R. Hicks, *A Revision of Demand Theory*, Clarendon Press, Oxford, 1956.

15 W. S. Jevons, *The Theory of Political Economy*, Macmillan, London, 1931.

16 A. Kaufmann and R. Faure, *Invitation à la Recherche Operationnelle*, Dunod, Paris, 1963.

17 A. Marshall, *Principles of Economics*, Macmillan, London, 1947.

18 P. Masse, *Le Choix des Investissements*, Dunod, Paris, 1959.

19 J. von Neumann and O. Morgenstern, *Theory of Games and Economic Behaviour*, Princeton U.P., 1944.

20 V. Pareto, *Manuel d'Economie Politique*, Giard, Paris, 1927.

21 L. J. Savage, 'The Theory of Statistical Decision', *Journal of American Statistical Association*, No. 48, 1947.
22 R. H. Thrall, C. H. Coombs and R. L. Davis, *Decision Processes*, Wiley/ Chapman and Hall, New York and London, 1954.
23 A. Wald, *Statistical Decision Functions*, New York, 1950.
24 L. Walras, *Elements d'Economie Politique Pure*, Librairie générale du Droit et de la Jurisprudence, Paris, 1952.
25 *Colloques Internationaux du CNRS: La Décision*, Éditions du CNRS, Paris, 1960.

3 The search for an optimal policy

26 J. Archer, *Algèbre linéaire et programmation linéaire*, Dunod, Paris, 1965.
27 R. L. Ackoff, *Progress in Operations Research*, Vol. 1, Wiley, New York, 1961.
28 J. C. G. Boot, *Quadratic Programming*, North Holland Publishing Co., Amsterdam, 1964.
29 A. Charnes and W. W. Cooper, *Management Models and Industrial Applications of Linear Programming*, Wiley, New York, 1961.
30 Danø Sven, *Linear Programming in Industry: theory and application*, Springer, Vienna, 1960.
31 G. B. Dantzig, *Linear Programming and Extensions*, Princeton U.P., 1963.
32 R. Dorfman, P. A. Samuelson and R. M. Solon, *Linear Programming and Economic Analysis*, McGraw-Hill, New York, 1958.
33 R. Frisch, *Maxima and Minima*, Dunod, Paris, 1960.
34 S. I. Gass, *Linear Programming: methods and applications*, McGraw-Hill, New York, 1958.
35 D. U. Greenwald, *Programmation Lineaire et Algorithme du Simplexe*, Dunod, Paris, 1960.
36 D. B. Hertz and R. T. Eddison, *Progress in Operations Research*, Vol. 2, Wiley, New York, 1964.
37 L. V. Kantorovitch, *Economicheskii Raschet Nailuckshego Ispol Lovaniia Resursov*, Akademii Nauk SSSR, Moscow, 1959.
38 S. Karlin, *Mathematical Methods and Theory of Games, Programming and Economics*, 2 vols., Addison, Westey, 1959.
39 T. C. Koopmans, *Activity Analysis of Production and Allocation*, Wiley, New York, 1951.
40 H. W. Kuhn and A. W. Tucker, *Linear Inequalities and Related Systems*, Princeton U.P., 1956.

41 O. Morgenstern, *Economic Activity Analysis*, Wiley, New York, 1954.
42 V. Riley and S. I. Gass, *Linear Programming and Associated Techniques*, O.R.O., Johns Hopkins Press, Baltimore, 1958.
43 B. Roy, *Les problèmes d'Ordonnancement Monographie AFIRO*, Dunod, Paris, 1956.

4 Dealing with chance

44 H. Cramer, *Mathematical Methods of Statistics*, Princeton U.P., 1946.
45 G. Dedebant and E. A. Machado, *Probabilidades*, Editoria Coni, Buenos Aires, 1963.
46 W. J. Dixon and F. J. Massey Jr., *Introduction to Statistical Analysis*, McGraw-Hill, New York, 1957.
47 W. Feller, *Introduction to Probability and its Applications*, Wiley, New York, 1950.
48 J. Ferrier, *Statistiques et Probabilités dans l'Administration des Entreprises*, Eyrolles, Paris, 1960.
49 M. Girault, *Calcul des Probabilités en vue des Applications*, Dunod, Paris, 1960.
50 M. Girault, *Initiations aux Processus Aléatoires*, Dunod, Paris, 1959.
51 B. V. Gnedenko, *Kuss Teorii Veroyatnostei*, Moscow, 1959.
52 B. V. Gnedenko and A. Ia. Khintchine, *Elemientarnoïé Viédiénié v Tiériou Viéroïatnostiéï*, Tiekhniko Tiérosetitcheskoï, Moscow, 1958 (French edition, Dunod, Paris, 1960).
53 S. Goldberg, *Probability: an introduction*, Prentice Hall, New York, 1960.
54 J. N. Hammersley and D. C. Handscomb, *Monte Carlo Methods*, Methuen, London, 1964.
55 P. G. Hoel, *Introduction to Mathematical Statistics*, Wiley, New York, 1947.
56 A. Kaufmann, *Cours Moderne de Calcul des Probabilités*, Albin Michel, Paris, 1965.
57 A. Kaufmann and R. Cruon, *Les Phénomène d'Attente*, Dunod, Paris, 1962.
58 P. Le Gall, *Les Systèmes avec ou sans Attente et les Processus Stochastiques*, Vol. 1, Dunod, Paris, 1962.
59 P. M. Morse, *Queues, Inventories and Maintenance*, Wiley, 1957.
60 V. Mothes, *Prévisions et Décisions Statistiques dans l'Entreprise*, Dunod, Paris, 1962.

61 E. Parzen, *Modern Probability: theory and applications*, Wiley, New York, 1960.
62 T. L. Saaty, *Elements of Queueing Theory with Applications*, McGraw-Hill, New York, 1961.
63 R. Schlaifer, *Probability and Statistics for Business Decision*, McGraw-Hill, New York, 1959.
64 A. Tortrat, *Principes de Statistique Mathématique*, Dunod, Paris, 1961.
65 One Million Random Digits, Table de nombres au hasard établie par la Rand Corp., Santa Monica USA, 1955.
See also sections 12, 13, 15; references 16, 27, 36.

5 Dealing with uncertainty

66 C. Berge, *Théorie génerale des jeux à* n *personnes*, Gauthier Villars, Paris, 1957.
67 D. Blackwell and M. A. Girshick, *Theory of Games and Statistical Decisions*, Wiley, New York, 1954.
68 Burger, *Einführung in die Theorie der Spiele*, De Gruyter, 1960.
69 H. Chernoff and L. E. Moses, *Elementary Decision Theory*, Wiley, New York, 1959.
70 G. Th. Guilbaud, *Stratégies et Décisions Économiques*, CNRS, Paris, 1954.
71 G. Th. Guilbaud, *Leçons sur les éléments principaux de la théorie des jeux*, CNRS, Paris, 1954.
72 S. P. Jacot, *Stratégie et Concurrence*, SEDES, Paris, 1963.
73 H. W. Kuhn and A. W. Tucker, *Contributions to the Theory of Games*, Vol. I and II, Princeton U.P., 1950–3.
74 R. D. Luce and H. Raiffa, *Games and Decisions*, Wiley, New York, 1957.
75 J. C. C. McKinsey, *Introduction to the Theory of Games*, McGraw-Hill, New York, 1952.
76 M. Shubik, *Strategy and Market Structure*, Wiley, New York, 1959.
77 S. Vajda, *The Theory of Games and Linear Programming*, Methuen, London, 1956.
78 E. S. Ventzel, *Lectures on Game Theory*, Hindustan Publishing Corporation, Delhi, 1961.
79 L. Weiss, *Statistical Decision Theory*, McGraw-Hill, New York, 1961.
80 J. D. Williams, *The Compleat Strategyst*, Rand Corporation Study, McGraw-Hill, New York, 1954.

6 The sequential processes of decision

81 R. Bellman, *Dynamic Programming*, Princeton U.P., 1952.
82 R. Bellman, *Adaptive Control Process: a guided tour*, Princeton U.P., 1959.
83 R. Bellman and S. Dreyfus, *Applied Dynamic Programming*, Princeton U.P., 1962.
84 A. T. Bharucha-Reid, *Elements of the Theory of Markov Processes and their Applications*, McGraw-Hill, New York, 1960.
85 I. B. Dynkin, *Osnovaniia Theorii Markovskih Protsessov ed. Litterature Psycho-mathematique*, Moscow, 1960 (French edition, Dunod, Paris, 1962.).
86 Kai Lai Chung, *Markov Chains with Stationary Transition Probabilities*, Springer, Berlin, 1960.
87 A. Kaufmann and R. Cruon, *La Programmation Dynamique (gestion scientifique séquentielle)*, Dunod, Paris, 1964.
88 L. S. Pontryagin and others, *The Mathematical Theory of Optimal Processes*, Wiley, New York, 1962.
89 P. Rosenstiehl and A. Ghouila-Houri, *Les Choix Économiques*, Dunod, Paris, 1960.
90 A. Vazsonyi, *Scientific Programming in Business and Industry*, Wiley, 1958.
See also: section 15, references 16, 18, 27, 31.

7 Learning by experience and simulation

91 O. G. Haywood, Jr., *Military Decision and Game Theory*, JORSA, 2, 365, 385, 1954.
92 H. Hierche, *Les Techniques Modernes de Gestion des Entreprises*, Dunod, Paris, 1962.
93 D. R. Fulkerson and S. M. Johnson, *A Tactical Air Game*, JORSA, 5, 704, 912, 1957.
94 A. Kaufmann, R. Faure and A. Le Garff, *Les Jeux d'Entreprises*, Presses Universitaires de France, Paris, 1960.
95 H. S. R. Murray, *A History of Board Games*, OUP, 1951.
96 G. H. Orcutt and others, *Microanalysis of Socioeconomic Systems: a Simulation Study*, Harper, New York, 1961.
97 R. D. Specht, 'War Games', in M. Davis and M. Verhulst (eds.), *Operations Research in Practice*, Pergamon Press, 1958.

98 V. Volterra, *Leçons sur la théorie mathématique de la lutte pour la vie*, Gauthier Villars, Paris, 1931.
99 V. R. Young, 'A Survey of Historical Developments in War Games', Staff Paper ORO, SP98, Johns Hopkins Press, Baltimore, 1959.
100 M. G. Weiner, 'An Introduction to War Games', in P. Rosenstiehl and A. Ghouila-Houri, *Les choix économiques*, Dunod, Paris, 1960.
101 R. E. Zimmerman, 'Simulation of Tactical War Games' in C. D. Flagle, W. H. Huggins and R. H. Roy (eds.), *Operations Research and Systems Engineering*, Johns Hopkins Press, Baltimore, 1960.
102 Journées AFCAL, SOFRO, RIMS, *Moyens Automatiques de gestion*, Dunod, Paris, 1961.

8 The flexible world

103 A. Besse, and others, *Le Capital Imagination* (*Brainstorming*), Edition de l'Entreprise Moderne, Paris, 1958.
104 J. E. Coulson and others, *Programmed Learning and Computer-based Instruction*, Wiley, New York, 1962.
105 A. Kaufmann and J. Cathelin, *Le Gaspillage de la Liberté*, Dunod, Paris, 1964.
106 A. A. Lumsdaine and R. Glaser, *Teaching Machines and Programmed Learning*, National Educational Association of USA, Washington, 1960.
107 S. Margulies and L. D. Eigen, *Applied Programmed Instruction*, Wiley, New York, 1962.
108 F. Zwicky, *Morphology of Propulsive Power*, Society for Morphological Research, Pasadena, California, 1962.
See also 1, 10.

Index

World University Library

Some books published or in preparation

Economics and Social Studies

The World Cities
Peter Hall, *London*

The Economics of Underdeveloped Countries
Jagdish Bhagwati, *Delhi*

Development Planning
Jan Tinbergen, *Rotterdam*

Leadership in New Nations
T. B. Bottomore, *Vancouver*

Human Communication
J. L. Aranguren, *Madrid*

Education in the Modern World
John Vaizey, *Oxford*

Soviet Economics
Michael Kaser, *Oxford*

Decisive Forces in World Economics
J. L. Sampedro, *Madrid*

Money
Roger Opie, *Oxford*

The Sociology of Africa
Georges Balandier, *Paris*

Science and Anti-Science
T. R. Gerholm, *Stockholm*

Key Issues in Criminology
Roger Hood, *Durham*

Society and Population
E. A. Wrigley, *Cambridge*

History

The Old Stone Age
François Bordes, *Bordeaux*

The Evolution of Ancient Egypt
Werner Kaiser, *Berlin*

The Emergence of Greek Democracy
W. G. Forrest, *Oxford*

The Roman Empire
J. P. V. D. Balsdon, *Oxford*

Muhammad and the Conquests of Islam
Francesco Gabrieli, *Rome*

The Age of Charlemagne
Jacques Boussard, *Poitiers*

The Crusades
Geo Widengren, *Uppsala*

The Medieval Economy
Georges Duby, *Aix-en-Provence*

The Medieval Italian Republics
D. P. Waley, *London*

The Ottoman Empire
Halil Inalcik, *Ankara*

Humanism in the Renaissance
S. Dresden, *Leyden*

The Rise of Toleration
Henry Kamen, *Warwick*

The Left in Europe since 1789
David Caute, *Oxford*

The Rise of the Working Class
Jürgen Kuczynski, *Berlin*

Chinese Communism
Robert North, *Stanford*

Arab Nationalism
Sylvia Haim, *London*

The Culture of Japan
Mifune Okumura, *Kyoto*

The History of Persia
Jean Aubin, *Paris*

Philosophy and Religion

Christianity
W. O. Chadwick, *Cambridge*

Monasticism
David Knowles, *London*

Judaism
J. Soetendorp, *Amsterdam*

The Modern Papacy
K. O. von Aretin, *Göttingen*

Sects
Bryan Wilson, *Oxford*

Language and Literature

A Model of Language
E. M. Uhlenbeck, *Leyden*

French Literature
Raymond Picard, *Paris*

Russian Writers and Society 1825–1904
Ronald Hingley, *Oxford*

Satire
Matthew Hodgart, *Sussex*

The Romantic Century
Robert Baldick, *Oxford*

The Arts

The Language of Modern Art
Ulf Linde, *Stockholm*

Architecture since 1945
Bruno Zevi, *Rome*

Twentieth Century Music
H. H. Stuckenschmidt, *Berlin*

Aesthetic Theories since 1850
J. F. Revel, *Paris*

Art Nouveau
S. Tschudi Madsen, *Oslo*

Academic Painting
Gerald Ackerman, *Stanford*

Palaeolithic Cave Art
P. J. Ucko and A. Rosenfeld, *London*

Primitive Art
Eike Haberland, *Mainz*

Romanesque Art
Carlos Cid Priego, *Madrid*

Expressionism
John Willett, *London*

Psychology and Human Biology

The Molecules of Life
Gisela Nass, *Munich*

The Variety of Man
J. P. Garlick, *London*

Eye and Brain
R. L. Gregory, *Cambridge*

The Ear and the Brain
E. C. Carterette, *U.C.L.A.*

The Biology of Work
O. G. Edholm, *London*

The Psychology of Attention
Anne Treisman, *Oxford*

Psychoses
H. J. Bochnik, *Hamburg*

Psychosomatic Medicine
A. Mitscherlich, *Heidelberg*

Child Development
Phillipe Muller, *Neuchâtel*

Man and Disease
Gernot Rath, *Göttingen*

Chinese Medicine
P. Huard and M. Wong, *Paris*

Mind in the Universe
Gösta Ehrensvärd, *Lund*

Zoology and Botany

The Age of the Dinosaurs
Björn Kurtén, *Helsingfors*

Animal Communication
J. M. Cullen, *Oxford*

Mimicry
Wolfgang Wickler, *Seewiesen*

Migration
Gustaf Rudebeck, *Stockholm*

Lower Animals
Martin Wells, *Cambridge*

The World of an Insect
Rémy Chauvin, *Strasbourg*

Biological Rhythms
Janet Harker, *Cambridge*

Life in the Sea
Gunnar Thorson, *Helsingore*

Primates
François Bourlière, *Paris*

The Conservation of Nature
C. Delamare Deboutteville, *Paris*

The Variation of Plants
S. M. Walters and D. Briggs, *Cambridge*

Earth Sciences and Astronomy

The Structure of the Universe
E. L. Schatzman, *Paris*

Climate and Weather
H. Flohn, *Bonn*

Anatomy of the Earth
Andrè Cailleux, *Paris*

The Electrical Earth
J. Sayers, *Birmingham*

Physical Science and Mathematics

Energy
Etienne Fischhoff, *Paris*

Crystals and Minerals
Hugo Strunz, *Berlin*

The Quest for Absolute Zero
K. Mendelssohn, *Oxford*

Particles and Accelerators
Robert Gouiran, *C.E.R.N., Geneva*

What is Light?
A. C. S. van Heel and C. H. F. Velzel, *Eindhoven*

Waves and Corpuscles
J. A. e Silva and G. Lochak, *Paris*
Introduction by Louis de Broglie

Mathematics Observed
H. Freudenthal, *Utrecht*

Science and Statistics
S. Sagoroff, *Vienna*

Applied Science

Words and Waves
A. H. W. Beck, *Cambridge*

The Science of Decision-making
A. Kaufmann, *Paris*

Bionics
Lucien Gerardin, *Paris*

Metals and Civilisation
R. W. Cahn, *Sussex*

Bioengineering
H. S. Wolff, *London*